DEPRESSION
the Way Out

NEIL NEDLEY, M.D.

Nedley Publishing
1010 14th St. NW
Ardmore, OK 73401
580-226-8007

ISBN 0-9661979-4-1

Caution: This book does not establish a doctor-patient relationship with the reader. Persons who are ill or on medication who wish to significantly change their lifestyle should do so under the direction of a physician familiar with the effects of lifestyle change on health.

Library of Congress Control Number: 2001118528

Nedley, Neil.
    DEPRESSION: the Way Out/Neil Nedley
    1st ed.
    p. cm.
    Includes bibliographical references
    ISBN: 0-9661979-4-1

    1. Health.   2. Mental health   3. Health promotion
    4. Self-care, Health   5. Depression

    I. Title.

Dedication

To my dear wife, Erica.

I first met Erica when she could not speak a word of English, at the tender age of 18. She was born and raised behind the iron curtain in Romania. Her entire immediate family legally immigrated to the United States (as part of the Helsinki Accord) in 1980 despite the cruel Communist dictatorship of Nicolae Ceausescu. It all happened so fast that she and her family did not have a chance to learn any English before they came. I saw her in the youth class of my home church in Troy, Michigan, just a few days after they arrived in the United States. I was only able to verbally communicate with her through a poor interpreter. I spoke English, the interpreter spoke to her in Spanish (Erica could understand a few Spanish words since Spanish and Romanian are both "Romance" Latin-based languages). She then spoke Romanian, and from what the interpreter could understand he interpreted into English. Our communication has steadily improved ever since!

When I went to medical school at Loma Linda University, I began to date California girls. My parents, however, would continue to report to me about Erica and her many talents. After spending my last summer at home in Michigan (1983) I got to know Erica better—by this time she could speak excellent English. It became obvious that our goals, interests, intellect, and affections were similar, although our personalities were quite different. She was about to enter physical therapy school in Michigan, but I persuaded her to take her training at Loma Linda University. We were engaged Memorial Day, 1985, and married in December of that year in the same church where our eyes had first met. We both graduated from our respective studies just a few months later.

Erica is my constant support, despite my busy greater-than-full-time medical practice. She has also wholeheartedly supported me in writing and publishing. She has willingly reviewed each picture and figure in this book and in *Proof Positive*. She has authored the largest and last appendix of this book, "Recipes to Elevate Mood," which has already helped scores of individuals on the way to optimal mental health. She has kept me accountable in time management, making sure that when I was supposed to be "working on the book" I was working on the book. Yet, she is a wonderful mother to our three boys, Joel,

Allen, and Nathan. She manages the expense account and payroll for the Nedley-Sabangan Clinic as well as for Nedley Publishing. In addition, she keeps up the Nedley ranch, orchard, and garden; leads out and directs several departments in our local church including children's ministry and the building committee; arranges our national and international health speaking appointments; plays the piano and organ for our home worships as well as for the church; and regularly conducts extensive vegetarian cooking schools. All of this labor is volunteer—a labor of love. She is without a doubt the busiest person I know, including myself, but still remains my very best friend and lover.

In short, the creating and writing of this book would never have been possible without Erica. As I said to you on our wedding day, Erica, I say to you today—I promise you my love forever, and ever, and ever—a promise that has not been hard to keep!

Acknowledgments

My gratitude and thanks to:

My father, Lloyd Nedley, who volunteered countless hours in making sure the book was readable for the lay public, and created a large number of figures to make it user-friendly. He also served as our lay editor. My father was the one who sparked my interest in health and personally demonstrated that a significant change in diet and lifestyle habits brings about dramatic improvement in physical and mental health. Although now in his late 70s, his mind remains healthy and sharp, and his body fit and strong. He still is one of the most enjoyable and intriguing persons to be around.

Paula Reiter, my office manager, for her continued pressure to complete the project. Her position on the front lines of health care and health fairs proved to her the urgent necessity to get this book in the hands of those who need it. She has expressed her belief that perhaps more lives will be saved by people reading and putting into practice the principles in this book than the lives individually being saved through my medical practice. If her enthusiasm and mission spirit in improving the lives of others physically, mentally, and spiritually were copied a hundredfold, this world would be much less sorrowful and would be a vastly different and better place.

Gery Friesen, who sacrificed time with his family and friends in coming to Oklahoma when the book was stagnating and willingly worked multiple, long, six-day work weeks to move the book closer to press. Gery's positive attitude and strong work ethic is contagious and refreshing. He performed the largest share of the layout and design of the book.

David DeRose, M.D., who assisted in editing chapters 3, 7, 8, and 9, and also helped us to find several "hard-to-find" references. David was instrumental as an instructor in my Internal Medicine program in bringing about positive changes in my own diet. His creative, yet scholarly writing, is educational and stimulating. I appreciate his friendship and his willingness to have me bounce ideas off him.

Mike McCullers for his willingness to spend multiple hours in the last few weeks cropping and retouching photographs. Mike also finished the layout and design of the book to get it press-ready. This meant working many late, additional evening hours after his full time day job was completed.

Sylvia Mayer, who set up some of Erica's completed recipes into the food settings photographed in Appendix X. Her talent and decorative skills are obvious.

Christopher Kelly, who photographed many of the pictures in the book. Although he has many other tasks, Chris was always willing to be of help when his schedule permitted.

Paula Wolfe, who had the unpleasant task of finding and correcting grammatical errors in the book. If you, the reader, find any mistakes that our team missed, please let us know so we can correct them for the next printing.

Skip Joers who assisted in the initial writing of Chapter 6 and Appendix V.

Each model who willingly submitted to be photographed in order to enhance the interest and readability of the book.

Matthew McVane who designed the book cover.

Mercy Memorial Health Center, Ardmore, Oklahoma, which not only "put up" with the times I was absent while writing or speaking, but provided research assistance through the help of their medical library and resource center. Cathy Ice, always pleasant and cheerful, obtained full articles even though they were sometimes difficult to find.

Joel Sabangan, M.D., Brian Shockey, M.D., and Zeno Charles-Marcel, M.D., who willingly provided medical coverage for my practice to permit me to author the book. I have truly been blessed by wonderful covering physicians who care for my patients as if they were their own. I also continue to enjoy the companionship of these three friends.

Mylas Martin, Barbara Watson, Robert Lynch, Kerri Reiter, Diana Skinner, Stella Thompson, Velda Lewis, The Brown Paper Bag in Ardmore, Oklahoma, and many others who contributed in various ways to the initiation and completion of the book.

My audiences who initially demanded the book.

My patients, who not only "put up" with my medical coverage while I was writing the book, but who were on my mind as I wrote many sections of the book. Although their names have been changed (along with occasional circumstances to keep confidentiality), they provided some of the many true examples cited in the book. Furthermore, this book is written for any patient to read, to learn, and to live a mentally healthier way of life.

My lovely wife, Erica. The book's dedication provides more details concerning Erica Nedley.

My three sons, Joel, Allen, and Nathan, who learned to respect the time that Daddy was home, but was busy "working on the book." I thoroughly enjoy swimming, running, and biking with my three little friends, as well as singing, reading the Bible together, and just plain "talking". My boys' happiness will almost be equal to my own in completing this project.

Contents

CONTENTS (CONTINUED)

About the Author

Neil Nedley, M.D., is a full-time practicing physician in Internal Medicine with emphasis in Cardiology, Gastroenterology, Preventive Medicine, Mental Health, and the difficult-to-diagnose patient. He did his undergraduate studies at Andrews University in Michigan, majoring in Biochemistry. He graduated from medical school in 1986 with a Doctor of Medicine (M.D.) degree from Loma Linda University in California, ranking in the top 10 percent of his class.

He completed his residency in Internal Medicine at Kettering Medical Center at Wright State University in Ohio in 1989, and in the same year he became certified by the American Board of Internal Medicine. He is a member of the American Medical Association, American College of Physicians, and Alpha-Omega-Alpha Honor Medical Society, as well as a number of other health and medical associations.

In 1989 he came to Ardmore, Oklahoma, to practice both acute care Internal Medicine, and Lifestyle and Preventive Medicine with the Ardmore Institute of Health, which operates the Lifestyle Center of America, a live-in Preventive Medicine facility. Dr. Nedley has served as Chairman of the Medicine Department at Mercy Memorial Hospital and Health Center, and President of the Medical Staff. He currently chairs the Medical Education and Medical Library Committees at Mercy Memorial Health Center, and is a board member of the Ardmore Institute of Health.

Dr. Nedley has lectured extensively in the United States, Canada, Europe, South America, and Russia on nutrition, lifestyle, and physical and mental health. He has held numerous nutrition seminars, cooking schools (with his wife, Erica), and depression and stress seminars. He has been a guest on numerous national television programs and radio stations throughout the United States. He has authored the widely acclaimed comprehensive, yet readable book on the relationship between nutrition, lifestyle, and health entitled *Proof Positive: How to Reliably Combat Disease and Achieve Optimal Health through Nutrition and Lifestyle*, now in its third printing.

The positive response by thousands of people around the world to this book helped launch Nedley Publishing, an organization that produces health materials based on solid documented scientific research and placed in an interesting and understandable format. Nedley Publishing currently produces books, CD-ROMs, and health presentation materials for the health professional and general public.

Dr. Nedley lives with his wife and three boys on a 100-acre ranch in Oklahoma and enjoys reading, running, bicycling, tennis, classical music, and riding his tractor.

Preface

Why a book on depression from a specialist in internal medicine? I openly admit that I did not know a lot about depression when I finished my internal medicine specialty. Yes, I had experienced psychiatric rotations and had performed psychiatric consultations under supervision. I had heard a few lectures from well-respected psychiatrists on the subject. I had to stay up to date on the effects, side effects, and potential drug interactions of the medications used for depression, simply because many of the patients I saw in consultation were taking these medications. But I was shocked when shortly after I had completed my residency, an article from "Archives of Internal Medicine," a scientific journal that publishes cutting edge studies in my own field, revealed that one out of three to six patients an internist sees in an outpatient practice are suffering from depression. If this was true, I reasoned, this would be the most common disease entity that my patients had; yet I felt so unprepared to assist them in overcoming depression.

I determined to find out as much about depression including what causes it, how it might be prevented, as well as how best to treat it. I began to search for and read the latest review articles written by some of the top psychiatrists in the field. Most of these articles centered on making an accurate diagnosis and the latest drug treatments. The articles that mentioned the possible causes of depression would usually just state the genetic tendency and a few social risk factors.

As a full-time practicing physician I take time almost every week, and often several times a week, to read the studies "hot off the press" that deal with my specialty of internal medicine. Internal medicine is a broad field that encompasses the diagnosis and treatment of adult diseases of the internal organs. One of those "internal organs" is the brain. I have always had a strong interest in brain science for several reasons, one of which is my desire to have my own brain function at the highest possible level.

Many of the consultations I perform on a daily basis are referred by other physicians who did not diagnose the actual condition causing a patient's particular symptoms. I am asked to diagnose and then treat the "difficult" patient. After my discovery that, indeed, many of my patients were depressed, I not only continued to read the latest research in brain science, but also began to study the latest research concerning depression.

Little by little, I began to realize that the potential causes of depression were voluminous, much more than just social factors and genetics. When the 1990s unfolded the major role that the frontal lobe of the brain played in the development of depression, I realized that most people with depression were not being told the actual cause of their condition. No diagnostic work-up was being performed by virtually any health care practitioner to determine the real cause of their disease. What was the result? Dependency on drug medication and/or counseling for life. This often meant trading the symptom of unexplained sadness for a list of physical and mental side effects of the medication. It sometimes even brought about the adverse social consequences of inappropriate counseling. These conflicting outcomes were compounded by the fact that depression was becoming much more prevalent in our modern society.

At this point, I began to utilize a new approach on my own patients with depression. Instead of just accurately diagnosing them and immediately placing them on the latest drug medication to counteract depression, I did an investigative work-up to determine the actual causes of their condition. I then put a treatment plan in place that dealt with these underlying causes. The results were truly amazing. In just 20 weeks the vast majority of my depressed patients were no longer dependent on drug medications, counseling, or even follow-up visits with me! Yes, they are truly cured from this dark condition. As I began to share my experience with colleagues and lay audiences, they requested that I compile this exciting information in a book so that many whom I will never meet might benefit from this approach. My desire is that you, the reader, will enjoy this book and find its information useful, practical, and motivating as you discover *Depression: The Way Out.*

CHAPTER ONE

THE MARVELOUS MIND *and the* Invisible Disease

Despondency was no stranger to A.L. At one time in his life he was so consumed with mental depression that he was totally incapacitated. On another occasion he expressed, "I am now the most miserable man living. If what I feel were equally distributed to the whole human family, there would be not one cheerful face on earth."

A.L. had reason for his gloomy outlook. He was born into an impoverished family, failed in business, and then was passed up for a job he felt he could put his heart into. His true love suffered an untimely death. He later proposed to another young lady who spurned his offer. A.L.'s life history and tendency to melancholy appeared to ensure that he would never rise above his circumstances and make anything of his life.

Half a world away and decades later a similar story was played out. This time the individual was from a different social strata. Born into a prominent family, W.C. nonetheless had challenges physically, mentally, and emotionally from an early age. When he was three years old he was thrown from a donkey and suffered a brain concussion. As a young boy of 11, he saw his life hanging in the balance as his physician tried to save him from rampant pneumonia. At the age of 18 he fell nearly 30 feet at the expense of a ruptured kidney and weeks of convalescence.

W.C.'s mental and emotional challenges often appeared about to overwhelm him. Twice he failed to pass the entrance exam for his chosen college. His father provided little solace when it came to W.C.'s academic failures. He told his son that he was leading an "idle, useless, and unprofitable life" and predicted— barring a change in life direction—that W.C. would become "a mere social wastrel, one of hundreds of public school failures" who would "degenerate into a shabby, unhappy, and futile existence." These challenges in W.C.'s early years provide a glimpse into the roots of depression that would plague him throughout his life. The picture that emerges is a life story that seems destined to end in obscurity. Truly, depression seems to steal away the very essence of who we are and robs the brain of its capacities for creativity, spontaneity, accomplishment, and joy.

However, depression does not have to be the end of any life story. A.L., whose full name was *Abraham Lincoln*, could have succumbed to his depression and never amounted to much. Instead, he forged ahead and became one of the most revered American presidents ever. His life testifies to the awesome power of the human brain. Lincoln's brain at one point in time appeared to be so compromised as to have lost its ability to function, but later enabled him to compose and deliver the Gettysburg address.

W.C.'s depression could have been the concluding chapter of another grim biographical footnote in the stream of time. However, *Winston Churchill* (which was his full name) also rose above circumstances and stirred the soul of Britain in one of its darkest hours. "Statesman," "Orator," "Motivator," "Leader" are all terms that have been applied to one who could well have succumbed to feelings of despondency.

Hope for Victims of Depression

The life histories of Abraham Lincoln and Winston Churchill offer hope to all who experience depression. They both engaged in many bitter conflicts on the battlefields of human opinion. However, their most important confrontations occurred on the level of their own minds.

ASTOUNDING FACTS ABOUT THE BRAIN

- Comprises only two percent of the total weight of the body

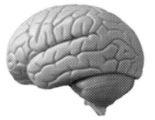

- Utilizes fifteen percent of the body's total metabolism

- Contains 100 billion nerve cells (neurons)

- Has thousands of different types of neurons (compared to ten or less in other organs)

- One neuron can communicate with as many as 200,000 other neurons.

Figure 1

Indeed, whether or not you have struggled with depression or other mental health challenges, your life history is dependent on how well you can harness the resources of your brain.

Harnessing those resources is no easy task, however. The brain is both amazing and powerful, yet it is probably the least scientifically understood organ in the human body. It is ironic that the disease of depression and its treatment provides some of the most marvelous examples of the brain's capacities and also its emerging secrets. Whether or not you have yet faced a full-blown bout of depression, a better understanding of the depths of this common disease can open new vistas for peak mental performance.

When we think of forces that have shaped our world and our lives it is indeed sobering to realize that a small organ weighing a mere three pounds can totally shape our destiny. Truly, the brain is central to our personal identity and our ability to successfully initiate and accomplish our goals in life.[1] The brain triggers all human behavior. Our memories, our desires, the ability to make sound decisions, the joy of laughter, deep sadness, and sobs of crying are all brain functions.

Complexity of the Human Brain

The human brain is the most complicated structure ever investigated by science. A few astounding facts about the brain are listed in **Figure 1**. Note that it represents a very small percentage of our total weight, but requires a much larger proportion of the body's energy to function. It is made up of literally billions of nerve cells called neurons. Note the large number of different types of neurons. Each type has its own distinct chemistry, shape, and connections.[2] The massive inter-communications of the neurons are a marvel. These facts just touch the surface of the brain's complexity.

The functions of a normal brain depend

on the ability of the neurons to effectively communicate with each other. In this communication process, electrical signals are transmitted to other neurons in the form of chemical signals. These functions are explained further in *Appendix I*.

The brain consists of sections called lobes. The lobes of the brain are shown in **Figure 2**. The back portion of the brain, called the occipital lobe, is shown on the middle right, and is the smallest of all the lobes. It is involved in vision as well as the initial stages of visual processing, such as identifying the color and shape of objects, or where they are in space. Damage to the occipital lobe can result in visual hallucinations, limited field of vision, inability to recognize faces and places, color blindness, or lack of understanding the meaning of what is seen.[3]

On the upper right, just behind the top center portion of the brain, is the *parietal* (pronounced pah-ri'-eh-tal) lobe. It interprets and integrates information from the sensory areas, allowing the identification of the "what" and "where" of objects. It is involved in touch and in initial stages of touch processing, interpreting the amount of pressure and the type of touch. Some of its functions include reading, writing, mathematical calculations, word comprehension and meaning, language comprehension, and spatial relationships.[4]

Shown on the upper left is the *frontal lobe*, which is involved in motor behavior. The frontal lobe is the largest of the cerebral regions, representing one third of the total brain surface area.[5] The front portion of the frontal lobe, known as the prefrontal cortex, is involved with the highest functions of the brain, including the ability to plan and to highly integrate data, both physical and emotional, and it also controls behavior. It allows us to accurately assess our behavior and respond to events and situations appropriately.

People with frontal lobe damage may perform well on some IQ tests, but in so-

THE LOBES OF THE BRAIN

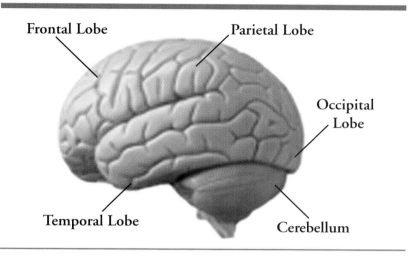

Frontal Lobe   Parietal Lobe

Occipital Lobe

Temporal Lobe   Cerebellum

Figure 2

cial and real-life situations requiring mental flexibility and planning, they may be completely unable to cope. The frontal lobe handles diverse functions such as fine finger movements, creative speech, music, eye movements, and abstract thought.[6]

The temporal lobe is on the lower left and includes the hippocampus, where the memory of persons, places, and things are consolidated. It controls hearing and understanding sounds, as well as instinctual and basic motor functions of the body. Damage to the temporal lobe can cause deafness, inability to interpret sounds, auditory hallucinations, impaired memory, confused speech, and impaired language comprehension.[7]

The cerebellum, shown on the lower right, is involved in fine coordination and athletic skills. It resides just above the brain stem. It controls body movements, balance, and eye movement. Damage to the cerebellum can cause impairment of posture, walk, movement of arms and legs, and eye movement.

The *amygdala* (pronounced awe-mig'da-la), albeit a small, almond-shaped portion of the brain, is important in emotional function. It is involved in assigning emotional meaning to events and

3

objects, and also plays a special role in negative emotions such as fear—specifically the fight-or-flight response. Other effects include control over food intake, sexual behavior, aggression, and desire.[8]

The emotional center of the brain is known as the *limbic system. Appendix II* is a sketch of the components of the limbic system of the brain. It plays a role in mediating the experience of emotions, basic responses, and storage of memories. A dam-aged limbic system can cause dream-like states, depersonalization, inappropriate fear, profound acute depression, extreme pleasure, and memory loss.[9]

The brain is not a static organ; its structure is constantly changing. The changes are explained in **Figure 3**.

The crowning wonder of the brain is that it is not static, physically or chemically. The brain is always changing. Each time a person learns something new, consciously or subconsciously, that experience alters the structure of the brain. Thus, neurotransmission not only contains current information, but if the learning occurs with the right intensity and pattern, it will alter subsequent neurotransmission. If an experience is notable enough to be retained in the memory, that experience will produce new synaptic connections, prune away old ones, and strengthen or weaken existing ones.

Some experiences such as stress, disease, or exposure to alcohol or other toxins can kill neurons. Current data demonstrates *that new neurons can develop even in adult brains,*[10] where they can help to create new memories. As a result of experience, information is now routed over a changed circuit. Many of these changes can be long-lasting or even permanent. This is how distinct memories of events that happened 20, 30, or even 50 years ago or more can exist, including many of our childhood memories.

The majority of our 35,000 human genes[11] are involved in building this truly amazing structure we call the brain, but genes are by no means the whole story. Brains are built and changed through experience and environment. Thus nutrition, lifestyle, and numerous every day choices have a profound effect on how well our brains function and behave. Instruction given almost 2000 years ago is even more relevant in light of modern science: "Be renewed in the spirit of your mind."[12]

THE CONSTANTLY CHANGING BRAIN

- As learning takes place, the brain structure changes.

- New neurons form, creating new memories.

- Alcohol, disease, and stress can kill neurons.

- Nutrition, lifestyle, and everyday choices change brain structure.

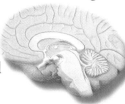

Figure 3

EXTENT OF MENTAL DISORDERS IN UNITED STATES

DISORDER	U. S. POPULATION
Mental disorder alone	19%
Addictive disorder alone	6%
Mental and addictive disorder	3%
Total	28%

Figure 4

Mental Disorders

With such a complex structure and function of the human brain, it should not be surprising that things occasionally go wrong with it. There are two basic classes of mental disorders. Disorders related to addictions, such as alcohol or drugs, are called "addictive disorders." All others are called "mental disorders." Why the distinction? All addictive disorders have a mental component, but may require a different approach to treatment than a mental disorder that does not involve addiction.

The fact is that mental and addictive disorders produce a heavy toll on our modern society. Almost 82 percent of the population of Manhattan, New York, have some signs and symptoms of mental distress. However, most of them do not have the cluster and duration of signs and symptoms that fit into a diagnosable mental illness.[13] Recent estimates are that 28 percent of the U.S. population (44 million people) suffer from a mental or addictive disorder in any given year, as listed in **Figure 4**.[14,15] Note that about 22 percent have a mental disorder, and the remaining 6 percent have an addictive disorder.[16,17,18]

Many people with a definite mental illness continue to function with only mild or even no obvious functional impairment, since they either have a disease that is mild or they learn to cover their symptoms and feelings well. However, nine percent of the U.S. population have a mental illness of such severity that they suffer significant functional impairment,[19] such as missed days of school or work, or even hospital-ization.

The Stigma of Mental Illness

Sally Lawson was one of those self-made women. She had started a hugely successful business from scratch and now, after selling her company for a handsome price, appeared destined for a life of perpetual luxury and freedom from financial worry. She brought the same initiative and decisiveness into her hobbies. Her first love was horsemanship. Sally prided herself on her quick thinking and problem solving even in difficult situations.

However, over the years things began to change for Sally. At first the signs seemed insignificant: some difficulty sleeping, more anxiety, and increased trips to her physician for physical health concerns. Now in her 70s, Sally did have some legitimate health concerns. However, her doctor repeatedly assured her that these issues were not dangerous and should be of no concern.

Unfortunately, those assurances did not lessen the mounting anxiety. Sally knew her problems had reached monumental proportions when she found herself struggling with indecision. She was the entrepreneur, the decisive voice at corporate board meetings, a champion equestrian. Indecision was not in her vocabulary.

Sally wondered if a mental health professional could help, but she repulsed the thought. She was a self-made women. There was just too much of a stigma associated with seeing a mental health professional.

It was not until Sally was hundreds of miles from home that she ventured to recite her concerns about her symptoms to a health professional. The confidante was not a psychiatrist but an Internal Medicine specialist. And she did get help. Her problem was diagnosed as depression. She had struggled with depression without realizing it for far too long. She distanced herself from a solution because of a perceived stigma resting on mental illness and mental health professionals.

Why do so many seem to fear a diagnosis of "mental illness?" Does the very term conjure up visions of institutionalized, de-humanized forms wandering aimlessly behind barred doors and windows? Do we fail to realize that *most mental health challenges can be successfully confronted on an outpatient basis?*

Depression—A Common Mental Illness

Depression is one of the most common, dangerous, and most feared forms of mental illness. We may not have secret fears of "going crazy" and falling into a psychosis where we lose touch with reality, but all of us have times when we are "down" or feel depressed.

Drifts in moods are a normal part of the human experience. But some will have a form of depression that lingers and can have serious consequences. Such a condition is not normal; it should receive medical attention. The sufferer may not be aware that medical attention is needed, or may not want to admit it. A misunderstanding of depression may be one of our greatest threats.

Depression—What is It?

So, what is "depression?" How common is it? Who is susceptible to it? Can a person have it and not know it? Is there more than one kind? What kind of physician deals with it? Is it strictly psychological? Can depression be accurately diagnosed and effectively treated? Can it be cured? Is it related to lifestyle? If I get it, will I need to be on medication, and if so will I need the medications for life? This book is dedicated to those who want answers to these questions.

Some of the facts about depression are listed in **Figure 5**.

A form of depression called *major depression* is the second most common mental illness in the United States. It is second only to simple *phobias*, such as fear of crowds or of enclosed spaces, etc. Major depression is far and away the most common mood disorder. Up to 10 percent of the population will suffer at least one episode in any given year.[20] It affects rich and poor, famous and infamous, cutting through all sectors of society.

Depression has been a misunderstood condition by most people. We need to understand what it is, not only because it is so prevalent today, but also because it is becoming more common year by year. I see it very frequently in my office as an Internal Medicine specialist. Such specialists deal with adult physical diseases of internal organs that do not require surgery, such as heart, lung, stomach, and intestinal diseases. This was and is my forte. However, one day an article crossed my desk in one of the major specialty journals showing that *about one out of every three patients in an Internal Medicine practice have depression when it is looked for.*[21]

SOME FACTS ABOUT DEPRESSION

- Major depression is the most common mood disorder.

- It knows no cultural, social, or economic barriers.

- It is largely misunderstood.

- One out of three Internal Medicine patients has it.

- Proper treatment can effectively reduce or cure it.

- Most cases can be treated on an outpatient basis.

Figure 5

Since this disease is so common in my field, I thought it was incumbent upon me to learn as much as I could about it. I not only wanted to recognize the disease, but also be able to adequately treat my patients who are afflicted with it. I was already familiar with the many standard medicines that are effective for depression, but I desired to go far beyond just the standard diagnosis and treatment.

As with any disease, there has to be a cause. I had been carefully taught by the esteemed and now late Albert Brust, M.D., never to simply label someone with the disease of, for example, congestive heart failure; it was mandatory that I find the underlying cause of congestive heart failure. Was it a valve or electrical problem of the heart, or could it be coronary artery disease (the most common cause), or even a primary heart muscle problem? It could be a hormonal problem stemming from elsewhere but having its effect on the heart. It was imperative that I find the answers. Why? So that I could treat the patient most effectively.

But isn't the treatment for congestive heart failure the same regardless of the cause? Yes and no. Some of the standard treatments are the same regardless of the cause, such as a low sodium diet and diuretic medication. But if the best treatment regimen is to be found, the cause needs to be established. Furthermore, depending on the cause, a cure may be possible such that the patient in due course may not need to be on any medication or treatment regimen.

I questioned whether this same reasoning was valid in dealing with depression. This launched me into a study that has turned out to be highly rewarding to my patients who are victims of this disease. It has also been rewarding to those whom I have had the opportunity to teach by way of lectures and seminars.

The results of my study form the basis of this book. The approach I outline here is unique at this point in time, but I do not believe it will be for long, for two reasons: (1) the outcome in most of my depressed patients has been nothing short of excellent, and (2) it makes good scientific and clinical sense.

Since reading the Internal Medicine article on depression and becoming more aware of its signs, I see at least some elements of depression in about one out of every four of my patients. Thus, I see depressive patients on a daily basis and often many times a day. It is unfortunate that so many people who are depressed do not seek medical attention for it. For every person who comes to a doctor with this disease, there are many more who suffer from the consequences of it but do not see a physician, psychologist, or any other medical professional. Many do not seek treatment because they fail to recognize that their suffering is caused by mental distress.

Depression is on the Increase

Depression is increasing worldwide and is now striking at an earlier age, as listed in **Figure 6**.[22,23,24,25]

Note that major episodes of depression now are occurring *frequently by the age of*

DEPRESSION IS INCREASING

• The number of people developing depression has increased since 1915.

• The disease seems to be striking at an earlier age.

• Major episodes of depression now occur frequently by age 25.

• Overall risk of depression has increased over time.

Figure 6

25, whereas they previously occurred in individuals at about an average age of 40 (the so-called mid-life crisis). The risk of an individual becoming afflicted by it has also increased over time.

This increased risk of depression is astonishing in light of the society in which we are living, particularly in the United States and the developed world. There is no question that we are living in an age in which more people are doing more "fun" things than ever before in human history. They range from amusement parks to movie theaters to sporting events, and countless other forms of entertainment and amusement, not to mention the constantly running television set that is in 99 percent of homes in America. Yet we have ever increasing rates of depression and sadness. Could there be a connection between seeking fun things and failure to find lasting happiness? We will explore this most interesting question in *Chapter 9*.

The large number of people inflicted by this disease and the resulting costs from a clinical standpoint are huge, as shown in **Figure 7**.[26,27]

At this writing, we see that it affects 200 million people worldwide, which is one person out of 30 of the world's population. In the U.S. it will affect 19 million Americans this year, or one person out of 16. In the U.S. alone the cost of dealing with this disease is over $70 billion per year.[28] It approaches the amount spent on heart disease, the number one cause of death in this country. U.S. anti-depressant sales have risen more than 800% to $10.2 billion since 1990.[29] The number of people taking anti-depressant medications has also steadily increased as shown in **Figure 8**.[30] We are indeed dealing with a major disease.

What Depression is Not

Some kinds of depression are not considered to be a disease. Depressive feelings will arise in the lives of all of us that result from traumatic events or other situations, but these are normal reactions that are not associated with a disease. Some of these sources of grief are listed in **Figure 9.**

Depressive feelings associated with these situations will ease with time as we learn to go on with life. Such depression is termed situational depression. Although many of the treatments outlined in this book will work for situational depression as well, this is not our main focus.

In addition to traumatic occurrences, the list includes "Blue Monday." From time to time, almost everyone will have a "Blue Monday" even when it isn't Monday. On such days, energy will be at a low ebb, and concentration is difficult. Comments which would ordinarily be regarded as jokes may seem like insults. At times these "off days" come as the result of something definite and identifiable, such as a loss of sleep—from the day-after-the-night-before kind of thing. At other times they come without warning and for no apparent reason. Fortunately, it is possible to prevent at least most of the down days, as *Chapter 5*, "Lifestyle Treatments For Depression," will explain. However, an occasional down mood obviously does not constitute a mental illness or disease.

IMPACT OF DEPRESSION

- Affects 200 million people worldwide

- Currently affects more than 19 million Americans

- Costs over $70 billion in treatment, disability, and lost productivity in the United states each year

Figure 7

Symptoms of Depression

What, then, are the symptoms of the disease of major depression? Is complicated medical testing required? We will see that it often does not require formal testing to make a diagnosis, nor does it require a physician or psychologist, although either or both might be helpful in confirming the disease. They certainly would be helpful in the attempt to find the cause and most effective treatment. Some people have problems calling depression a disease, since it may be knowingly or unknowingly self-induced. But labeling a condition a disease does not take away responsibility of the person involved. For instance, coronary artery disease, the number one cause of heart disease and premature death in America, is often self-induced by a pattern of high-cholesterol eating habits and/or cigarette smoking, yet it is still a disease that can cause death. The same is true for depression. Listing it as a disease does not necessarily mean that it is not self-induced.

There are nine symptoms associated with the disease of major depression, as listed in **Figure 10**.[31] In the absence of emotional trauma, a diagnosis of depression can be made by determining how many of the following symptoms an individual has:

A person who experiences at least *five of the nine symptoms for at least two weeks* has clinically defined *major depression*.

A person who experiences *two of the four symptoms for at least two weeks* has a clinically defined *mild form of depression* called subsyndromal depression.

A person with the disease of major depression will rarely have all nine; however, I have seen some patients who do have them all. Of course, emotional trauma could produce all of the symptoms, but they

would not indicate the disease of depression, as previously explained.

A person with a mild form of depression, called subsyndromal depression, may not be suffering from a diminished quality of life. Yet, the importance of diagnosing the disease

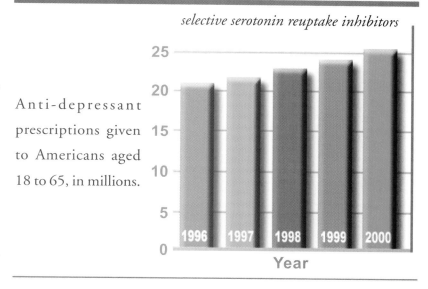

STEADY GROWTH

selective serotonin reuptake inhibitors

Anti-depressant prescriptions given to Americans aged 18 to 65, in millions.

Year

Figure 8

SITUATIONS THAT PRODUCE NORMAL DEPRESSIVE FEELINGS

• Loss of job
• Divorce
• Death of a loved one
• Disappointment in love
• "Blue Monday"

Figure 9

should not be minimized because of the high risk of it being transformed into major depression.

Let us now look at each of the nine symptoms for major depression as outlined in **Figure 10**.[31]

The first symptom, deep sadness, is what most people equate with feeling depressed. People qualify for this symptom if they personally acknowledge that almost every day they feel sad or empty most of the day, or if a reliable person makes a similar observation about them. For example, an observer may notice that the person in question becomes tearful without an obvious cause. Often my patients with depression will be explaining something to me in the exam room and then will lose

SYMPTOMS OF MAJOR DEPRESSION

1. Deep sadness or emptiness

2. Apathy

3. Agitation or restlessness

4. Sleep disturbances

5. Weight/appetite disturbances

6. Lack of concentration

7. Feelings of excessive guilt or worthlessness

8. Morbid thoughts

9. Fatigue

Figure 10

control and begin to cry, saying that they don't know why they are crying. If they feel ashamed, as they often do, I reassure them that there is nothing to be ashamed of. I have a box of facial tissues in every room and invariably hand them one and provide reassurance. Children or adolescents will qualify for this symptom even if their mood is not sad, but irritable instead.

It is important to note that I often see people with depression that do not have the symptom of deep sadness, and thus will deny that they are depressed; to them, sadness equals depression, and since they don't feel sad, they think that they can't be depressed. On the other hand, it is equally important to realize that not everyone who experiences deep sadness or even crying spells is suffering from a mental disease. If they do qualify for this symptom, it will often be because of their feelings of emptiness.

Also, those who do not qualify for this symptom or symptom number two, apathy, do not have major depression, regardless of how many other symptoms they exhibit.

Apathy is described by a markedly diminished interest or pleasure in almost all activities for most of the day, nearly every day. Even doing "fun" things is no longer enjoyable. The motivational level of the affected person is often decreased significantly.

The third symptom, agitation, is a disturbance without a definite cause, often described as restlessness. A person will also qualify for this symptom if the body's general level of activity is significantly slowed. The individual may not be aware of his slower walking pace unless he sees himself on a home video. Other usual activities will often be significantly slowed.

The fourth symptom, sleep disturbance, may vary from one person to another. Some individuals will have insomnia almost every night, while others will feel sleepy or may even be found sleeping much of the time, even during the day. These people characteristically will not want to get up in the morning, but will have to "drag themselves" out of bed.

The fifth symptom, weight or appetite change, can also go either direction. For an established patient of mine, I will check the individual's previous weight. If a loss or gain of five or more percent of body weight occurs in one month without significantly attempting a weight change, this symptom applies. It will also apply if they have a marked increase or decrease in appetite nearly every day. Children will qualify if they fail to undergo expected weight gains with time.

The sixth symptom, lack of concentration, is most notable in students or brain workers. Those who have difficulty in making decisions or say that clear thinking is difficult nearly every day will also qualify for this symptom.

The seventh symptom of feelings of worthlessness makes a person feel that he is of no use to any other person on almost a daily basis. Excessive or inappropriate guilt would also qualify him for this symptom. Merely self-reproach or guilt about being sick does not qualify this person for this condition.

The eighth symptom, morbid thoughts, includes recurrent thoughts about death or suicide, whether or not the person has actually formed a specific plan for carrying it out. Obviously, if the person has already attempted suicide he would qualify for this condition.

The ninth and last symptom is the one I see most often in my practice—fatigue or lack of energy nearly every day. Many people come to me with this complaint. I usually ask questions about the other symptoms to see if depression could be the underlying cause. Although most of my patients with fatigue do not have depression as the cause, many do; for those who do, I take the approach described in *Chapter 3* to find the real cause of their depression as I compile a profile of their condition. It often takes some convincing that they have

depression if they have the symptom of fatigue, but are not experiencing the symptom of deep sadness. This realization must occur if a lasting treatment program is to be followed by the patient. It is the important first step to initiate a lasting treatment to reach the goal of a lasting cure.

A more detailed explanation of major depression symptoms is found in *Appendix III*. For those who may be interested in the symptoms of another mild form of depression called dysthymic disorder, you will find them in *Appendix IV*.

ABRAHAM LINCOLN'S DEPRESSION

"I am now the most miserable man living. If what I feel were equally distributed to the whole human family, there would be not one cheerful face on earth. Whether I shall ever be better, I cannot tell. I awfully [fearfully] forbode [predict] I shall not. To remain as I am is impossible. I must die or be better it appears to me."

—*Abraham Lincoln*

Conclusion

The human brain is a marvelous organ in structure and function. Its amazing inter-communications linking electrical and chemical signals have been the subject of ongoing studies by scientists and physicians ad infinitum. However, like any other organ of the body, it can have malfunctions that afflict people in every walk of life in the U.S. and around the earth. Depression is one of these maladies.

The percentage of the U.S. population afflicted by depression is at an all-time high, and continues to increase. The increase is much greater among the 15 to 25-year-old age group. Such disorders may be an embarrassment to the victims that results in a denial or cover-up of the disease, and thus the victims go untreated.

The good news is that recent discoveries in the diagnosis and treatment of depression have markedly increased the opportunity for recovery. These new lines of attack are a departure from the customary medicines in common use today for treating this disease. The approach has proven to be very beneficial to my patients, which should be an encouragement to all who are suffering from depression or who know someone who is. This book is committed to spelling out the workings of this unique method of treatment.

References—

[1] *Mental Health: A Report of the Surgeon General* Department of Health and Human Services, National Institutes of Health, National Institutes of Mental Health, 1999 p. 32.

[2] *Mental Health: A Report of the Surgeon General* Department of Health and Human Services, National Institutes of Health, National Institutes of Mental Health, 1999 p. 32.

[3] Simon R, Sunseri M, Goldman:Cecil Textbook of Medicine, 21st Ed., 2000:2036,2037.

[4] Simon R, Sunseri M, Goldman:Cecil Textbook of Medicine, 21st Ed., 2000:2036.

[5] Simon R, Sunseri M, Goldman:Cecil Textbook of Medicine, 21st Ed., 2000:2034.

[6] Simon R, Sunseri M, Goldman:Cecil Textbook of Medicine, 21st Ed., 2000:2035.

[7] Simon R, Sunseri M, Goldman:Cecil Textbook of Medicine, 21st Ed., 2000:2037.

[8] Goetz C, Pappert E, Textbook of Clinical Neurology, 1st Ed., 1999:34.

[9] Simon R, Sunseri M, Goldman:Cecil Textbook of Medicine, 21st Ed., 2000:2037,2038.

[10] Gould E, Reeves AJ, et al. Neurogenesis in the neocortex of adult primates. *Science* 1999 Oct;286:548-552.

[11] Frances Collins, director of the human genome project, quoted at a speech to the National Institutes of Health, January 18, 2001. Previous numbers of genes were estimated to be 80,000 but new research puts the number at about 35,000. Published work on this due soon.

[12] Ephesians 4:23. *The Holy Bible*. KJV.

[13] Srole L. Mental health in the metropolis: the Midtown Manhattan study. 1962 New York:Mcgraw-Hill.

[14] Epidemiologic Catchment Area (ECA) Program of the national institute of mental health, division of biometry and epidemiology. 1981, 82.

[15] Kessler RC, McGonagle KA, et.al., Lifetime and 12 month prevalence of DSM-III-R psychiatric disorders in the United States. Results from the National Comorbidity Survey. *Arch Gen Psychiatry* 1994 Jan;51(1):8-19.

[16] Regier DA, Narrow WE, et.al., Community estimates of medical necessity. G.Andrews & S. Henderson, Unmet needs in mental health service delivery. Cambridge, England: Cambridge University Press 2000.

[17] Kessler RC, Berglund PA, et.al., The 12 month prevalence and correlates of serious mental illness. Manderscheid, R., & Sonnenschein MA, Mental health, United States, 1996. p. 59-70 Washington D.C.

U.S. Government Printing Office.

[18] Kessler RC, McGonagle KA, et.al., Lifetime and 12 month prevalence of DSM-III-R psychiatric disorders in the United States. Results from the National Comorbidity Survey. *Arch Gen Psychiatry* 1994 Jan;51(1):8-19.

[19] National Advisory Mental Health Council 1993.

[20] Kessler RC. Comorbidity of DSM-III-R major depressive disorder in the general population: results from the US National Comorbidity Survey. *Br J Psychiatry Suppl* 1996 Jun;(30):17-30.

[21] Rucker L. Feasibility and usefulness of depression screening in medical outpatients. Arch Intern Med 1986 Apr;146(4):729-731.

[22] Birmaher B, Ryan ND, et al. Childhood and adolescent depression: a review of the past 10 years. Part I. J Am Acad Child Adoles Psychiatry 1996;35(11):1427-1439.

[23] Klerman, GL, Weissman, MM. Increasing rates of depression. *JAMA* 1989;261:2229-2235.

[24] Cross-National Collaborative Group The changing rate of major depression: cross-national comparisons. JAMA 1992;268:3098-3105.

[25] Kessler RC, McGonagle KA, Nelson CB, Hughes M, Swartz M, and Blazer DG. Sex and depression in the National Comorbidity Survey. II: cohort effects. J Aff Disord 1994;30:15-26.

[26] Narrow WE. One-year prevalence of depressive disorders among adults 18 and over in the U.S.: NIMH ECA prospective data. Population estimates based on U.S. Census estimated residential population age 18 and over on July 1, 1998. Unpublished but cited by the National Institute of Mental Health in a paper entitled "The Invisible Disease: Depression" found at www.nimh.nih.gov/publicat/invisible.cfm.

[27] Regier DA, Narrow WE, et al. The de facto mental and addictive disorders service system. Epidemiologic Catchment Area prospective 1-year prevalence rates of disorders and services. *Arch Gen Psychiatry* 1993;50(2):85-94.

[28] Mental Illness: A Rising Workplace Loss. *Wall Street Journal* June 13, 2001.

[29] IMS Health as quoted by *Wall Street Journal* June 13, 2001. Mental Illness A Rising Workplace Loss.

[30] IMS Health as quoted by *Wall Street Journal* June 13, 2001. Mental Illness A Rising Workplace Loss.

[31] Mental Health: A Report of the Surgeon General Department of Health and Human Services, National Institutes of Health, National Institutes of Mental Health, 1999 p. 247.

CHAPTER TWO

DEPRESSION'S HIDDEN DANGERS

Depression is a familiar word describing an often-baffling illness portrayed by many faces.

Ed Harris wore one of those faces. A successful businessman and a respected elder in his local church, Ed had health problems. He heard that my excellent success in treating patients resulted from searching for the identity and root cause of an illness, not just medicating the symptoms—so he scheduled an appointment with me. I met Ed and his wife, Carrie, in the exam room. After exchanging pleasantries, I asked him about the severe headaches he had listed as his chief complaint.

The headaches occurred almost daily for nearly two years. Ed had already seen his family physician, who gave him a prescription and ordered an MRI (magnetic resonance imaging)—an expensive and sophisticated series of three-dimensional pictures of the brain, skull, and sinuses. Despite the medication, Ed's headaches did not improve. The physician sent him to a specialist, a reputable neurologist. After seeing Ed's satisfactory MRI, the neurologist prescribed a stronger pain medication. At first the intensity of Ed's headaches lessened, but later, the pain increased as Ed developed a tolerance to the stronger medication.

After hearing Ed's description of the headaches I asked, "Do you ever experience fatigue?" He replied that he had absolutely no energy and said, "It is a chore just to get up in the morning."

I asked, "Do you ever feel deep sadness or worthlessness?" and "Do you ever have trouble sleeping or concentrating?" Ed replied that he didn't, but Carrie vigorously nodded her head.

Drawing Carrie into the conversation I said, "Obviously your wife disagrees, Ed." Then I asked, "Why are you nodding your head, Carrie?" When she described several of Ed's experiences, he insisted that these experiences weren't important. But as Carrie continued to add examples, Ed finally said, "Doctor, I hadn't quite thought about it like that before, but I will have to say that she is right."

When Ed's medical history was completed, he acknowledged that seven of the symptoms of major depression (listed in *Chapter 1*) applied to him. The remaining two, "morbid thoughts" and "appetite changes," were the only symptoms that he had not reluctantly acknowledged. After finishing the physical examination, I looked at Ed's blood laboratory work and X-rays and then explained my diagnosis. I told him that major depression was the likely cause of his chronic headache. I recommended a special interview and exam to determine the cause of his depression (the subject of *Chapter 3*). I also recommended changes in nutrition and lifestyle along with medical treatment.

Ed seemed embarrassed and continued to question the diagnosis. He reasoned that he had a *physical* disease with real, physical pain that at times was almost disabling. He was unconvinced that his physical pain could be caused by depression, a *mental* illness. Finally, Carrie insisted, "Look Ed, nothing you have done up to now has really relieved your headaches. I think this is at least worth a try!"

Ed and many other depressed individuals find it difficult to believe that depression is not simply a mental illness with mental symptoms (outlined in *Chapter 1*, **Figure 10**). This perception is partially the result of a centuries-old misconception taught by ancient Greek philosophers—the *artificial separation of mind and body*. The term "mental illness" frequently becomes an obstacle to public understanding, as it did in Ed's case.

DEPRESSION'S IMPACT ON DEADLY DISEASES

Depression increases risk of:

- Fatal stroke by 50%

- Sudden cardiac death in heart attack survivors by 2 1/2 times

- Death from cancer

- Death from pneumonia

Figure 1

Failure to recognize the hand-and-glove relationship of mind and body leads to inaccurate understanding of health and illness. It is a misconception that mental illness is unrelated to physical health, and that physical illness is unrelated to mental health. *In reality, the mental and physical aspects of health and disease are completely inseparable.*[1] As both cause and effect, depression complicates other illnesses.

Depression would be serious enough if it simply produced *mental* symptoms. But depression can also be the root cause of symptoms that are *life threatening*. When a person is physically ill, depression can dramatically intensify the disease to the point of causing death. Several major diseases that are seriously impacted by depression are listed in **Figure 1**.[2,3]

Depression and Stroke

Stroke is the first physical illness on the list that can be worsened by depression. The most common physical factor in strokes is atherosclerosis, or the build-up of plaque in the arteries supplying the brain. The arteries eventually clog, causing the death of brain tissue supplied by these damaged arteries. Note that the risk of having a fatal stroke is increased by 50 percent for people who suffer from depression.[4] Why? Depression alters the *platelets* (small cell particles) circulating in the bloodstream, causing them to become overactive, which increases the risk that an artery with a cholesterol build-up will become blocked.[5] The likelihood of stroke is also increased by the release of stress hormones from the adrenal glands,[6] located above the kidneys.

Depression and Heart Disease

Heart disease, the second malady on the list impacted by depression, is the number one cause of death in the U.S. and the entire world.[7] Heart attack patients, after recovering from their physical symptoms, may feel unable to step back into their simplest routines. They may feel an uneasy sadness or a lack of energy that they cannot explain. It is normal for heart attack patients to feel sadness because of their illness. However, it is abnormal for that sadness to continue more than two weeks, particularly when recovery is satisfactory. Prolonged despondency should receive appropriate treatment, as explained in **Figure 2**.

Studies show that heart patients experiencing fatigue, but not depression, have a 50 percent greater risk of dying within two years after a heart attack,[8] compared to healthy people. Heart patients who experience major depression are 150 percent more likely to die within two years than their non-depressed counterparts.[9] This alarming increase in death may be partially explained by physical factors related to depression. Depression increases disturbances in heart rhythm and decreases the heart's ability to speed up with activity or slow down with rest.[10,11] These ominous numbers suggest that *getting adequate treatment for depression or fatigue may be even more important than being on the right medication following a heart attack.*

When significant coronary heart disease is diagnosed, bypass surgery is often performed to improve the blood flow to the heart. After recovery from surgery, patients frequently feel that the heart problem is corrected and that they no longer have to worry about the heart. As I describe in my book *Proof Positive*, if the blood cholesterol level, blood pressure, and tobacco dependency status of the patient is not corrected, blockages will develop in the bypass grafts, usually within one to ten years.

What was not known at the writing of *Proof Positive* is that there is a more important factor than cholesterol level, blood pressure, or smoking status—the *mood status* of the bypass patient. Research shows that being depressed after coronary bypass surgery is a good predictor that a person will suffer a recurrence of chest pain and the blockages that cause them within one to five years.[12] The studies indicate that

DEPRESSION FOLLOWING A HEART ATTACK

If a recovering heart attack victim becomes depressed:

- Depression is a threat to recovery.

- Depression sharply increases the risk of dying within two years.

- Treatment for depression is a "must."

Figure 2

in the development of recurrent heart disease, *depression outweighs the well-known heart disease risk factors.*

Another study shows that depression triples the risk of contracting heart disease in men who have never had heart problems.[13] This risk is independent of other known risks of heart disease, including smoking, blood cholesterol levels, diabetes, and high blood pressure.

Risk to the elderly for coronary heart disease is increased by depression. A large study of depressed men and women older than 65 was recently completed. These 4,493 subjects, who did not have any known heart disease, were analyzed for depression symptoms. Some participants had high depression scores while others had no symptoms of depression. For those who had high depression scores, the risk of heart disease increased by 40 percent and risk of death by 60 percent. The study's authors concluded that among elderly Americans, symptoms of depression point toward additional risk for coronary heart disease and death.[14]

Regarding diabetics, depression strongly increases the risk of heart disease for the insulin-dependent,[15] but does not seem to increase the risk in non-diabetic women under the age of 65.[16]

DEPRESSION AFFECTS CANCER RISK

- Good mental health may improve the chance of recovery from cancer.

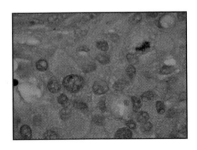

- Depression weakens the immune system's power to attack cancer cells.

- Older adults having depression for six years have greater risk of getting cancer.

Figure 3

Depression and Cancer

What about the effects of depression on cancer, the second leading cause of death in the U.S.? When cancer spreads beyond the originating organ, it is often fatal. Whether or not it is fatal, and how long an individual lives after getting terminal cancer, are influenced by several factors that include: (1) the type of cancer, (2) where it has spread, (3) what type of treatment has been prescribed, and (4) the patient's mental health.[17,18,19]

Research indicates that good mental health may improve the chance for recovery from cancer as shown in **Figure 3**. Good mental health can counteract the negative effect depression has on the immune system.[20]

One study from the National Institute on Aging in Bethesda, Maryland, indicates that adults older than 70 years of age who have chronic depression for at least six years have twice the risk of contracting cancer, compared with mentally healthy peers.[21] The higher risk applies to almost all types of cancer.

Depression and Pneumonia

Along with cancer and heart disease, pneumonia ranks among the five leading causes of death in the U.S.[22] Like cancer and heart disease, depression can seriously complicate pneumonia. Although most people who develop pneumonia recover, studies show that the risk of dying from pneumonia significantly increases if the patient is also depressed.[23]

Mortality

Depression can be a risk factor for death at any age, but is especially true in older adults. A six-year study of 5,200 Americans 65 and older examined the relationship between depressive symptoms and death.[24] The risk of mortality was 25 to 43 percent higher among individuals with major depression. Further examination of data showed that among older adults even milder forms of depression were found to increase the risk of death.[26]

What Body Functions are Harmed by Depression?

You saw the potentially fatal effects of depression on each of four major illnesses in **Figure 1**. Depression can also be detrimental to a host of body functions which may or may not increase the risk of death, but do decrease the quality of life. A total of 11 potentially harmful effects of depression on body functions are listed in **Figure 4**.

Let us take a closer look at each of these 11 body functions.

Depression Reduces Brain Size

The first harmful effect on our list involves *the brain*. Depression not only causes well-defined temporary changes in the structure and function of the brain, but may also cause permanent changes according to a study at the Washington University School of Medicine in St. Louis. An MRI was used to take three-dimensional pictures of the brains of depressed and healthy women.

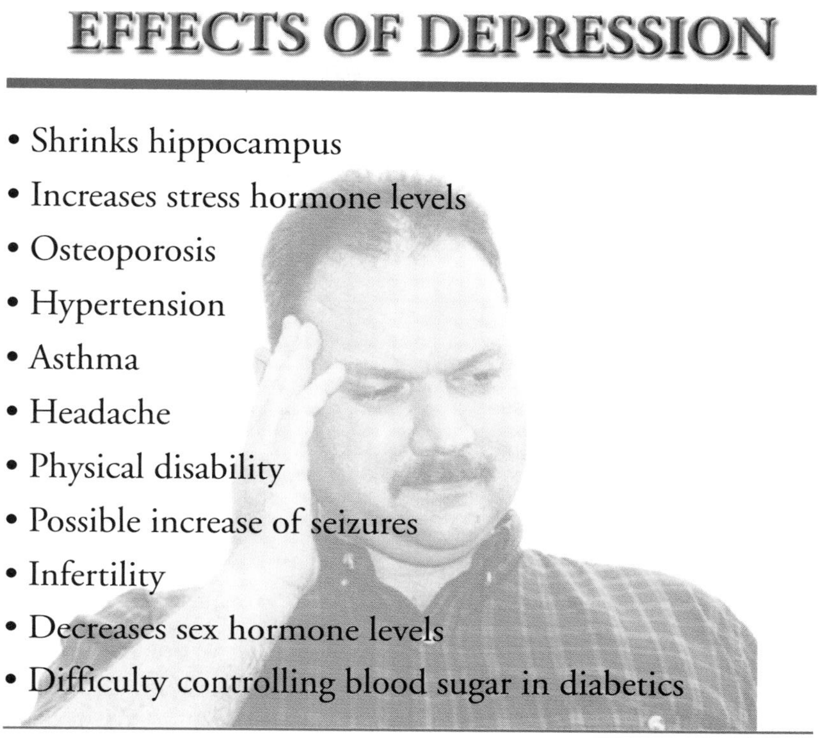

Women with a history of depression had 9 to 13 percent *smaller hippocampal sizes.*[27]

The hippocampus area of the brain is involved in *learning and memory,* as explained in *Chapter 1.* Women in the study group reported an average of about five episodes of depression, with one woman reporting 18 occurrences. The study participants who reported the most occurrences of depression had smaller hippocampal sizes than women who reported fewer episodes. Women with a history of depression had lower scores on a test that measured verbal memory, a key function of the hippocampus. The study also found that the amygdala, an area of the brain associated with emotion, was also smaller in women with a history of depression.

One of the authors of the study, Yvette L. Sheline, M.D., stated, "The finding that depression can result in [cause] volume loss and that more depression can result in [cause] even greater volume loss underscores the importance of treating and preventing depression." Adequate treatment can prevent suffering, restore the quality of life, and may limit long-term damage to specific areas of the brain.

Increased Stress Hormone Levels

The second harmful effect in **Figure 4** is *stress hormones.* While depression suppresses certain mind and body functions, it actually increases the output of at least three hormones: a *hypothalamic hormone,* one of the *pituitary hormones,* and *blood cortisol,* a stress hormone produced by the adrenal glands. Like a domino effect, the increased output of the first hormone may trigger the output of the second one, etc..[28] These increases in stress hormone levels explain long-term decreases in the size and function of certain areas of the brain.

In healthy individuals who experience stress, a high cortisol level may generate a feeling of *increased energy,* helping them to "fight" stress, but in depressed individuals

EFFECTS OF DEPRESSION

- Shrinks hippocampus
- Increases stress hormone levels
- Osteoporosis
- Hypertension
- Asthma
- Headache
- Physical disability
- Possible increase of seizures
- Infertility
- Decreases sex hormone levels
- Difficulty controlling blood sugar in diabetics

Figure 4

a high cortisol level tends to *decrease the energy level* and make the depression last longer. A high cortisol level may also make the depression more likely to return after an initial recovery.[29]

A high level of cortisol in the bloodstream for more than a few days is undesirable for healthy as well as depressed individuals. In fact, in some instances cortisol may be related to a gradual shrinking of areas of the brain responsible for verbal memory.[30,31] In *Chapter 7,* "Stress and Anxiety," we take a more detailed look at this important hormone. We also teach how to lower cortisol levels. This important reduction may also reverse some of the effects of aging on the brain.[32]

Osteoporosis

Osteoporosis (thinning of the bones) has become a household word. Worldwide, this disease affects one in three women past the age of 50.[33] Although the disease especially affects white women after menopause, it also affects all other races and both sexes. Hip fractures are among the most feared complications of osteoporosis, but fractures of the backbones (vertebrae) and wrists are also commonly related to this bone-thinning process.

You probably know one or more people who have suffered broken bones after a simple fall. About 1.3 million osteoporosis-related fractures occur each year in the U.S. More than half of all postmenopausal women will suffer a fracture due to osteoporosis at some time in their lives. These fractures can decrease the quality of life and set the stage for premature death through such complications as pneumonia. The media has primarily emphasized calcium as a deterrent for bone thinning, but this mineral is far too simplistic, considering that countries with the *highest calcium intakes* also *have the highest rates of osteoporosis in the world*.[34] For more complete information on the role of diet and lifestyle in the management of this disease, see my book *Proof Positive*.

You may ask, "What does depression have to do with osteoporosis?" Research discovers a close relationship. In one study, 24 depressed women were compared with 24 mentally healthy women. Their average age was 41. The depressed women's average bone mineral density was 6 percent lower in the spine and 10 to 14 percent lower in the hip. The authors of this study note, "the lifetime risk of fracture related to depression is substantial."[35]

This observation is supported by another study of both men and women, that compared those who reported major depression with others who were mentally healthy. The study showed that among the depressed participants, significant bone loss occurred during a two-year period. The degree of bone loss was greater in depressed men than in depressed women. Although this new research shows a rather surprising connection between seemingly disconnected systems of the body—the brain and the bones—Solomon of old seems to have recognized this connection more than 2500 years ago. Three of his proverbs are recited in **Figure 5**.[37]

Hypertension

The fourth body function in **Figure 4** that is affected by depression is blood pressure. *Hypertension* (high blood pressure) affects one out of every six Americans. This condition is a major contributor to the buildup of plaque and blockages in the body's many arteries. Although there are many other causes of high blood pressure, depression and stress are emerging as conspicuous causes. Many depressed patients experience anxiety, which is a stress-related mental disorder. A combination of depression and anxiety significantly increase the risk of developing hypertension, as portrayed in **Figure 6**.[38]

In this study of more than 3,000 people, ages 25 to 64, it would be reasonable to expect a variety of health histories, including lifestyles and risk factors. I have found that in order to adequately treat some patients' elevated blood pressure, I first have to determine the source of their depression and anxiety before attempting to offer a lasting solution to the problem.

Blood Sugar

The broad consequences of depression can also be seen in the management of insulin-dependent *diabetes*. Research indicates that controlling blood sugar is harder when the diabetic patient is also depressed, anxious, or excessively stressed.[39] For example, prescribing certain relaxation therapies that are done daily at home may help reduce blood sugar for a depression-free patient. However, relaxation therapy does not affect the blood sugar of a depressed or stressed diabetic. Depression prevents the therapy from being effective. As in the previously mentioned research, this study confirms that the best approach is to *find and treat the cause* of an illness.

Asthma

Asthma is number six on the list of maladies aggravated by depression. Adults who report higher levels of stress and depression are more than twice as likely to develop asthma.[40] In fact, depression and anxiety seem to be major contributors to the development of asthma, particularly in non-smokers. Adequately controlling stress and treating depression may not only *prevent* asthma but can also assist in *controlling relapses* in those who already have the disease.

Headache

Two to three percent of Americans have *chronic tension headaches* causing pain on both sides of the head and neck that can persist from half an hour to several weeks. A study shows that nearly half of those reporting chronic tension headaches also have anxiety or depression. Many headache patients do not show obvious signs of these mental symptoms, which are only identified after an interview and evaluation, according to lead author Dr. Gay Lipchik of Ohio University.[41]

Many of the patients in Dr. Lipchick's study had been troubled by headaches for so long that they could not remember which symptom came first, the headache or the depression. Thus the researchers were unable to determine whether the psychological problems arose before the onset of the headaches or were caused by the headaches. I have found in my practice that when a good treatment regimen for depression is followed, the headache often ceases. This is exactly what I told Ed Harris, our patient at the beginning of this chapter.

Physical Disability

About 20 percent of the elderly show

PROVERBS ON THE BRAIN AND BONES

"The light of the eyes rejoiceth the heart: and a good report maketh the bones fat."
Proverbs 15:30
"Pleasant words are as an honeycomb, sweet to the soul and health to the bones."
Proverbs 16:24
"A merry heart doeth good like a medicine; but a broken spirit drieth the bones"
Proverbs 17:22

Figure 5

DEPRESSION CAN RAISE YOUR BLOOD PRESSURE

Risk of hypertension of 3,310 depressed and anxious individuals:

Group	Increased risk of hypertension
Men	50%
White Women	70%
Black Women	200%

Figure 6

some signs of depression. If otherwise healthy persons past the age of 70 display just one symptom of depression, they are more likely to become *disabled* within the next four years.[42,43] The more symptoms displayed (see *Chapter 1* for the list of symptoms of depression) the greater the risk of disability. Research indicates that, "the prevention and treatment of depressive symptoms may be one of the most effective targets for interventions aimed at reducing physical decline and increasing the number of years during which older people are free of disability."[44] Thus, treating even very mild depression in the elderly may prevent their decline by short-circuiting the interactive and progressive downward spiral of depression and physical disability. Whether or not an aging person requires nursing home care may be more closely related to mental health than to physical health. The risks of disability faced by depressed elderly are listed in **Figure 7.**

Seizures

Admittedly, not all of the physical effects of depression are known at this time. Also, some of the consequences already understood may be due indirectly to effects other than depression. For example, as

previously stated, too much cortisol put out by the adrenal glands in response to depression can cause osteoporosis and high blood pressure. But one fact is clear— *depression is closely associated with a host of physical diseases and symptoms.*

Further study of these numerous other associations is needed. For instance, older adults who are depressed are six times as likely to have a *seizure* as their happier peers.[45] This finding suggests that, at least in some cases, an underlying third factor may be the cause of both depression and seizures.

Infertility and sex hormones

The final two items on the effects of depression on body functions involve *infertility and sex hormones.* Another connection suggesting a need for further study shows that women who experience infertility are frequently depressed. According to some studies, they may be as depressed as those with cancer, AIDS, or heart disease. Some of these cases of infertility may be linked directly to depression.

A study involved 174 infertile women. Some were depressed and others were not. They were all given a ten-week course in stress management to see if it would cure the infertility. About 60 percent of the depressed women had a baby after completing the course, but only 24 percent of those who were not depressed had a baby after completing the same course.[46] The conclusions are that (1) depression was the cause of infertility in many of the women, and (2) that treating the depression will solve the problem in many cases.

Depression also increases the risk of *infertility* in men according to a separate study.[47] Men with depression severe enough to be hospitalized had significantly lower testosterone levels throughout the day and night. Elevated blood cortisol levels, linked to depression, could possibly be the explanation.

DEPRESSION AMONG THE ELDERLY

- Risk of disability is increased with only one depression symptom.

- The more symptoms there are, the greater the risk.

- By treating the symptoms the risk is reduced.

•Treating even mild depression can reduce the risk.

Figure 7

Depression Affects Behavior

We have seen many of the ways depression can affect body functions. It can also have damaging effects on our behavior, some of which are listed in **Figure 8**.

Let us now explore these five behaviors.

Interference with Learning and Job Prospects

Depression in the young can inflict long-term or even permanent damage, as explained in **Figure 9.**

Students, whatever their age, who are afflicted by depression find it difficult to function appropriately in school and social settings. Older students and adults suffering from moderate to severe depression commonly miss days of work. Depression can prevent students from successfully completing an education and make it difficult for them to get and keep a job in the adult world. Job performance is usually poor when they do work. Absences and poor performance eventually affect their current employment and future job prospects.

Unfortunately, depression is now occurring more frequently in younger age groups in our society. The younger the person when depression strikes, the more likely it is that the illness will reduce learning ability and eventually job prospects. In a study of 500 depressed 30-year-olds, 43 percent of the subjects had depression prior to the age of 22, or early-onset depression. The men and women with early-onset depression were more likely to have never married and less likely to have obtained a college degree. Women with early-onset depression were 50 percent less likely to have obtained a college degree than were women with late-onset depression. This probably not only limited job choices but also the women's annual income by age 30. It is obvious that when depression occurs at a young age, it is even more important to find the cause and adequately treat it.

BEHAVIORS AFFECTED BY DEPRESSION

- Interference with learning and job prospects

- Increases the likelihood of having problem children

- Nicotine addiction

- Alcoholism

- Suicide

Figure 8

DEPRESSION IN THE YOUNG

Depression in the young can have serious consequences:

- Reduces learning ability
- Impairs job performance
- Weakens pursuit of a college degree
- Tends to create social isolation

Figure 9

21

Problem Children

Depressed mothers are more likely to have problem children, as described in **Figure 10**.

In a study of 1,215 mothers and their children at the University of North Carolina,[48] 55 percent of the moms were never depressed, 38 percent were sometimes depressed, and 8 percent suffered from clinical major depression. Three-year-old children of the clinically depressed mothers were less cooperative and exhibited more problem behaviors than those of the other two groups.

These children also fared worse on tests

CHILDREN OF DEPRESSED MOMS TEND TO HAVE:

- Weak verbal skills

- More defiant attitudes

- More behavior problems

Figure 10

that measure expressive language and verbal comprehension. Children of moms who were never depressed scored highest, while children of mothers who were depressed at times but did not have major depression, scored somewhere between the other two groups. This study indicates that maternal depression can have profound effects on young children.

Fortunately, depression in the mother was not the only factor determining the child's outcome. Sensitive moms who were respectful of their children, supportive of their activities, and did not interfere unnecessarily, had children who fared better on intelligence and language tests and were

more helpful in cleaning up play things. The negative effects of clinical depression seemed to be somewhat weakened when a depressed mother was also sensitive.

The study's lead author cautions, "One implication of these findings is that those who are endeavoring to help depressed mothers with young children might do well to focus on other factors in addition to the depression itself. A lack of maternal sensitivity and a low quality of mother-child interaction have their negative effects, especially in families in which the depressed mother feels unsupported by her social network and is under financial stress."

Nicotine Addiction

One of the potential effects of depression is nicotine addiction. People diagnosed with major depression are three times more likely to become smokers.[49] This regression from depression to smoking usually begins in adolescence. There is good news, however. Once depressed smokers decide to kick the habit, they have no more difficulty in succeeding than do their non-depressed peers.[50] For information on how to successfully take the misery out of kicking the habit see *Chapter 16* in **Proof Positive**.[51]

Alcohol Addiction

Many people who have at some point in their lives been heavy smokers or drinkers find it necessary to avoid environments that support these practices. It is important for them to know that once any addictive habit is overcome, there is always the possibility of relapse and return to harmful behavior. To avoid relapse, a former alcoholic cannot afford even one social drink but must maintain complete abstinence.

Depression can reduce the moral strength needed to overcome any kind of addiction. In one study of people hospitalized for alcohol dependence, depressed patients after treatment relapsed three times faster than those not having major depression.[52] Some patients did not relapse, however. This fact provides encouragement and removes an across-the-board excuse for others who are struggling with addictions.

Antidepressant medications did not help. Depressed patients who were taking antidepressant medications relapsed at about the same point in time as depressed patients on no medications. This fact again emphasizes *the need to go beyond the simplistic approach of prescribing medication* to find and treat the *cause* of depression.

Suicide: Depression's Close Relative

Suicide is responsible for 31,000 deaths per year and is the eighth leading cause of death in the U.S..[53] Suicide attempts bring 500,000 people to this country's emergency rooms every year.[54] More firearm-related fatalities result from suicide than from homicide (50 percent more people kill themselves than others) in this country.[55] The purchase of a handgun may increase the risk of suicide.[56] The status of suicide in the U.S. is outlined in **Figure 11**.

Suicide is now the fourth leading cause of death between the ages of 10 and 15, and the third leading cause of death between the ages of 15 and 25.[57] Suicide among those who are 10 to 20 years old have dramatically increased during the last 50 years.[58,59] Although fatalities occur in all age groups, depressed adolescents and the elderly commit suicide more often than all other age groups. The problem is not confined to the Western world. Suicide in some developing nations such as Sri Lanka, particularly via poisoning, is five times higher than in the West.[60]

Studies prove that movies, certain kinds of music, and news reports frequently trigger depression and suicide. *Depression diseases* (including major depression) are the *leading cause of suicide*, and are present in about 35 percent of all cases.[61] Furthermore, *the more severe the depression, the greater the risk of suicide.*

In cases of depression severe enough to

THE STATUS OF SUICIDE

- One-half million people per year attempt suicide.

- Less than 10% succeed.

- The severely depressed are at highest risk.

- Adolescents and the elderly are at high risk.

Figure 11

be hospitalized, as many as 15 percent will eventually be successful in a suicide attempt.[62] The risk of suicide increases when depression is not treated adequately. In a study of people with major depression who committed suicide during one calendar year in Finland, 45 percent were receiving psychiatric care at the time of death. Obviously, a majority of these patients were not receiving adequate treatment for their depression. Depressed individuals who were receiving no treatment for their condition committed more than half of the suicides. This observation underscores the urgent need for depressed individuals to locate an appropriate treatment program promptly.

Research reveals that there are many factors that contribute to increased risk for suicide. Fourteen are shown in **Figure 12**.[63,64,65,66,67,68,69]

As you examine this list, you will notice that some of these risk factors cannot be changed, such as gender, family history, and stressful loss. Fortunately, others can be changed, such as unwillingness to seek help, choice of music, alcohol or drug usage, and body image disorder. Appropriate management of these factors is the basis of treatment and recovery.

Let us examine some of these risk factors.

Gender and Suicide Risk

Men are more than four times as likely to commit suicide than women. Women are more likely to be depressed than men, and four times as likely to *attempt* suicide,[70] which means that men who attempt to end their lives *are more than 16 times as likely to succeed.*[71]

Various Mental Illnesses and Suicide Risk

Panic disorder (episodes of severe stress symptoms such as chest pain, heart racing,

flushing, and feelings of severe anxiety without apparent cause) increases risk of suicide, particularly if depression is also present.[72] Also, depression in combination with any other mental illness such as *schizophrenia* can become a deadly combination.

A person with *bipolar disorder* is one who experiences alternating periods of euphoria and depression. Such a person has a greater suicide risk than does a person without mental illness. This disease is explained in *Appendix V.*

Alcohol or Drug Abuse Increases Suicide Risk

Alcohol or drug use can lead to suicide even in those who are not depressed. According to Ronald Kessler, professor of healthcare policy at Harvard Medical School in Boston, Massachusetts, "You don't have to be an alcoholic; just the fact that you're disinhibited [lost your normal inhibitions due to the influence of alcohol or a drug] at the moment is enough—which is bad news." While the temporary suspension of good judgment by alcohol or drugs is often thought of as a secondary cause of death, Dr. Kessler found that when an individual is depressed, the use of alcohol or drugs often leads directly to the suicide attempt.[73]

Some sad or anxious people drink alcohol or use drugs to dull their emotional pain. What many of these individuals do not realize is that these drugs eventually worsen their moods and heighten suicidal thoughts. For years, therapists have recognized that using alcohol or drugs increases the risk of suicide. Thirty percent of suicide victims have alcohol in their bloodstream.[74] Many healthy people die each year from suicide—people with absolutely no depression or mental illness. Often their only risk factor is the alcohol they consume.

New research confirms that being under

14 SUICIDE RISK FACTORS

- Male gender
- Various mental illnesses
- Alcohol or drug abuse
- Prior suicide attempts
- Family history of suicide
- Refusal to seek help
- Stressful life event

- Serious physical illness
- Anniversary of a loss
- Withdrawal
- Homosexuality
- Heavy metal music
- Body image disorder
- Access to lethal methods such as guns

Figure 12

the influence of a mind-altering substance is not associated with the *planning* of suicide, which is in agreement with the traditional assumption. However, it is closely associated with suicidal *thoughts* and *unplanned* attempts.[75] These thoughts and attempts can be the result of consuming only "moderate" quantities of alcohol. Thus, my recommendation is *complete abstinence from alcohol* for those who are healthy as well as for those who are suffering from a mental illness such as depression.

The news media is preoccupied with promoting the use of alcohol "in moderation." They widely report any study showing that moderate alcohol consumption decreases the risk of heart disease, but when studies such as Dr. Kessler's are released, the media remain strangely silent. Their reports fail to acknowledge that alcohol use in moderation not only increases the risk of death by suicide but also increases the risk of accidental death, homicide, death attributable to cancer, hepatitis C, and a host of other causes. The risk of suicide among moderate drinkers is explained in **Figure 13**.

How can the media be silent on these evident disadvantages, while touting the advantages of a potentially lethal substance well documented as the third leading cause of death in America?[76] Could it be advertising dollars? More complete information on the dangers of moderate alcohol consumption is available in *Proof Positive*.[77]

This important information about alcohol and suicide underscores the significance of legislative policy. Many states have wisely increased the legal drinking age from 18 to 21, but some groups are calling on the federal government to demand a reversal of this decision. Studies show that this would increase the annual number of suicides by approximately 125 among 18-to-20-year-olds, who would not have attempted it without the available alcohol.[78]

Beyond the lives lost from suicide, alcohol takes a greater number of lives from homicides and accidents in this same age group.

You might ask, "If alcohol is not good for a 20-year-old, why is it good for a 21-year-old, or a 40-year-old, or even a 70-year-old?" I believe it is important to teach each generation to objectively examine the advantages of abstaining from alcohol. This knowledge can go a long way toward reducing the experience of misery, disease, and death worldwide.

Alcohol is not the only mind-altering substance that increases the risk of suicide. In *Chapter 6* we mention that antidepressant drugs like SSRIs (select serotonin reuptake inhibitors), and even the herb Kava-Kava, increases the possibility of suicide, but recent research also shows that some stimulant drugs *equally* increase suicide risk.[79] This connection will be explored in *Chapter 9* in relation to the frontal lobe of the brain. Abstinence from any mind-altering drug should be recommended, especially for those who have additional suicide or depression risk factors.

MODERATE DRINKERS ARE AT RISK OF SUICIDE

Effects of moderate drinking:

- Heightens suicidal thoughts and unplanned attempts

- Temporarily impairs judgment

- May lead directly to suicide attempt

- Alcohol is in the blood of many suicide victims.

Figure 13

Refusing to Seek Help and Suicide Risk

Suicidal thoughts are extremely private thoughts that most people find embarrassing. As a physician, I first establish rapport with a depressed patient before asking about suicidal thoughts. I approach this subject in a sympathetic, calm, and uncritical manner. Depressed patients frequently avoid discussing the topic of suicide, but asking them about suicide does not put the idea in their head. Instead, I have observed that patients who are actively contemplating suicide often are relieved to be able to discuss these unspoken thoughts. An appropriate approach to the seriousness of these thoughts gives the depressed individual tools for managing them.

I first determine whether these patients have a realistic interest in the future. Hopelessness is the element of depression most often connected to suicidal behavior.[80] Instead of trying to convince these patients to surrender their suicidal thoughts, I offer them reassurance and hope. This offer is based on the opportunity to find and treat the underlying cause of the suicidal thoughts and on the effectiveness of a tailored treatment program. After conversation with the patient, if I am convinced that there is a high risk for suicide, I intervene—even to the point of hospitalizing a patient against his will if necessary. Prompt action is often necessary to prevent the death of a depressed and suicidal person.

Many suicidal individuals will not voluntarily seek help unless someone intervenes on their behalf. Their reasons range from hopelessness to fear. Some may inaccurately assume that there is no treatment for their condition, or they may dread the stigma of being labeled mentally ill and suicidal. Others may fear financial collapse due to the cost of medical care. Still others may be socially isolated, with no close friends or family to recognize the changes in their mental state. Isolation increases the suicide risk for people who live alone, are single, or move frequently.[81] It is essential that depressed and suicidal persons get the help they need. Their friends and family must lovingly *insist* on getting that help to save a life.

Stressful Life Event and Suicide Risk

No age group is exempt from the tragedy of suicide. Each stage of life presents its own forms of stress and loss. Young people experience the stress of an illness, a job loss, or loss of a friend. The elderly frequently suffer multiple losses and are especially vulnerable to suicide. The suicide rate among white men older than 84 is six times that of the general population.[82] Age and illness frequently conspire with depression to produce suicidal thoughts. Individuals who have been diagnosed with cancer, who have had a stroke,[83] or who are disabled from a disease face an increased risk of suicide.[84] These individuals frequently feel that there is no hope for them or that they are of no value. They need treatment not only for their physical disease but also for their depression. Spiritual resources are profoundly important to such persons. *Chapter 7*, "Stress and Anxiety," is especially important to read for those who have suffered loss or other stressful life events.

Homosexuality and Suicide Risk

Homosexuality is a factor in many suicide attempts. Adult men who have had same-sex relations (whether they are bisexual or homosexual) are up to five times as likely to have attempted suicide as heterosexual men.[85] High school students who are homosexual, bisexual, or "not sure" of their sexual orientation are more than three times as likely to attempt suicide as their heterosexual classmates.[86]

Music and Suicide Risk

A study of 121 Midwestern high school students' music preference indicated that 75 percent of the girls who preferred heavy metal music had considered suicide compared with 35 percent of the girls who preferred other types of music. *Nearly 50 percent of the boys who preferred heavy metal had considered suicide* compared with 15 percent of the boys who listened to "nonmetal" music."[87]

Conversely, *serious music has been demonstrated to improve mood*, both subjectively and objectively. I explore this topic in *Chapter 5* on lifestyle treatments for depression.

Body Image and Suicide Risk

We are part of a society that praises the attractive face and body and ridicules what it considers unattractive. This attitude may explain why overweight women and underweight men tend to be more depressed and inclined to consider suicide. People who feel depressed often are impulsive and will binge on fatty foods in hope of feeling better.[88]

A large study of more than 40,000 U.S. adults found that obese women were 26 percent more likely to think about suicide and 55 percent more likely to have attempted suicide in the past year than women of normal weight.[89] The opposite was true of men. Underweight men were 80 percent more likely to think about suicide compared to men of normal weight. They were also 77 percent more likely to have attempted suicide.

The study's author, Dr. Myles Faith, stated that "there are many prejudices and discrimination against obese people, especially women, so one thought is that being obese puts [women] at risk for depression." On the other hand, he says that Western culture tends to value hyper-masculine, muscular male physiques more than thinner builds, and Dr. Faith specu-

lates that some underweight men may view themselves as "scrawny or being a weakling," which may lower their self-esteem and raise their risks for depression. The intense competition among commercial advertisers demonstrates their understanding of the popular views of body image.

When an undesirable physique is perceived as a physical impairment, it is called *body dysmorphic disorder*. This problem is on the increase and is beginning to get more attention. While it is of some concern to many adults, it can be devastating to teenagers and adolescents. Taken to an extreme, such perception becomes an anxiety or stress disorder, which is a mental illness.

Such unhealthy, delusional obsession with imagined or slight physical imperfections drives some teens to depression, isolation, and even suicide.[90] Individuals suffering from body dysmorphic disorder are almost continually thinking about their appearance and may look in the mirror at every opportunity. It increases the risk of developing an eating disorder such as anorexia, which is an aversion to food, or bulimia (eating followed by self-induced vomiting). These disorders have been shown to increase the risk of suicide.[91]

Conclusion

The information in this chapter should make it very clear that finding and adequately treating the causes of depression will remove an enormous amount of misery and save many lives. Millions of people who now suffer could again thoroughly enjoy more efficient and productive lives, free from pain and disease. But first they must find the help they need and begin the right treatment program. There is hope.

Unfortunately, not every story has a happy ending. Did you wonder what happened to Ed Harris, whom I told you about at the very beginning of this chapter? He kept only one follow-up appointment. I recommended a highly successful treatment program, but he was embarrassed and rejected the diagnosis of major depression. Ed never made a follow-up appointment with me to implement the recommended program.

I understand from secondary sources that he still has severe headaches that require ever-increasing doses of narcotic medi-cations. The outlook for Ed is not good. He is now dealing with the miserable lifestyle of narcotic dependency, and the uncertainty of what additional harm his depression may cause. He remains unconvinced of his condition with its subtle clues of emptiness and low self-worth.

No happy ending here. Ed cannot believe that taking personal responsibility and completing an adequate treatment program would end not only his mental symptoms but also his physical symptoms. He could, with a little effort, remove many of the symptoms that complicate his life: fatigue, difficulties with sleeping and concentrating, and the headaches.

Read on to learn what Ed and so many others need to do to be free from depression and its miserable effects.

References—

[1] Mental Health: A Report of the Surgeon General. Executive Summary. Department of Health and Human Services. National Institutes of Health, National Institute of Mental Health, 1999, p 5,6.

[2] Takeida K, Nishi M, Miyake H. Mental depression and death in elderly persons. *J Epidemiol* 1997 Dec;7(4):210-213.

[3] Hippisley-Cox J, Fielding K, Pringle M. Depression as a risk factor for ischaemic heart disease in men: population based case-control study. *BMJ* 1998;316:1714-1719.

[4] Everson SA, et al. Depressive symptoms and increased risk of stroke mortality over a 29-year period. *Arch Intern Med* 1998 May 25;158(10):1133-1138.

[5] Roose SP. Treatment of depression in patients with heart disease. *J Clin Psychiatry* 1999; 60 Suppl 20: 34-37.

[6] Harbuz MS. Stress, hormones and your brain. *J Neuroendocrinology* 2000;2(5):381-382.

[7] Murray CJ, Lopez AD. Mortality by cause for eight regions of the world: Global Burden of Disease Study. *Lancet* 1997 May 3;349(9061):1269-1276.

[8] Irvine J. Depression and risk of sudden cardiac death after acute myocardial infarction: testing for the confounding effects of fatigue. *Psychosom Med* 1999 Nov-Dec;61(6):729-737.

[9] Irvine J. Depression and risk of sudden cardiac death after acute myocardial infarction: testing for the confounding effects of fatigue. *Psychosom Med* 1999 Nov-Dec;61(6):729-737.

[10] Carney RM, Freedland KE, et al. Major depression, heart rate, and plasma norepinephrine in patients with coronary heart disease. *Biol Psychiatry* 1999 Feb 15;45(4):458-463.

[11] Watkins LL, Grossman P. Association of depressive symptoms with reduced baroreflex cardiac control in coronary artery disease. *Am Heart J* 1999 Mar;137(3):453-457.

[12] McKhann GM, Borowicz LM, et al. Depression and cognitive decline after coronary artery bypass grafting. *Lancet* 1997 May 3;349(9061):1282-1284.

[13] Hippisley-Cox, J. Depression as a risk factor for ischaemic heart disease in men: population-based case-control study. *BMJ* 1998;316:1714-1719.

[14] Ariyo AA, Haan M, et al. Depressive Symptoms and Risks of Coronary Heart Disease and Mortality in Elderly Americans *Circulation* 2000;102:1773-1779.

[15] Forrest KY, Becker DJ, et al. Are predictors of coronary heart disease and lower-extremity arterial disease in type 1 diabetes the same? A prospective study. *Atherosclerosis* 2000 Jan;148(1):159-169.

[16] Hippisley-Cox, J. Depression as a risk factor for ischemic heart disease in men: population-based case-control study. *BMJ* 1998;316:1714-1719.

[17] Fawzy FI, Cousins N, et al. A structured psychiatric intervention for cancer patients. Changes over time in methods of coping and affective disturbance. *Arch Gen Psychiatry* 1990;47:720.

[18] Fawzy FI, Fawzy NW, et al. Malignant melanoma: Effects of an early structured psychiatric intervention, coping, and affective state on recurrence and survival 6 years later. *Arch Gen Psychiatry* 1993;50:681.

[19] Spiegel D, Bloom JR, et al: Effects of psychosocial treatment on survival of patients with metastatic breast cancer. Lancet 1989;2:888.

[20] Stein M, Miller AH, Trestman RL. Depression, the immune system, and health and illness. *Arch Gen Psychiatry* 1991;48:171.

[21] Penninx BW, Guralnik JM, et al. Chronically depressed mood and cancer risk in older persons. *J Natl Cancer Inst* 1998 Dec 16;90(24):1888-1893.

[22] Preliminary data on births and deaths-United States, 1995. *MMWR Morb Mortal Wkly Rep* 1996 Oct 25;45(42):914-919.

[23] Takeida K, Nishi M, Miyake H. Mental depression and death in elderly persons. *J Epidemiol* 1997 Dec;7(4):210-213.

[24] Schulz R, Beach SR, et al. Association between depression and mortality in older adults: the cardiovascular health study. *Arch Intern*

Med 2000;160:1761-1768.

[25]Schulz R, Beach SR, et al. Association between depression and mortality in older adults: the cardiovascular health study. *Arch Intern Med* 2000;160:1766.

[26]Schulz R, Beach SR, et al. Association between depression and mortality in older adults: the cardiovascular health study. *Arch Intern Med* 2000;160:1766-1767.

[27]Sheline YI, Sanghavi M, et al. Depression duration but not age predicts hippocampal volume loss in medically healthy women with recurrent major depression. *J Neuroscience* 1999 June 15:19(12):5034-5043.

[28]*Tasman: Psychiatry,* 1st ed. W. B. Saunders Company. 1997, p 998-999.

[29]O'Toole SM, Sekula LK, Rubin RT. Pituitary-adrenal cortical axis measures as predictors of sustained remission in major depression. *Biol Psychiatry* 1997;42:85.

[30]Lupien SJ, de Leon M, et al. Cortisol levels during human aging predict hippocampal atrophy and memory deficits. *Nat Neurosci* 1998 May;1(1):69-73.

[31]Porter NM, Landfield PW. Stress hormones and brain aging: adding injury to insult? *Nat Neurosci* 1998 May;1(1):3-4.

[32]Cameron HA, McKay RD. Restoring production of hippocampal neurons in old age. *Nat Neurosci* 1999 Oct;2(10):894-897.

[33]World Health Organization (WHO). The World Health Report 1995: Bridging the Gaps. Geneva, Switzerland: World Health Organization, 1995.

[34]Abelow BJ, Holford TR, Insogna KL. Cross-cultural association between dietary animal protein and hip fracture: a hypothesis. *Calcif Tissue Int* 1992 Jan;50(1):14-18.

[35]Michelson D, Stratakis C, et al. Bone mineral density in women with depression. *NEJM* 1996 Oct 17;335(16):1176.

[36]Schweiger U. Weber B. et al. Lumbar bone mineral density in patients with major depression: evidence of increased bone loss at follow-up. *Am J Psychiatry* 2000 Jan;157(1):118-120.

[37]Proverbs 15:30, 16:24, 17:22. *The Holy Bible.* KJV

[38]Jonas BS, Lando JF. Negative affect as a prospective risk factor for hypertension. *Psychosom Med* 2000 Mar-Apr;62(2):188-196.

[39]McGrady A. Horner J. Role of mood in outcome of biofeedback assisted relaxation therapy in insulin dependent diabetes mellitus. *Appl Psychophysiology Biofeedback* 1999 Mar 24;(1):79-88.

[40]Jonas BS, Wagener DK, et al. Symptoms of Anxiety and Depression as Risk Factors for Development of Asthma. *J Appl Biobehav Research* 1999;4:91-110.

[41]Lipchik GL, Rains JC, et al. Recurrent headache: a neglected women's health problem. *Women's Health Issues* 1998 Jan-Feb;8(1):60-64.

[42]Penninx BW, Guralnik JM, et al. Depressive symptoms and physical decline in community-dwelling older persons. *JAMA* 1998 Jun 3;279(21):1720-1726.

[43]Penninx BW, Leveille S, et al. Exploring the effect of depression on physical disability: longitudinal evidence from the established populations for epidemiologic studies of the elderly. *Am J Public Health* 1999 Sep;89(9):1346-1352.

[44]Penninx BW, Guralnik JM, et al. Depressive symptoms and physical decline in community-dwelling older persons. *JAMA* 1998 Jun 3;279(21):1720-1726.

[45]Hesdorffer DC, Hauser WA, et al. Major depression is a risk factor for seizures in older adults. *Ann Neurology* 2000 Feb 47(2):246-249.

[46]Domar AD. Distress and conception in infertile women: a complementary approach. *J Am Med Womens Assoc* 1999 Fall;54(4):196-198.

[47]Schweiger U. Deuschle M., et.al. Testosterone, gonadotropin, and cortisol secretion in male patients with major depression. *Psychosom Med* 1999;61(3):292-296.

[48]Berndt ER, Koran LM, et al. Lost human capital from early-onset chronic depression. *Am J Psychiatry.* 2000 Jun;157(6):940-947.

[49]Breslau N, Peterson EL, et al. Major depression and stages of smoking. A longitudinal investigation. *Arch Gen Psychiatry* 1998 Feb;55(2):161-166.

[50]Breslau N, Peterson EL, et al. Major depression and stages of smoking. A longitudinal investigation. *Arch Gen Psychiatry* 1998 Feb;55(2):161-166.

[51]Nedley N. *Proof Positive: How to Reliably Combat Disease and Achieve Optimal Health through Nutrition and Lifestyle.* Ardmore, OK: Nedley Publishing, 1998, pages 408-412.

[52]Greenfield SF, Weiss RD, et al. The effect of depression on return to drinking: a prospective study. *Arch Gen Psychiatry* 1998 Mar;55(3):259-265.

[53]Angst J, Angst F, Stassen HH. Suicide risk in patients with major depressive disorder. *J Clinical Psychiatry* 1999;60 Suppl 2:57-62;discussion 75-76,113-116.

[54]U.S. Department of Health and Human Services: Mental Health: A Report of the Surgeon General. U.S. Department of Health and Human Services, Substance Abuse and Mental Health Services Administration, Center for Mental Health Services, National Institutes of Health, National Institute of Mental Health, Rockville, Maryland, 1999, p. 245.

[55]U.S. Department of Health and Human Services: Mental Health: A Report of the Surgeon General. U.S. Department of Health and Human Services, Substance Abuse and Mental Health Services Administration, Center for Mental Health Services, National Institutes of Health, National Institute of Mental Health, Rockville, Maryland, 1999 p 245.

[56]Wintemute GJ, Parham CA, et al. Mortality among recent purchasers of handguns. *NE M* 1999;341:1583.

[57]Potter LB. Suicide in youth: a public health framework. *J Am Acad Child Adolesc Psychiatry* 1998 May; 37(5):484-487.

[58]Public Health Advisory Board Report, May 1999.

[59]U.S. Department of Health and Human Services: Mental Health: A Report of the Surgeon General. U.S. Department of Health and Human Services, Substance Abuse and Mental Health Services Administration, Center for Mental Health Services, National Institutes of Health, National Institute of Mental Health, Rockville, Maryland, 1999, pp 150-152.

[60]Eddleston, Sheriff MH, Hawton K. Deliberate self harm in Sri Lanka: an overlooked tragedy in the developing world. *BMJ* 1998 Jul 11;317(7151):133-135.

[61]Angst J. Angst F. Stassen HH. Suicide risk in patients with major depressive disorder. *J Clin Psychiatry* 1999;60 Suppl 2:57-62;discussion 75-76,113-116.

[62]Angst J. Angst F. Stassen HH. Suicide risk in patients with major depressive disorder. *J Clin Psychiatry* 1999;60 Suppl 2:57-62;discussion 75-76,113-116.

[63]U.S. Department of Health and Human Services: Mental Health: A Report of the Surgeon General. U.S. Department of Health and Human Services, Substance Abuse and Mental Health Services Administration, Center for Mental Health Services, National Institutes of Health, National Institute of Mental Health, Rockville, Maryland, 1999, p. 245.

[64]Cornelius JR, Salloum IM, et al. Disproportionate suicidality in patients with comorbid major depression and alcoholism. *Am J Psychiatry* 1995;152:358.

[65]Weiss RD, Hufford MR. Substance abuse and suicide. The Harvard Medical School Guide to Suicide Assessment and Intervention. Jacobs DG, Ed. Jossey-Bass Publishers, San Francisco, 1999, p 300.

[66]Hyman SE, Rudorfer MV. Depressive and Bipolar Mood Disorders. Scientific American May 2000.

[67]Garofalo R, Wolf RC, et al. Sexual Orientation and Risk of Suicide Attempts Among a Representative Sample of Youth *Arch Ped Adolesc Med* 1999 May;153(5):487-493.

[68]Cochran SD, Mays VM. Lifetime prevalence of suicide symptoms and affective disorders among men reporting same-sex sexual partners. *Am J Public Health* 2000 Apr;90(4):573-578.

[69]Scheel KR, Westefeld JS. Heavy metal music and adolescent suicidality: an empirical investigation. *Adolesc* 1999 Sum-mer;34(134):253-273.

[70]Blumenthal SJ. Suicide: A guide to risk factors, assessment, and treatment of suicidal patients. *Med Clin N Amer* 1988;72:937-971.

[71]U.S. Department of Health and Human Services: Mental Health: A Report of the Surgeon General. U.S. Department of Health and Human Services, Substance Abuse and Mental Health Services Administration, Center for Mental Health Services, National Institutes of Health, National Institute of Mental Health, Rockville, Maryland, 1999, p 244.

[72]*Tasman: Psychiatry*, 1st ed. W. B. Saunders Company. 1997, p 995.

[73]Borges G, Walters EE, Kessler RC. Associations of substance use, abuse, and dependence with subsequent suicidal behavior. *Am J Epidemiol.* 2000 Apr 15;151(8):781-789.

[74]Smith GS, Branas CC, Miller TR. Fatal nontraffic injuries involving alcohol: A metaanalysis. *Ann Emer Med* 1999 Jun;33(6):659-668.

[75]Borges G, Walters EE, Kessler RC. Associations of substance use, abuse, and dependence with subsequent suicidal behavior. *Am J Epidemiol.* 2000 Apr 15;151(8):781-789.

[76]McGinnis JM, Foege WH. Actual causes of death in the United States. *JAMA* 1993 Nov 10;270(18):2207-2212.

[77]Nedley N. *Proof Positive: How to reliably combat disease and achieve optimal health through nutrition and lifestyle.* Ardmore, OK: Nedley Publishing, 1998, p. 425.

[78]Birckmayer J, Hemenway D. Minimum-age drinking laws and youth suicide, 1970-1990. *Am J Public Health* 1999 Sep;89(9):1365-1368.

[79]Borges G, Walters EE, Kessler RC. Associations of substance use, abuse, and dependence with subsequent suicidal behavior. *Am J Epidemiol.* 2000 Apr 15;151(8):781-789.

[80]Beck AT, Kovacs M, Weissman A. Hopelessness and suicidal behavior: an overview. *JAMA* 1975;234:1146.

[81]Whitley E, Gunnell D, et al. Ecological study of social fragmentation, poverty, and suicide. *BMJ* 1999 Oct 16;319(7216):1034-1037.

[82]Cole MG, Bellavance F, Mansour A. Prognosis of depression in elderly community and primary care populations: a systematic review and meta-analysis. *Am J Psychiatry* 1999;156:1182.

[83]Stenager EN, Madsen C, et al. Suicide in patients with stroke: epidemiological study. BMJ 1998 April 18;316:1206-1210.

[84]Cassem EH. Depressive disorders in the medically ill. An overview. *Psychosom* 1995 Mar-Apr;36(2):S2-10.

[85]Cochran SD, Mays VM. Lifetime prevalence of suicide symptoms and affective disorders among men reporting same-sex sexual partners: results from NHANES III. *Am J Public Health* 2000 Apr;90(4):573-578.

[86]Garofalo R, Wolf RC, et al. Sexual Orientation and Risk of Suicide Attempts Among a Representative Sample of Youth *Arch Ped Adolesc Med* 1999 May;153(5):487-493.

[87]Scheel KR, Westefeld JS. Heavy metal music and adolescent suicidality: an empirical investigation. *Adolesc* 1999;34(134):253-273.

[88]Tice DM, Bratslavsky E. Emotional Distress Regulation Takes Precedence Over Impulse Control: If You Feel Bad! *J Pers Soc Psych* 2001;80:53-67.

[89]Carpenter KM, Hasin DS, et al. Relationships between obesity and DSM-IV major depressive disorder, suicide ideation, and suicide attempts: results from a general population study. *Am J Pub Health* 2000 Feb;90(2):251-257.

[90]Albertini RS, Phillips KA. Thirty-three cases of body dysmorphic disorder in children and adolescents *J Am Acad Child Adolesc Psychiatry* 1999 Apr;38(4):453-459.

[91]Herzog DB. Mortality in eating disorders: a descriptive study. *Int J Eat Disord* 2000 Jul;28(1):20-26.

CHAPTER THREE

WHAT CAUSES DEPRESSION?

During her first visit to my office, Tanya told me that she was tired of being tired. She had gone through this routine too many times. When she didn't feel well, she usually delayed calling a doctor, hoping that the problems would take care of themselves. But when some symptom eventually demanded her attention, she reluctantly made an appointment to find a doctor who could take her immediately.

She had seen several doctors for these symptoms in the last two years, but her delays frequently made it necessary to take whatever emergency appointments were available. In most cases, the routines had been familiar and the visit would end with the doctor handing her a prescription.

She told me that she was "just too busy to do all of those complicated things, like thinking about changes in diet, getting more exercise, and taking a vacation once in awhile. The medication is easier."

Today, when doctors make a diagnosis of depression it is almost automatic for them to prescribe a medication. This is a typical practice and *may* help to "treat the depression." It may also decrease the risk of suicide, but it may *not* be the ticket to depression-free living. Simply put, *medications may treat the symptoms of depression but miss the underlying cause.*

On Tanya's first visit to the office she was clearly in abdominal pain. She bent forward, guarding the middle of her body with both arms. As a new patient, Tanya was still learning about my medical philosophy. She clearly expected to be given something for the pain before being "poked and prodded."

Medical school stresses the importance of never giving someone pain medication for abdominal pain, no matter how severe, until a thorough exam is performed. Why? Medication can mask the pain and make it much more difficult for the physician to pinpoint the cause. There are a number of different causes of this common malady. The same is true of depression. Antidepressant medication for "the pain" can help relieve symptoms, but may make it more difficult for a health professional to determine the cause of the depression. If the cause of the abdominal pain or the depression is not found, the pain will often continue, recur, or become more severe.

Also, pain is not always connected to what may seem the most obvious. So we begin with the process of questioning for understanding. Eventually, I discovered that Tanya's pain was not directly connected with the part of her body she cautiously guarded.

By definition, major depression includes a combination of symptoms, but the diagnosis of symptoms does not pinpoint the *cause* of the disease. To find a long-term solution, it is imperative to identify the causes of depression and to treat each one systematically. Unfortunately, as Tanya observed, this is not usually as simple a process as prescribing a drug. Like most chronic diseases, depression is a complex disease with many factors interacting to produce depression. The most effective treatments broadly attack each identifiable cause.

There are eight major factors that can either cause or contribute to depression. These factors are categorized in **Figure 1**, which provides the framework that we will use to explore the intricacies of depression and its treatment.

Unchangeable Risk Factors For Depression

Clearly, there are some risk factors for depression that cannot be changed. Sometimes simply becoming aware of these can fuel depression. After all, it can be discouraging to think that the deck may be stacked against you, making perpetual bouts of depression seemingly unavoidable.

When I called Tanya's unchangeable risk factors to her attention, she understood that my reason for highlighting them was not to discourage her. Instead, this information gave her encouragement to fight the pain and depression by *focusing her energy on factors that she could change.*

The truth about Tanya's case is encouraging—no one is doomed to perpetual depression. By addressing factors that can be changed, even the person with the worst set of non-changeable risk factors can often beat the odds altogether and stave off depression, or greatly decrease its severity. Let's look carefully at the risk factors as listed in **Figure 2**. The more of these factors present in our lives, the more thought we should give to preventive strategies *before* this common mood disorder strikes.

But let me add an important footnote. If you seem to have escaped all of the familiar, unchangeable factors, keep two things in mind. First, you may have an inherited tendency to depression that has never been noted in any immediate family members. Secondly, depression can strike anyone—including those who have none of the unchangeable factors.

The fact is sometimes overlooked that knowing your non-modifiable factors can provide an early warning and help prevent the disease. "An ounce of prevention is worth a pound of cure." Tanya found a more permanent solution to many of her symptoms, and now believes that it is healthier to choose a lifestyle that decreases the risk of depression and its complications than to temporarily medicate them.

Genetics

It is important to emphasize that inherited tendencies (called "genetics"), can set the stage for depression. But inherited roots alone are not always sufficient to cause depression. People who have inherited depressive tendencies may avoid the condition by giving attention to other risk factors.

One of the applications of genetics is to identify specific genes associated with any

FACTORS THAT CAN CAUSE OR INCREASE RISK OF DEPRESSION

- Unchangeable factors
- Diet-related factors
- Social factors
- Other lifestyle factors
- Medical conditions
- Imbalanced brain electrical activity
- Uncommon causes of depression
- Unproven causes of depression

Figure 1

given condition. Unfortunately, there does not appear to be a single gene that is responsible for a depressive tendency.[1] It is more likely that multiple genes play various roles in setting the stage for depression, with lifestyle and other factors being the final players.

In a broader sense, genetics accounts for our gender and is related to our ethnic roots. Nonetheless, despite the relation between genes and these so-called "demographic factors," when it comes to gender and race, significant social factors are also involved. Let us look at these factors along with age in the following section.

Depression Among Our Youth

Depression is not an adults-only disease. A summary of depression among our youth is listed in **Figure 3**.

The facts cited in this figure are astounding. The message is clear. We must get the word out that the youth of this country are at high risk of becoming depressed, and the consequences of their depression are very serious. We see that rates in adolescents reach as high as 20 percent, indicating that young adults suffer from this disorder nearly as frequently as do older adults.[2]

Adolescents who are depressed are particularly vulnerable to what is probably depression's most tragic outcome—*suicide*. Attempted suicide rates peak during the adolescent years. By age 15, an overwhelming 14 percent of youth report having attempted suicide.[3]

Teen and young adult women are at higher risk for depression than men.[4] Although not necessarily typical of the entire U.S. population, recent data from Los Angeles is extremely disturbing. Researchers studied 155 young women age 17 and 18 for five consecutive years. Almost 50 percent of these women had at least one episode of major depression in that relatively short time span.[5] Academic difficulties or

UNCHANGEABLE RISK FACTORS FOR DEPRESSION

- Genetics
- Age
- Gender
- Ethnic differences
- History of depression in adolescence
- Family history of depression

Figure 2

DEPRESSION AMONG OUR YOUTH

- Up to 20% of adolescents and adults have depression.

- 14% of youth have attempted suicide by age 15.

- 47% of 17- and 18-year-old women in L.A. had major depression in a 5-year span.

- Hispanic and black adolescents report more depression than white adolescents.

- 2 to 3 times more women are depressed than men.

- Depressed adolescents have a 60% chance of recurrence as adults.

Figure 3

romantic problems appeared to increase the risk of depression in members of this high-risk age group.

In the previously cited study by Emslie and colleagues, students of African-American and Hispanic ethnicity reported significantly more depression than did white students.[6] This stands in sharp contrast to statistics for older adults where there does not seem to be a racial influence for depression.[7]

Gender is another consideration. Even into adulthood, women are at greater risk of depression than men.[8] It has been noted that between two to three times as many women have major depression compared to men.[9] International surveys suggest that, in the larger number of these females, depression is not due to cultural factors only. While gender and culture do not explain all of the statistics, the numbers clearly establish the fact that in many nations, with few exceptions, women suffer from depression more frequently than do men.[10]

A History of Depression in Adolescence

No matter how unpleasant our past physical and mental health struggles may have been, no one can rewrite personal medical history. If you have experienced depression *as an adolescent*, you have an *increased risk for major depression in your adult years*. Weissman and colleagues from Columbia University forcibly illustrated this fact in a study. Among the people they studied, *nearly two-thirds* of those who experienced depression as adolescents *were also depressed in their adult years*.[11]

Family History of Depressive Disorder

There is broad consensus that risk of depression is substantially increased when there is a family history of depressive disorder, particularly if it exists in first-degree relatives, such as siblings or parents.[12,13]

Family history of depression, if present, should clearly raise red flags.

Mental illness can pass from parent to child. A study showed that children whose parents suffered from major depression were nine times more likely to be depressed than children from unaffected families.[14]

I strongly urge these individuals to take seriously the possibility of experiencing depression. If you do not take depression seriously, statistics warn that you may be the next victim.

The strategy should be to seriously address risk factors that you can do something about. Among the controllable factors to be considered are *what you eat.*

Nutrition

Diet has such a profound effect on human metabolism that it comes as no surprise that there are many interrelationships between the foods we eat and our risk of depression. However, because we all have different genetic backgrounds and live in different environments, our susceptibility to nutritional causes of depression varies widely from one individual to another.

Consequently, some of the areas that I have categorized as "diet-related" may require a certain genetic background or other factors to be in place for depression to result. This consideration does not minimize the importance of these factors or their nutritional relationships. Instead, since underlying genetic or metabolic susceptibilities of an individual are often not known, it behooves us to *choose the most widely nutritious diet possible.*

Some of the diet-related areas that can cause or contribute to the risk of depression are listed in **Figure 4.**

Inadequate Serotonin and Depression

Low serotonin levels in the brain are a contributing factor to depression. Furthermore, serotonin is produced in larger amounts in the region of the frontal lobe (called the prefrontal cortex) than in any other portion of the brain. And, as might be expected, if the frontal lobe is depressed, serotonin levels will also be lower. *A high level of serotonin in the brain* is an important factor in treating depression, but serotonin is not found in any food or food supplements. *It can only be manufactured within the body.*

The body needs certain "raw materials" to make serotonin. One of these materials is the amino acid (or "protein building-block") known as tryptophan. *Eating foods with adequate amounts of tryptophan optimizes serotonin production.*

One study considered 15 women who had a past history of depression but were recovered and currently mentally healthy and happy without drug treatment. These women were put on a diet low in tryptophan. The diet produced a 75 percent reduction in plasma tryptophan concentrations. Ten of the fifteen women experienced temporary but clinically significant depressive symptoms.[15] Some of the women claimed they experienced a "full relapse." The researchers noted that one woman "experienced a sudden onset of sadness, despair, and uncontrollable crying."

This study was highly praised as the first to show a direct link between diet and mood. One of my female patients has noticed that going just one day on a low tryptophan diet will cause a relapse into depression and anorexia—having no desire to eat—which is a prominent symptom for her when she is depressed. *Chapter 4* explains how to get enough tryptophan in the diet.

Omega-3 Fats and the Brain

Fish oil has been strongly publicized as being healthful. It contains an important fat, found abundantly in the fatty tissues of cold-water fish. It is of the "omega-3" variety (a designation used to refer to its particular chemical structure).

Omega-3 fats have many beneficial effects, ranging from heart disease prevention to anti-inflammatory properties. They deserve our attention in this chapter because of their *profound mental health implications.* The serious effects on the brain of a diet deficient in omega-3 fatty acids are listed in **Figure 5**.[17,18]

It is obvious from the figure that

DIETARY FACTORS AFFECTING MENTAL HEALTH

- Serotonin
- Omega-3 fats
- Folic acid
- Vitamin B_{12}
- Homocysteine
- Protein intake & early puberty

Figure 4

MENTAL EFFECTS OF OMEGA-3 DEFICIENCY

A diet deficient in Omega-3:

- Increases the risk of depression

- Has been linked to increased aggression in prisoners

- For infants, will lower IQ 9 to 10 points by adulthood

Figure 5

omega-3 fatty acids are a very important nutrient in reducing risk of depression. The relationship to IQ deserves some comment.

Some thought-provoking studies have focused on infant brain development. It is clear that omega-3 fats are necessary for optimal brain development during the critical formative time of early life. Unfortunately, *cow's milk and traditional baby formulas are both low in omega-3 fatty acids. Human breast milk,* on the other hand, *contains much higher amounts.* Even as late as 2001, these important omega-3 fatty acids had not yet found their way into infant formulas.

These relationships are not merely theoretical. Researchers have discovered that the brain effects of omega-3 deficiency last a lifetime. Today's adults who were given infant formulas and cow's milk have, on average, a *9 to 10 point lower IQ than those who were receiving human breast milk.*

This finding raises an additional question. Might individuals who were not given breast-milk experience an increased risk of depression, even if they currently consume an adequate amount of omega-3? Since a lack of breast milk results in a learning handicap, might it also handicap the resistance to depression? If researchers find that growth of the frontal lobe is impaired by omega-3 deficiency, then we may rightly expect an increased risk of depression in those who were not fed breast milk in their infancy.

How do we protect ourselves from a diet low in omega-3? Fish are not the only sources. In fact, fish should be avoided because of their negative effects on health. These effects include lake contamination with heavy metals and other contaminants. The dangers of heavy metal contamination are explained later in the chapter. Other negative effects of fish are spelled out in *Chapter 4.*

Many plant foods are rich in omega-3. A long list of these foods is found also in *Chapter 4.*

Folic Acid and Mental Health

Depression can be caused or worsened by insufficient blood levels of a B vitamin called folic acid (also referred to as folate). It has received a lot of media attention lately. This attention is a response to the fact that if folic acid is not consumed in high enough amounts by pregnant mothers, the unborn can have heart disease, stroke, and brain or spinal cord defects. The dangers of low folic acid in the blood are listed in **Figure 6**.

The drugs in the figure that will fail to relieve depression caused by deficient folic acid are *Prozac,® Zoloft,® Paxil,® Elavil,®* and imipramine (or potentially any other currently available antidepressant).[19] We learned that the correct treatment of any disease depends on *proper diagnosis of the cause* or causes. When a person does not respond well to antidepressant medication, a blood test for folate content may reveal why there has been no improvement. *Raising the folic acid level by diet as outlined in Chapter 4 will typically cure this form of depression.*

It has been found that a low blood folate level not only increases the risk of depression but also increases the risk of Alzheimer's disease.[20]

Vitamin B12 and Depression

Vitamin B_{12} is vital to optimal health of the nervous system. Symptoms of a deficiency of this vitamin are poor coordination, frequent forgetfulness, and depression.[21] It can even affect the personality. Many patients with B_{12} deficiency have been mistakenly diagnosed as having Alzheimer's disease.

Information on this essential nutrient appears in **Figure 7**.

This essential vitamin is found most reliably in animal products and fortified plant foods. However, even a diet that is adequate in B_{12} does not ensure adequate *blood levels* of this vitamin. Vitamin B_{12} has one of the most complicated absorption processes of any nutrient. It requires appropriate interaction in the mouth and stomach before it is successfully absorbed in the small intestine.

As we age, it is common to lose some of the stomach's absorptive capacities. Consequently, by the time we reach 80, if we rely on food alone to give us our B12, we have about a one-in-five chance of developing serious problems and deficiencies. *Taking B12 supplements is advised, and they should be chewed rather that swallowed whole.*

Although many associate B12 deficiency with a vegan or vegetarian diet, only a small percentage of people with B12 deficiency are vegetarian.

Homocysteine and Depression

Homocysteine is an amino acid (or "protein building-block"). Elevated levels of this compound have been convincingly linked to stroke, heart attack, and other problems related to blood vessel blockage. Individuals with higher homocysteine levels also appear to have an increased risk of depression.[22,23] However, it is very difficult to tell whether homocysteine itself is doing the damage.

This perplexity arises from the fact that many of the known causes of high homocysteine levels are also causes of depression. As we have seen, deficient levels of the B vitamins, including Vitamin B6, folic acid, and B12 can cause depression, and *lower blood levels of these vitamins* also tends to *elevate concentrations of homocysteine.* This raises the question, "Is homocysteine a problem when it comes to depression—or are higher levels of homocysteine simply an indication of the presence of other depression risk factors?"

To make the issue even more complex, as we will explore later, strokes—even unrecognized ones—can lead to depression. Since higher homocysteine levels appear to cause strokes, we have a similar question to that involving the B vitamins. Does homocysteine alone cause depression, or do the small strokes it causes do the dirty work?

DANGERS OF FOLIC ACID DEFICIENCY

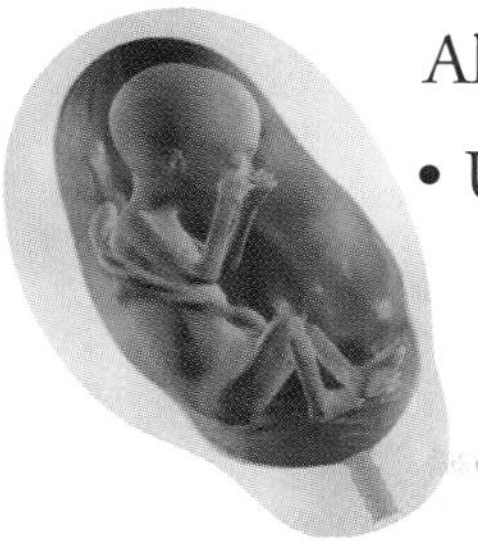

- Increases risk of depression and Alzheimer's
- Unborn fetuses can have heart disease, stroke, and spinal cord defects
- Standard depression drugs will not work

Figure 6

VITAMIN B12 FACTS:

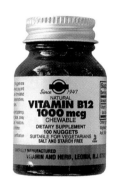

- Found in fortified plant food and animal products.
- Vegans and meat eaters can have the deficiency.
- Taking B12 supplements is advised.
- The supplement tablets should be thoroughly chewed.

Figure 7

Thus, the link between low homocysteine and depression may not be a simple cause and effect relationship.

Protein Intake and Early Puberty

Among females, the *risk of depression later in life* is related to *early puberty*. Girls who are at the middle of their puberty phase of development by age 11 or younger have an increased risk of depression. The risk of developing depression symptoms in their teenage years and into adulthood is twice as great.[24]

The timing of puberty is no longer a perfect mystery. We now understand many factors that influence the age at which a girl begins her reproductive years. Information on early puberty among girls is presented in **Figure 8**.[25]

A *lower amount of animal protein in the diet, especially before adolescence, seems to promote later puberty.*

A recent study suggests that the problem is indeed the high amount of animal protein in the U.S. diet. Dietary patterns of 67 white females in the United States were examined. The study found that *the higher the animal protein intake at ages three to five, the earlier the first menstrual period.* In contrast, girls that consumed *higher amounts of vegetable protein at ages three to five* had a *much later onset of menstruation.*[26]

The adolescent growth spurt occurred earlier in girls who had *higher fat intakes* between the ages of one and two, and higher animal protein intakes between the ages of six and eight. Of course, early-age menstruation carries with it other physical and social

risks. It opens the door for higher levels of teen pregnancy, and significantly increases breast cancer risk.[27] The risk of developing panic or eating disorders in these girls is also increased.

These significant facts should encourage people in the western hemisphere to rethink their love affair with foods high in animal protein. This, plus a great amount of other evidence, confirms that *the average American consumes too much protein contained in meat and dairy products.*[28]

There is some conjecture based on solid scientific evidence as to why a high protein diet could cause depressed symptoms even in adults. As mentioned, tryptophan is needed in the diet to make serotonin, which in turn can help prevent or even treat depression. Tyrosine, valine, isoleucine, leucine, phenylalanine, and also large neutral amino acids compete with tryptophan in traveling from the arteries into the brain tissue.[29] These are amino acids that are abundantly found in *animal protein.*

Researchers from the University of Milan in Italy measured and considered the ratio of tryptophan to these five amino acids in the bloodstream. They found that the lower the ratio, the greater the risk for depression or other mental illness.[30] In the future, we may have to consider a food's ratio of these amino acids to determine the effect the food may have on our moods. A figure in *Chapter 4* shows the ratio of these amino acids in a variety of foods.

In addition to promoting early puberty, higher protein intake can have other indirect effects on depression. A high protein diet, with no other complicating factors, increases the risk of breast cancer even if puberty is delayed.[31] Other chronic diseases, such as prostate cancer, kidney stones, and osteoporosis are also linked with increased consumption of animal protein.[32]

These and other chronic physical illnesses actually increase the risk of experiencing depression. Keeping in good physical health actually decreases the risk of de-

EARLY PUBERTY AMONG GIRLS

- Average age of menstruation in Japan is 17 years

- Average age of menstruation in the U.S. is 12 years

- Japan has a diet lower in animal protein than the U.S.

Figure 8

pression and in the long run, avoiding "high protein" eating habits may tip the scale against depression and in favor of a number of health dividends.

Other Nutrients Help to Protect Against Depression

It is important to eat a balanced diet that includes enough of all of the basic vitamins and minerals, not just the nutrients mentioned above. For instance, one study found a substantial percentage of depressed patients' diets contained less than the RDA (recommended daily allowance) of one or more nutrients.[33] A point worth considering is that many depressed patients do not feel hungry. This can lead to an inadequate food intake, which may also lead to a deficient diet and a worsening of depression.

Toxins Damage the Brain

In an apparently evermore-polluted world, toxins are often implicated as causes of chronic behavior changes and mental illness. Human contact with metals has co-existed with the development of civilization. The toxic effects of metals have been chronicled for centuries. Exposure to metals is not confined to industrial sites, since metallic substances have been known to contaminate water and enter the food chain.

Some of the metals and toxins that have been associated with mental illness are listed in **Figure 9**.[34]

The hazards of lead poisoning have been found in several environments, as listed in **Figure 10**.

Lead

Lead poisoning captured world headlines in October 2000 when the famous composer Ludwig Van Beethoven's hair analysis was reported. He had such high concentrations of lead in his hair that he was thought to have suffered (possibly losing his hearing) and died from lead poisoning.

Lead was one of the earliest nerve and brain toxins researched. Currently, it is used mainly in a few industries such as battery manufacturing, and the populations at risk are mainly exposed workers. It is no longer used in the production of paint, gasoline, plumbing components, and other products.

Exposure among workers in some industries continues to be high, and the risk of toxicity remains significant. With cases

METALS AND MENTAL ILLNESS

- Lead
- Mercury
- Manganese
- Arsenic
- Bismuth
- Organotin
- Trimethyltin Chloride

Figure 9

LOCATIONS OF LEAD POISONING

- Dust
- Dirt
- Drinking water
- Calcium supplements
- Lead-based paint
- Manufacturing environments

Figure 10

of severe poisoning becoming less common, attention has shifted to more subtle forms of toxic exposure to lead.

A number of studies found that exposure to lead can result in many disorders. Some of them are listed in **Figure 11**.

In those who are daily exposed to lead, the blood lead level is associated with how much fatigue is present on that particular day.[35] Increased rates of depression as well as confusion, fatigue, and anger have been noted in those with blood lead levels greater than 40 mg/dl.[36,37]

Lead exposure in children has not been linked to depression, but has been linked to increased reaction time, antisocial behavior, and impairment of attention.[38] Decreased intelligence and hearing loss can also occur in exposed children.

Lead in paint was banned in 1975 in the United States, which has helped decrease the incidence of lead exposure in children. Exposure can also occur through dust, dirt, and drinking water, especially if the water passes through lead pipes.

Another source of exposure is burning a candle with a metallic core in its wick, such as a scented or ceremonial candle. Dr. Jerome Nriagu, professor of environmental health sciences at the University of Michigan, cautions that burning certain candles made in both China and the U.S. for one hour in an enclosed room can make airborne lead levels soar. The levels can reach 30 times higher than the level that has been determined unsafe by the U.S. Environmental Protection Agency (EPA). If the wick looks shiny, it could have lead or zinc in it and should not be burned in an enclosed environment.

Herbs and vitamins from India and possibly other countries can be a source of very toxic lead levels.[39] Another more common source is calcium supplements. Investigators from the University of Florida in Gainesville recently examined 22 brands of calcium supplements for lead and found that eight had measurable levels of the toxic heavy metal, including the most commonly taken calcium supplement—the calcium carbonate of Tums.[40] Although none of the supplements had high levels that could produce nerve problems while taking the pills short-term, the lead in the calcium supplements is still troubling because many people take the products every day for years.

Children in lower-income families are most likely to be exposed to lead, and in a study of 296 inner-city preschoolers, nine months to three-years-old, the researchers found that those with high levels of fat in their diet were more likely to have dangerous levels of lead in their blood.[41] The children exposed to lead will actually *absorb less lead* if they *eat less fat.*

Blood lead levels are useful for recent or chronic lead exposure, but are usually not helpful in determining past exposure. A child who was once described by the parents as "a little angel" but later undergoes an aggressive personality change that may include bullying, vandalism, setting fires, and shoplifting, may have been exposed to lead. Unfortunately, an expensive X-ray, capable of showing lead deposits in the bone, is required to help determine the cause of the behavior change.[42] At this time, only high blood lead levels can be treated by drug

DISORDERS CAUSED BY LEAD

- Increased rates of depression
- Apathy
- Irritability
- Fatigue
- Confusion
- Diminished ability to control anger
- Impairment of brain ability and behavior

Figure 11

therapy (chelation therapy), and the results of distant past exposure have no known treatment. These facts underscore the importance of avoiding lead exposure, especially in childhood.

Lead exposure can not only affect and damage the brain but can also damage the kidneys and increase the risk of dental cavities.[43]

Mercury

Occupational mercury poisoning has been noted for centuries, the most prominent being the case of hat makers, who used the closely guarded proprietary compound, mercury nitrate, to cure their felt. This historical fact is the source of the phrase "mad hatters." There are potentially four neurological consequences of mercury toxicity, as outlined in **Figure 12**.

The emotional symptoms include an increased sensitivity in interaction with others, irritability, avoidant behavior, depression, fatigue, and lethargy.[44] A classic example is a person who becomes nervous, timid and shy, blushes readily, and becomes embarrassed in social situations. He or she may object to being watched and seeks to avoid people, or may become irritable and quarrelsome. This behavior may result in the individual giving up his job. Lethargy, tremors, lack of fine coordination, and at least some degree of impaired intelligence usually accompany these symptoms.[45]

Where do we find mercury hazards? The answer is found in **Figure 13**.

Mercury poisoning does not always occur from industrial exposure. It also can come from some herbs or vitamins produced in India and China.[46] According to the Hong Kong Consumer Council, two variants of the Chinese herb "Water Melon Frost" were found to have toxic levels of mercury. A beauty cream manufactured in Mexico caused mercury poisoning in consumers and their family members in Texas and Arizona recently. The contaminated

cream, called "Crema de Belleza Manning," prompted a statewide health investigation in Arizona and highlights the hazards of purchasing certain products abroad. Of the 89 people who were found to have used the cream, many had early symptoms of mercury poisoning, including headaches, weakness, mood changes, and dizziness.[47] Low levels of mercury are found in thimerosal, a

NEUROLOGIC CONSEQUENCES OF MERCURY TOXICITY

- Lack of coordination
- Inability to walk normally
- Impaired intelligence
- Alterations in emotion and mood

Figure 12

SOURCES OF MERCURY CONTAMINATION

- Imported herbs and vitamins
- Industrial exposure
- Certain beauty creams
- Certain vaccines
- Fish
- Certain beef and other meats

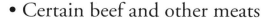

Figure 13

preservative used in some vaccines prior to 2001 in the United States.[48]

Mercury in Fish

One of the most prevalent sources of mercury in the food chain is fish. In 1996, the Environmental Protection Agency (E.P.A.) stated that mercury intakes greater than 0.1 micrograms per kilogram of body weight are unsafe, although I believe any mercury in food is unsafe, particularly when eaten regularly. Fish such as bass, crappie, dolphin, halibut, mackerel, pike, snapper, and tuna contain 0.2 to 0.3 parts per million (ppm) of mercury.[49]

An adult woman weighing 132 pounds would meet the "safe" threshold for mercury consumption by eating four ounces of such fish once a week. According to the E.P.A., any more than this amount of fish consumed would be unsafe. This underscores the importance of obtaining the omega-3 fats that help to prevent depression from plant sources instead of from fish. *Chapter 4* explains how this can be done.

A report from France on October 30, 2000, highlighted what was already known—that *contaminated beef* and other meats can also have *toxic levels of mercury and other heavy metals*. The French newspaper, the daily *Le Parisien* reported that cows consumed lead, mercury, cadmium, nickel, chromium, copper, and zinc as a result of a polluted canal that repeatedly overflowed, flooding the pasture in which the animals grazed. "Instead of being born black and white, some of my calves came out of the womb reddish-brown and white," the farmer who owned the herd was quoted as saying. The newspaper said that of the 84 cows that lived in the pasture between 1998 and 2000, more than 40 died as a result of the contamination. Most of the others, some of which took on a rusty hue because of the amount of copper they consumed, were sold to slaughterhouses and became ground beef.

Most dentists believe that the mercury amalgam fillings used to fill dental cavities do not pose a significant human risk. They are designed not to leak. Other orthomolecular scientists state that only composite non-mercury fillings or gold be used to fill dental cavities, since they believe that any risk is too high a risk.

Mercury exposure in pregnant mothers can affect the unborn, increasing the likelihood of low birth weight and high blood pressure in their offspring.[50]

Recent toxic mercury exposure is treated with drug therapy (chelation therapy). If lethal amounts are absorbed through the skin or ingested orally, chelation therapy usually will not spare the life of the patient.[51,52]

Manganese

Unlike lead and mercury, manganese is a trace mineral that the body needs in small amounts for optimal health. In large amounts, manganese is toxic and is associated with impulsive, hyperactive behavior that is similar to the mania symptoms of bipolar disorder.[53] Other possible symptoms include anorexia, weight loss, and insomnia. Typical major depression usually does not result from manganese toxicity. However, long-term occupational exposure to manganese or copper may result in Parkinson's disease.[54] Manganese poisoning is largely an occupational disease and is much less common than lead or mercury poisoning.

Arsenic

Arsenic has a long history of use for criminal purposes. Occupational poisoning currently occurs in the pharmaceutical and agricultural industries, in ore refining, manufacture of glass, and in the fur industry. Mass poisonings have occurred when arsenic was accidentally mixed with foodstuffs, killing several persons.

Chronic arsenic intoxication causes several neurological effects, including weakness, lethargy, dizzy spells, fatigue, progressive anxiety, emotional instability, insomnia, depression, and in severe cases a psychosis characterized by paranoid delusional thinking, and progressive disturbance of judgment and self-care functions.[55] Other symptoms include diarrhea and hot flashes.

Chronic arsenic exposure can come from contaminated drinking water and may contribute to cancers of the skin, bladder, lung, and prostate. It has also been linked to anemia, diabetes, and heart disease. You can determine whether your drinking water has arsenic or other harmful substances by sending $12 to the Environmental Quality Institute (EQI) at the University of North Carolina at Asheville. The Institute will send you the containers to send your sample back to them and issue a report to you of their findings. Filtration systems such as reverse osmosis, distillation, and anion exchange filters will remove arsenic.

Bismuth

Bismuth, found in *PeptoBismol*,® is used as a medication for indigestion, diarrhea, and to treat a stomach infection called Helicobacter Pylori. Bismuth, if used chronically or in high amounts, can cause depression, anxiety, irritability, and tremors that may last from weeks to months.[56] Sudden deterioration is known to occur without warning several years after exposure, with the development of symptoms reminiscent of stroke. A unique pattern of gray matter abnormalities can be seen on CT scans or MRIs.

Organotin

Organotins are used in insect and rodent killers and disinfectants. A unique mood disorder has been reported in workers exposed to organotin, with alternating bouts of rage and deep depression lasting from several hours to days. These mood changes may be long lasting, being noted on reevaluation between 9 and 34 months after exposure. It is not yet clear whether these changes are direct effects of organotin, the consequence of posttraumatic stress after exposure, or a reflection of personality and coping styles.[57]

Trimethyltin chloride

Chemical workers exposed to trimethyltin chloride have reported symptoms of forgetfulness, fatigue, loss of motivation, periods of headache, and sleep disturbance.[58]

Toxins Under Suspicion But Lacking Evidence

Solvents comprise compounds largely used in industry and include carbondisulfide, toluene, perchloroethylene, and trichloroethylene. Although there have been case reports suggesting that some or all of the above chemicals may cause depression or another mental illness, there is a shortage of good research available stating the specific effects these chemicals actually have.[59]

The same is true of insecticide compounds such as *organophosphates*.

Social Factors That Increase Risk of Depression

Although many causative factors for depression are underrated, the social factors that can contribute to depression appear, for the most part, to be overrated. While social factors are very important, I find that many patients begin to focus on these as sole causes of their depression. For example, a 19-year-old girl who has broken up with her boyfriend is clearly at higher risk for depression. If this young lady should actually experience depression, I would encourage her to consider factors in addition to her social turmoil as potential causes of her mental illness.

It is important to note that social factors are significant—but not necessarily the inevitable causes of such depression. The fact that many 19-year-old girls break up with boyfriends without becoming depressed serves as a balancing consideration for the effect of social influences on depression.

Why is it that two people may face apparently identical social challenges and yet only one of them becomes clinically depressed? As I see it, social factors never happen in a vacuum. Many other factors that influence the risk of depression are also operative. The message of this broadly focused chapter is, "Do not fall into the common trap of focusing on a single cause of depression and feel that this factor is the only one that you must deal with."

Depression (or your concerns about depression before its symptoms become fully evident) is always best addressed by viewing a *broad range of factors*. When all of the influences that generally determine depression risk have been considered, you can then more effectively attack those that apply specifically to you.

Figure 14 lists several social factors that have been found to increase the risk of depression.

Let us look at each of the seven social circumstances that can increase the risk of depression. The first one is parental separation.

Parental Separation

As we have seen, adolescents are not free from the risk of depression. On the contrary, they experience a relatively high risk of developing this common condition, and adolescents *who do not live with both biological parents are at an even higher risk of depression*.[60] For this and other reasons, the mental health benefits of living with both biological parents cannot be overstated. When conflict enters the home, however, parents may use justifications for separation and divorce that do not match the evidence. Their clichés may sound catchy, such as "It is better for our children to come from a divided home than to live in one." But when it comes to the mental health of their children, this saying is not necessarily true. Trying to save—or to tolerate—an "on the rocks" marriage is often the better solution.

Grandparents Taking on Parental Responsibility for Young Children

Shane's grandmother brought him to the office. She was worried about his loss of appetite, his moodiness, and frequent skipping of school. After talking to Shane and his grandmother and completing a routine exam, I was more concerned about Mrs. Latham's health than Shane's.

Unfortunately in this generation, divorce is more common than ever before in the history of the U.S.. This does not only increase the risk of depression in the children involved but also can have other extensive consequences. Often, the most available and most consistent caregivers of the children left behind by a divorce are not the

SOCIAL FACTORS THAT INCREASE RISK OF DEPRESSION

- Grandparents raising children
- Parental separation
- Severe sexual abuse
- Codependency
- Low social class
- Absence of social support
- Negative, stressful events

Figure 14

parents, but the grandparents.

Between 1980 and 1990 *the number of children living with grandparents or other relatives increased by almost 44 percent.* By 1997, almost 4 million U.S. children were, like Shane, living primarily with grandparents. Statistics show that *grandparents who raise their grandchildren double their risk of depression.*[61] They also experience higher rates of disability. While it is easy to speculate as to why this is so, research has been established that if grandparents are the primary caregivers of their grandchildren, they increase their own risk of depression.

Sexual Abuse

In our age of *do-it-yourself* psychotherapy, you would think that any history of sexual abuse could be labeled as a cause of depression. However, many types of sexual abuse actually do not increase the risk of depression. Nonetheless, severe or repeated instances of sexual abuse do increase the risk.[62]

Absence of Social Support

Linda's major complaint was depression. Her general knowledge of how to maintain good health was impressive. Along with enjoying a flower garden, she had developed her own fitness routine to manage her diet, exercise, and need for rest. But she had been unable to manage the mood swings that left her feeling dull and unmotivated. Worst of all were the times when she felt despondent. After we studied the possible causes of her symptoms, we focused on the most evident ones for immediate treatment. Linda listed loneliness among the possible causes of her depression. She recently left her job for a new one.

The value of social support is generally apparent in the mental health of humans. Interestingly, it has also been demonstrated to influence depression risk in primate animals. In Harlow's classic experiments, monkeys separated from their mothers demonstrated overt symptoms of despair.[63] The importance of social support is stated in **Figure 15**.[64]

Note that the *perception* of strong social support is important. For social support to be effective in helping a depressed person, it must be clearly demonstrated to the victim. Many psychology theorists include lack of social support in their model of depression causation and treatment.[65,66,67]

I explained to Linda that, like her transplanted flowers, she was suffering from root damage. After realizing that her new job had temporarily disturbed the roots she had established earlier, she made a list of activities and people who could help her form new connections. She then gave some thought to the kinds of stress that might be disturbing her mental health.

Negative Stressful Life Events

Many reports link recent negative stressful life events with the precipitation of depression.[68,69] Severe stressful events such as the death of a spouse or the loss of a job can bring about a "situational depression." This can potentially lead to major depression. Ongoing stress can also lead to depression. Researchers from Johns

DEPRESSION AND SOCIAL SUPPORT

- There is a compelling connection between depression and the lack of social support.

- Individuals who believe they have inadequate social support face an increased risk of depression.

Figure 15

Hopkins University interviewed 905 people living in Baltimore who had full-time jobs, including secretaries, teachers, construction workers, and executives.[70] Having little say at work and having a high workload increased the occurrence of a condition known as job strain. Job strain has been found to be a high risk factor for depression, as expressed in **Figure 16**.

If your boss doesn't listen to you and the work keeps piling up, you may be on a collision course with depression. This may be one of the reasons that there is quite an overlap between anxiety and depression. We address this important reason more fully in *Chapter 7*.

Codependency

Every person is a social being. The Holy Scriptures say that the Lord God, after creating Adam, said, "It is not good for the man to be alone; I will make him a helper suitable for him."[71] He then created Eve, his wife. It is good for each of us to be dependent upon others, and to realize that dependency. We are all created to be social beings. In a broad sense, every person should be "codependent," as it is a vital part of healthy living. This is why one of the worst punishments given a prisoner is solitary confinement.

JOB STRAIN

Workers with high job strain were five times more likely to have a depressive disorder compared to those with low job strain.

Figure 16

In the world of psychology, the term "codependency" has a different meaning. It is used to describe an *unhealthy, extreme dependency upon others*. From here on, I will be using the word "codependent" in its psychological meaning—an *unhealthy social state*. People with addictions, such as alcoholics, are often associated with people who have codependency. It is the term used to describe an obsession or even addiction to relationships, which often develops because of unfulfilling or unhealthy parent-child relationships.[72] The parents may be abusive and/or emotionally unavailable due to alcoholism, mental, or physical illness.[73]

Within every person is the God-given need to love and be loved. When children do not receive adequate love and nurturing from their parents, they can become insecure and in essence may spend their lives looking for love. They develop a virtual "love hunger." In the book, **Love Is A Choice**, Hemfelt, Minirth, and Meier postulate that codependency stems from empty "love tanks".[74] These individuals lack the security in their inner psyche that results from being openly loved and nurtured by two emotionally stable parents.

A more recent analysis by Natasha R. Lindley looked at the particular self-concepts possessed by codependent individuals. Upon examining multiple studies she concluded that indeed, *low self-worth* is the underlying trait that causes one's relationship skills to become faulty.[75] Not surprisingly, there is a *high incidence of depression* in individuals who possess codependent traits.[76]

Many psychologists focus on codependency alone as the root cause of any addiction or all unhealthy social relationships. They also tend to assume that virtually every depressed person has the condition, at least to some degree. This is an extreme oversimplification of the cause of depression and often leads to incorrect and even harmful psychological counseling. The fact is that many addictions, as well as some unhealthy social relationships, stem from poor judgment—and not necessarily from parental flaws or parental unavailability. But the traditional therapies for codependency take the emphasis away from the individual's own poor judgment and assign blame to the childhood environment and ultimately to the parents. The counselor then has the client go back in time and "deal" with the people (older adults) who caused this condition. This supposedly allows the victim of codependency to "move on" and overcome the sad state of unhealthy social relationships. Unfortunately, *counseling directed toward dealing with the troubled past has not been found to be effective in most cases.*[77]   *Chapter 5* will discuss therapies that work for overcoming codependency.

Other Lifestyle Factors That Increase Risk of Depression

Our daily choices and habitual routines have much to do with our mental health. Good choices can decrease the risk of depression. At the same time poor choices can dramatically increase that risk. We have already looked at the important connection between dietary factors and mental health. Let's consider several other choices that can influence health. Poor lifestyle practices that increase one's risk of depression are listed in **Figure 17**.

Let us explore each of these five factors.

Physical Inactivity

A wealth of evidence indicates that *physical exercise* is a powerful protector of our *mental health* and can be used to treat depression. A recent study is particularly instructive when it comes to preventing depression.

A group at particular risk for depression are those who have recently had a heart attack. The value of exercise is especially notable here. Dr. Richard Milani and colleagues at the Ochsner Clinic in Louisiana found that structured *cardiac rehabilitation exercise* powerfully combats depression among those who had recent heart attacks.[78] They studied more than 300 enrollees in a cardiac rehabilitation program. Results of the study are summarized in **Figure 18**.

HABITS THAT INCREASE RISK OF DEPRESSION

- Physical inactivity
- Interruption of circadian rhythms
- Legal drugs
  - Tobacco
  - Caffeine
  - Alcohol
- Illicit drug use
- Head injury

Figure 17

EXERCISE IN CARDIAC REHABILITATION REDUCES DEPRESSION RISK

Study of 300 cardiac victims that included exercise in their recovery program showed:

- 20% suffered from depression when they began their exercise commitment.

- After a 36-session exercise program during a 3-month period, depression was totally resolved in 2/3 of the individuals.

Figure 18

The findings outlined in the figure are particularly encouraging when we recall that among those with a recent heart attack, depression increases one's risk of death substantially over the next six months.[79]

Circadian Rhythm Interruption

Our bodies run on an *internal clock* that operates on roughly a 24-hour schedule. This schedule is so much a part of us that even if sealed in a cave, away from all time cues, our vital body processes will continue to function on essentially the same 24-hour rotation.[80] This natural rhythm is called a *circadian rhythm*. The term literally means "about" (Latin "circa") "a day" (Latin "dies"), and expresses this vital but often neglected part of physiology.

We all have some basic appreciation of circadian rhythms. Have you noticed that you function most efficiently when you consistently keep "on schedule?" For example, if every day you eat lunch at noon, your body will expect a meal at that time, and will coordinate your body processes to best facilitate digestion at the noon hour. What happens when you skip, or just postpone, your normal mealtime? Typically, if you usually have a regular mealtime, your body will protest the change, informing you with stomach rumblings and the like. These discomforts give you the message that your body does not appreciate it when you ignore your "body clock."

However, skipping a meal or staying up later than usual are not the greatest insults to our circadian rhythms. Probably our most extreme offense is the total disregard for these natural timekeepers that occur during shift work.[81] Recently, I have seen tangible examples of this in my own practice.

A large manufacturing company where I live operates around the clock. New ownership recently took over and switched the employees to rotating shift work. Instead of remaining on the same shift, every four weeks the workers are obligated to totally ignore their circadian rhythms as their schedule alternates from day shift to afternoon shift and then to the midnight shift.

Without doing a scientific study of the impact of these changes, I have noted a stunning rise in the number of cases of depression among the employee population. On the four-week shift program, these workers' bodies are never able to lock into a predictable rhythm. They start to feel better after the third week on the same shift, but two weeks later their work-rest cycle shifts again. Anyone with this kind of schedule soon becomes painfully aware of the importance of having regular times for going to bed and getting up each morning, including weekends. We feel better Monday through Friday when we keep the same schedule for the weekend. Most of us, even those working a steady day shift, tend to get out of step on the weekend. The result is usually impaired function on Monday mornings.

Some of the symptoms that have their root in violating our body's circadian rhythm are listed in **Figure 19**.

Even *mentally healthy people* with no known risk factors for depression *can become depressed* if the *circadian rhythms are significantly disturbed.*[82] This fact suggests

SYMPTOMS OF CIRCADIAN RHYTHM VIOLATION

- Depression
- Stomach disorders
- Anxiety
- Poor appetite
- Sleep disorders

Figure 19

that circadian rhythm disturbance is one of the root causes of depression. Interestingly, in about 50 percent of depressed individuals, depressed mental symptoms are temporarily resolved when they stay up and are sleep deprived. The depressed symptoms will return in force after sleeping, even if only a short nap is taken. This is why some individuals who are depressed have a tendency to become night owls and have a tendency to stay up "until they drop." They feel "normal" during these late hours, and they have a tendency not to want to get up after sleeping since their depressed symptoms return upon awakening.[83]

Winter Depression

Circadian rhythms can be disrupted by *normal seasonal changes.* Depression can be triggered by changes in the light-dark cycle that accompany the winter months, particularly in latitudes further from the equator.[84] Depression of this type can be treated or prevented either with interventions that boost brain serotonin levels[85] or by direct exposure to bright artificial light.[86]

Legal Drugs and Depression

Smoking and alcohol are both on the hit list when it comes to decreasing your risk of depression. Smoking and depression are strongly interrelated, as explained in **Figure 20.**[87,88,89]

A person with either pair of problems outlined in this figure is indeed in a vicious cycle.

It is important to note that concerns of alcohol and depression are not limited to occasional alcohol abusers. Even moderate drinkers have a higher risk of depression than those who do not drink. Reasons for this are explored in *Chapter 9.*

Like the use of tobacco and alcohol, caffeine also appears to increase the risk of depression. In the famous Tromso heart study, women who were heavier users of coffee dramatically increased their risk of depression.[90]

Even some medications can produce depression. The popular acne drug called *Accutane®* now comes with a warning from the FDA that includes suicidal thoughts, emotional instability, and depression.[91]

Illicit Drug Use

Depression can occur both in the context of using illicit drugs and withdrawing from them. Two common drugs of abuse, amphetamines and cocaine, are notorious for their connection with depression during drug withdrawal.[92]

Head Injury

The final lifestyle factor listed in **Figure 17** that can set the stage for depression is head injury. Severe head injury that causes obvious damage to the brain that is detected on an MRI often results in major depression. It is not common knowledge that even minor head injuries not detectable on an MRI can precipitate depression. Persons who experience a loss of consciousness or memory of events surrounding the head injury have a significant risk of developing

ALCOHOL AND NICOTINE INCREASE RISK OF DEPRESSION

- Nicotine habit increases risk of depression.

- Depression increases risk of acquiring the nicotine habit.

- Similarly, alcohol increases the risk of depression.

- Depression increases the tendency to use alcohol.

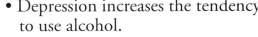

Figure 20

49

depression in the weeks that follow the injury. Even those who do not lose consciousness or memory, but experience headaches, dizziness, or difficulty concentrating within several days of the injury are at risk for developing major depression.[93,94]

I saw this form of depression with a person in my own medical office staff several years ago. While leaving her house, our office manager, who always had a positive, cheerful, and "can-do" attitude, slipped on a thin layer of ice on her sidewalk. She fell and injured the side of her head. Although scans showed no visible brain injury, she suffered from severe headaches for quite some time. Within two weeks of the fall she began to cry for no apparent reason while talking to patients or other employees. Work-up revealed that she had indeed developed major depression. Fortunately, after following the program outlined in this book, she was fully recovered within nine months.

Head Injuries in Contact Sports

Recent research reveals that the set-up for long-term brain damage often occurs following a head injury that causes a concussion. Risks for concussion are especially high in contact sports such as football or soccer. The chance that a college football player has had a concussion while playing football, either before or during college, is very high—about one in three. Players with two or more concussions perform significantly worse on tests that measure memory, learning ability, and other brain functions, as well as speed of information processing.[95] Sports that have resulted in concussion for some players are listed in **Figure 21.**[96]

Trauma to the head that causes just one concussion may trigger a cascade of biochemical events in the brain, which in time will result in degenerative nerve changes similar to those found in patients with Alzheimer's disease.[97,98]

There is a reason that the brain is enclosed within a hard bony structure called the skull—to protect it from mechanical injury. That means we should wear seat belts and shoulder harnesses at all times when in motor vehicles and choose recreational activities that will not put the brain at risk.

Medical Conditions That Increase Risk of Depression

Research indicates that *physical* illness can be a powerful factor in upsetting our *mental* health. In the United States, four to ten percent of people in an average community will be dealing with depression. That statistic jumps to as much as 36 percent of those who have medical afflictions of one kind or another.[99] When medical afflictions strike, not all groups are at the same increased risk of depression. For example, younger individuals, those with less education, and those in lower income brackets are more likely to develop depression under the stress of physical illness.[100]

A variety of medical conditions—once they are present—could be considered to be unchangeable risk factors for depression. But I don't find it useful to classify physical health

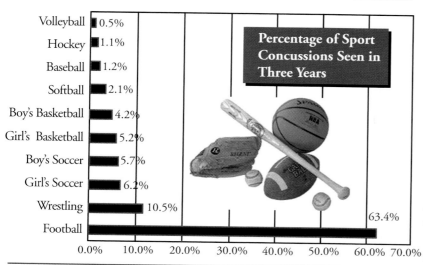

SPORTS AND BRAIN TRAUMA

Percentage of Sport Concussions Seen in Three Years

Sport	Percentage
Volleyball	0.5%
Hockey	1.1%
Baseball	1.2%
Softball	2.1%
Boy's Basketball	4.2%
Girl's Basketball	5.2%
Boy's Soccer	5.7%
Girl's Soccer	6.2%
Wrestling	10.5%
Football	63.4%

0.0%   10.0%   20.0%   30.0%   40.0%   50.0%   60.0% 70.0%

Figure 21

problems in this manner. Frankly, many of these conditions can be totally prevented (or at least delayed or improved) by paying appropriate attention to a *healthy lifestyle*. In fact, this is the basis of my book ***Proof Positive***.

Any medical condition, particularly if chronic, can tip the emotional balances and promote a slide into depression. But some health problems are *particularly high risk* when it comes to depressive illness. These conditions are listed in **Figure 22**.

Let us take a closer look at some of the conditions listed in the figure.

Stroke Brings on Depression

Ann had been experiencing increasing depression over a period of several weeks. She had noticed other unexplained symptoms that troubled her as well. We eventually discovered that she had been having minor strokes. These small, often-undetected strokes can cause depression. Healthy function of certain brain areas appears to be critical to warding off—or treating—depression. One such area is the prefrontal cortex of the brain. Another vital region to mental health is housed deep in the brain and is called the *basal ganglia*. Recent research by Dr. David C. Steffens and colleagues at Duke University has revealed that depressed individuals are more likely to have MRI evidence of small strokes in the basal ganglia.[101]

For those who have recognizable strokes, *40 percent will be depressed* three to four months after the stroke occurs.[102]

Heart Disease Increases Risk of Depression

Following a heart attack, individuals also face an increased risk of depression. For example, in one series of 99 hospitalized patients with coronary artery disease, 23 percent of the patients met the criteria for major depression.[103] This statistic is even more sobering when you recall that depres-

sion dramatically increases the risk of death in patients with heart disease, as explained in *Chapter 2*.[104]

Strokes and heart attacks are excellent examples of potentially preventable conditions. Whether by improving blood pressure control, addressing dietary factors, or getting serious about a host of other risk factors, these diseases can often be prevented—or at least greatly minimized in severity. In the book ***Proof Positive***, I have carefully detailed these compelling connections.[105]

Cancer and Other Terminal Illnesses are Linked to Depression

It is not surprising to find a link between depression and terminal illnesses such

MEDICAL CONDITIONS THAT MAY CAUSE DEPRESSION

- Stroke
- Heart disease
- Cancer and terminal illness
- AIDS
- Parkinson's disease
- Diabetes
- Postpartum status
- Premenstrual syndrome
- Sleep disorders
- Thyroid disease
- Adrenal gland disease
- Parathyroid gland disease
- Lupus

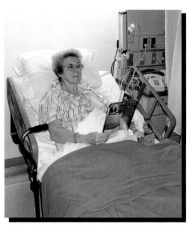

Figure 22

51

as cancer. Up to 42 percent of cancer patients also have major depression.[106] However, there are definite challenges to a physician when dealing with terminal conditions. Consider the situation with cancer. Making the diagnosis of depression may be extremely difficult in that context because the disease itself can cause symptoms that meet the criteria for depression, even when true depression is not present. Sleep disturbances, weight loss, fatigue, changes in eating habits, and recurrent thoughts of death can occur even in patients who are psychologically coping well with their cancer. Recognizing the fact that depression can coexist with such illnesses and treating the depression may not only significantly reduce the patient's psychological load but may also improve the patient's response to medical treatment.[107]

AIDS and Major Depression

It stands to reason that anyone contracting AIDS (acquired immunodeficiency syndrome) would become a likely candidate for

significant depression in view of the disabling disease process and the dismal prognosis. It is not surprising that various studies have demonstrated a significant association between AIDS and major depression.[108] One study found that AIDS patients are about seven times more likely to commit suicide than the general population.[109]

Stressors such as unemployment and unresolved grief do contribute to depression in the AIDS patient, but researchers suggest that specific physical aspects of the disease begin to have effect. As the disease progresses, three effects combine as factors to produce major depression. They are spelled out in **Figure 23**.

The root cause of AIDS and the irrefutable method of preventing it are both well understood, as explained in my book **Proof Positive**.[110]

While depression may seem unavoidable in the AIDS victim, the recognition and treatment of psychological distress may successfully reduce the inevitable physical and emotional pain associated with this devastating terminal illness. Christian counseling is always an important option in cases where individuals are making personal decisions that may affect their eternal destiny.

Parkinson's Disease and Depression

Parkinson's disease is a progressive disease of the nervous system characterized by tremors and impaired movement. It affects more than one million Americans. A decrease in the production of dopamine, a critical brain chemical, is responsible for producing the symptoms.

The cause or causes of Parkinson's disease has eluded researchers, though they are making gains. Some suspected causes include on-the-job exposure to solvents like paints and glues,[111] welding fumes,[112] pesticides,[113] job-related exposure to metals,[114] prions from infected meat,[115] iron accumulation in the brain,[116] and even your genetic

THREE FACTORS IN AIDS VICTIMS CAUSE DEPRESSION

- Effects of the HIV virus on the central nervous system

- Direct toxic effects of the virus itself

- Effects of medications used to treat the disease

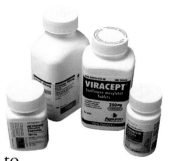

Figure 23

make-up.[117]

During her regular appointment, Maggie explained that recently she felt unexplainably sad on several occasions. Always an active person, she still maintained a rigorous schedule of activities despite the annoying tremors caused by Parkinson's disease. Maggie was learning to cope with the tremors, but she wanted to know what she could do about coping with the depression.

Nearly 50 percent of patients with Parkinson's disease will suffer from major depression at some point in their protracted illness.[118,119] Depression is believed to result from actual changes in brain electrical patterns that accompany the condition. Later in this chapter I discuss the answer to Maggie's question, the importance of healthy brain circuitry for all of us—whether or not we have Parkinson's disease, depression, or are just trying to keep in top mental health.

Many other diseases of the brain, including brain tumors, multiple sclerosis, Alzheimer's disease, and brain infections can also cause depression.

Diabetes and Depression

Research suggests that individuals with diabetes—whether on insulin or not—have a substantially increased risk of depression. Risk may approach triple that of those without blood sugar abnormalities. One of the tragedies of this relationship is that many practitioners do not make this connection. The result is that depression appears to be seriously under-treated in individuals with diabetes.[120]

Having a Baby and Getting Depressed

The research literature is very clear that immediately after giving birth, women experience a higher risk of depression.

Some new mothers seem embarrassed to admit that they have become depressed after giving birth. An episode of "*baby blues*" following childbirth is so common and usually so mild that it is considered normal by most people, and it doesn't get much attention. Occurring in 50 to 80 percent of mothers, maternity blues is characterized by a mildly depressed mood state during the first two weeks postpartum.[121] Apparently caused by a rapid change in hormone balance, these episodes are resolved without a need for treatment.

While the term *baby blues* is a common term, less commonly understood is the fact that mothers who experience it are at higher risk for a much more significant episode of depression in the months that follow.

This condition, termed *postpartum depression*, is considered a psychiatric disorder that occurs in about 7 to 14 percent of adult women. It usually begins between 2 to 10 weeks after giving birth, although it may not develop until up to two years postpartum.[122,123] Postpartum depression is also characterized by mood swings.[124] A longer-term inability to adjust to the new demands of motherhood can have a devastating effect on both the mother and the infant.[125]

A history of difficult premenstrual syndrome (PMS), as well as a personal or family history of depression, especially postpartum depression, places a woman at a greater risk for a serious bout with depression after childbirth. In more than 50 percent of cases, a postpartum episode is the woman's first experience with serious depression. It seems reasonable to suspect that the cause is primarily hormonal; however, various lifestyle and social factors have also been evaluated as risk factors.

Most often, marital tension, stressors related to child-care, and a lack of strong emotional social support seem to be the triggers.[126,127] Furthermore, adoptive mothers and fathers also suffer an increased incidence of depression during this time of adjustment.[128,129] Further evidence that psychosocial stressors are the strongest causative factors in depression is that a full 26 percent of teenage mothers develop post-partum depression, a higher incidence than any other age group.[130]

Unfortunately, most depressed moms of newborns are only given the options of counseling and taking drug medications. Abstaining from drug therapy when breast feeding is a valid consideration, which narrows the mother's options further. But there are many nutritional and lifestyle factors in addition to the known social factors that should work together to reduce the risk and treat postpartum depression.

It may not be possible for new mothers to avoid the baby blues completely. Their high risk factors for depression are shown in **Figure 24**.

If a new mother is aware of the four risks for depression listed in **Figure 24** and follows the treatment program outlined in subsequent chapters of this book, it will help her meet the challenges of depression.

HIGH RISK FACTORS FOR DEPRESSION IN MOTHERS

- Family history of mental disorders

- Teenage mother

- Marital problems

- Lacking social support system

Figure 24

Monthly State of Depression in Women—PMS

For a woman to be somewhat depressed or "moody" around the time of her menstrual period is so common that it is almost considered normal. For centuries a variety of symptoms relating to the menstrual cycle have been described, but only during the past two decades have studies been performed to examine the sometimes disabling physical discomfort and emotional distress commonly referred to as PMS.

PMS (premenstrual syndrome) is characterized by physical, behavioral, and psychological symptoms of sufficient severity to interfere with interpersonal relationships or normal activities. About 80 percent of women in their reproductive years may experience mild symptoms, including abdominal cramps and bloating, breast tenderness, or depressed mood for a day or two before the menstrual period. Up to 8 percent of women will experience debilitating symptoms around the time of ovulation that continue for two weeks, through the first few days of menses. This more severe form of PMS is called premenstrual dysphoric disorder (PDD).[131]

While the incidence of PMS is of concern because it is so common, PDD is of particular concern because it is constituted by predictable monthly episodes of significant depression amidst a host of other potentially disabling symptoms. These might include severe anxiety, migraine headache, mania (severe hyperactivity), and even psychosis. Diagnosis and treatment of both PMS and PDD are complex because approximately one half of women who have premenstrual complaints actually have a pre-existing medical or psychiatric condition which is intensified during the premenstrual period. These not only include major depression but also allergies, asthma, bulimia, seizures, and genital herpes.[132]

PMS and PDD appear to be related to hormone fluctuations associated with the menstrual cycle. Various lifestyle and social factors have been examined as possible contributors to premenstrual syndrome, but no consistent association has been found. A prior incidence of mental disorders, particularly major depression, has been linked to PDD. One study also suggested that a previous bout with postpartum depression places a woman at greater risk.[132]

Some women report their PMS symptoms beginning or worsening in severity after childbirth, after starting or stopping the use of oral contraceptives, or after pelvic surgery such as tubular pregnancy. Studies have not been performed to determine whether these particular variables are true risk factors for PMS. It has been established that adolescent daughters are more likely to have PMS if it also occurred in their mothers.[133]

While the most prevalent treatment for PMS currently is antidepressants, there are some natural measures that have been shown to have potential benefit. Low doses of Vitamin B_6 have provided relief in some women with premenstrual symptoms.[134] Some studies suggest a benefit with magnesium, Vitamin B_6, and Vitamin E, but the use of supplemental calcium has proven to be more effective in many cases.[135]

Researchers have found that a disturbance in calcium regulation, which triggers premenstrual symptoms, can be addressed by taking 1200 mg of calcium carbonate per day. Women who took the calcium supplement had a near 50 percent decrease in symptoms compared with a 30 percent decrease in women who took a placebo.[136]

Reportedly, PMS symptoms can be relieved with administration of evening primrose oil and other products containing long-chain fatty acids. Despite its popularity, studies have not shown it to be any more effective than a placebo.[137] Some women have found relief using herbs such as black cohosh, blue cohosh, wild yam root, chaste tree fruit (also called chasteberry), or raspberry leaf tea, but no conclusive studies regarding their effectiveness have been performed.

A carefully planned program based on attention to diet and exercise can be effective in solving the PMS problem. Mood swings can be minimized with lifestyle changes.

Dr. Neal D. Barnard, president of the Physicians' Committee for Responsible Medicine based in Washington, D.C., and the department of obstetrics and gynecology at Georgetown University School of Medicine performed a study. The result is stated in **Figure 25**.

Menstrual cramps can be caused by prostaglandins, whose production is triggered by sex hormones like estrogen. A low fat vegan diet (with about 10 percent fat) has been shown to reduce estrogen production, and is also high in fiber, which helps the body to excrete excess estrogen. Lower estrogen means lower prostaglandin production and a decrease in the intensity and duration of menstrual cramps. While this regimen was not effective in all women,

DIET CHANGE REDUCES PREMENSTRUAL SYMPTOMS

Consuming a low-fat vegetarian diet reduced the length and severity of premenstrual symptoms.

Figure 25

many found profound relief.[138]

Pain and emotional distress in general are better tolerated when a person is rested, well hydrated, and in good physical condition. These facts suggest that drinking adequate water, getting plenty of rest, and staying in good physical shape would presumably benefit anyone suffering from the discomfort and emotional distress associated with premenstrual syndrome.

Depression and the Thyroid

Depression and low thyroid function are so interwoven that psychiatrists do not allow a diagnosis of "major depression" unless the clinician can ensure that thyroid function is normal. Despite this diagnostic criterion, there are no doubt thousands of individuals who have been diagnosed with depression who really have untreated *hypothyroidism*.

About 40 percent of individuals with hypothyroidism will have depression as a result.[139] Obviously, the treatment of choice for their depression is the same as the treatment for their thyroid disease (usually oral thyroid hormone). Anyone who is depressed and does not know why should have his or her thyroid status adequately tested (which should include a blood test called a TSH).

For a more complete list of internal medicine and neurology diseases that can be the cause of depression see *Appendix VI*.

After reviewing the number of diseases that can result in depression, it is no wonder that internal medicine physicians like myself see so many patients with depression. In fact, a good internal medicine physician may be the best health care provider to determine the actual cause of depression, whereas the psychiatrist may be the best person to deal with the resistant or hard-to-treat cases of depression.

Medications Can Cause Depression

There is a long list of medications that can increase one's risk of depression. Ironi-

cally, a medication that is *intended to treat a medical condition* may increase the risk of depression, and *the medical condition itself may also increase the risk of depression*. We have one risk adding to another risk. It may seem that I'm opening the door to a difficult dilemma. You may ask, "What should I do?" Should you take a high blood pressure medication that could increase your risk of depression? Or should you avoid the medication and gamble that your uncontrolled blood pressure will not contribute to a depression-inducing heart attack or stroke? Perhaps that does not sound like a difficult decision—after all, heart attacks and strokes can do more than cause depression. But what about that medication for chronic knee pain? Is *that* relief worth the increased risk of depression?

In my mind, none of these scenarios are really *either/or* situations. In short, a variety of lifestyle — and other non-drug factors—can usually help to address many common diseases. Drug therapy often does not need to be the first line of attack. Even when medications do seem to be indicated, there are often a variety of options that work equally well. If I know that a patient is at higher risk of depression than average, I am less likely to prescribe a drug that would further increase depression risk.

On the other hand, if you are prescribed a depression-implicated medication, do not despair. Your doctor may feel that there are no other options, but by paying special attention to the other causative factors discussed in this chapter you may tip the scale in your favor and avoid depression's visit.

A list of common medications that have been associated with the onset of depression appears in **Figure 26**.[140] For a complete list of medications reported to possibly cause depression, see *Appendix VII*.

Imbalanced Brain Electrical Activity Related to Depression

Depression risk appears to be increased

by any factor that decreases the electrical activity in the master control center of the brain. This center is known as the pre-frontal cortex, which makes up the largest region of the frontal lobe of the brain. *Almost all depression victims suffer from decreased electrical activity in this vital brain area.*[141] The decrease can be *40 to 50 percent, and more at times.*

You may wonder how a person's brain activity can be measured. The answer is provided by a sophisticated diagnostic procedure called *PET* (positron emission tomography). Commonly referred to as a *PET scan*, this test is done using equipment similar to an MRI or CT scan, but it provides vital information that the MRI or CT scan cannot furnish. The MRI and CT tests reveal brain anatomy, or *brain structure*, but cannot detect *brain activity*. A PET scan shows both brain structure and the activity levels of each part of the brain. PET scanning is a modern technique that has allowed us to determine that there is a marked decrease in prefrontal activity in depressed individuals.

The discussion of frontal lobe activity, of course, raises that "chicken or egg" question. Is it the depression that causes the frontal lobe abnormality, or do problems with prefrontal cortex activity help to precipitate the depression? Research suggests that there are elements of truth in both propositions. In fact, because of the importance of this subject, all of *Chapter 9* addresses this critical area. In that chapter I make a strong case for doing whatever is possible to enhance frontal lobe function.

Uncommon Causes of Depression

Although we have placed our primary emphasis on the more common causes of depression, the discussion would not be complete without also listing some uncommon causes of this malady. Several of these factors are worthy of our attention and are listed in **Figure 27**.

COMMON MEDICATIONS ASSOCIATED WITH DEPRESSION

1. Heart and blood pressure drugs:
   - Clonidine
   - Water pills (diuretics) in the thiazide family
   - Digitalis (e.g. Digoxin or Lanoxin)

2. Hormones:
   - Oral contraceptive pills
   - Cortisone and related medications
   - Anabolic steroids

3. Medications used for mental health:
   - Anti-anxiety drugs in the Benzodiazepine family (e.g. Valium, Ativan, Xanax, etc.)

4. Anti-inflammatory drugs:
   - Common over-the-counter and prescription
   - NSAIDs (Nonsteroidal anti-inflammatory agents)

5. Anti-infective agents:
   - "Sulfa" antibiotics
   - Ethambutol (a tuberculosis drug)
   - Interferon

6. Drugs used for intestinal problems:
   - Medications used to improve intestinal motility
     Metoclopramide (Reglan)
   - Anti-acid/anti-ulcer drugs
     Cimetide (Tagamet)
     Ranitidine (Zantac)

Figure 26

Sick Building Syndrome

Sick building syndrome typically occurs in buildings with recirculating ventilation systems that are not open to fresh air. However, the condition can still occur even when outdoor air ventilation is available. The of-

UNCOMMON CAUSES OF DEPRESSION

- Sick building syndrome
- Metabolic causes
- Infectious causes:
  Borna virus
  Prions
  Influenza in infants

Figure 27

Infection and Depression

Certain infectious diseases have been linked with depression. Some individuals look at these diseases as comparable to "snakes in your back yard" or "poisonous spiders in your dresser drawers." What I mean is that they regard these factors as unusual (at least in most settings) and even if present, never completely avoidable. I see infectious illnesses differently. First of all, we can often decrease or eliminate the risk of exposure to certain germs. Second, even when exposure is unavoidable, our lifestyle can make a significant difference in whether or not we succumb to serious illness when exposed. The book *Proof Positive* explains many ways in which we can strengthen the immune system.[144] Although many people think in terms of a good immune system and cancer prevention, the diseases that follow depression should prompt us to add it to the list of illnesses potentially avoided by good immune mechanisms.

Borna Infection

The Borna virus is one of many that can be transmitted from animals to humans. It infects domestic animals, including horses, cattle, sheep, and cats, as stated in **Figure 28**.

It can actually cause depression in the infected animal. Many veterinarians have learned to suspect Borna disease-related depression when a horse suffers telltale personality changes.

As expressed in **Figure 28**, the Borna virus can infect human mononuclear cells (a type of white blood cell). Once established in those cells, the virus can remain dormant for many years. For this reason, a person may not have any symptoms immediately following Borna exposure. Unfortunately, the virus can later raise its ugly head and cause very severe depression in humans.[145]

When it comes to this uncommon cause of depression, diagnosis is extremely

fenders are harmful substances that build up in the air and cause physical illness. Implicated substances may include allergens, molds, and chemicals that are "off-gassed" from newer building materials. Although sick building syndrome is characterized by symptoms as varied as eye irritation, headaches, and sinus problems, it can also be a contributing factor to depression.[142] But depression may not occur until after a month or two of daily exposure. Proper ventilation of the building, ultraviolet light exposure, either in the ventilation ducts or through large windows, combined with a cleaning that rids the place of molds may relieve the occupants' symptoms.[143]

important. Once the Borna virus is found, an antiviral agent (amantadine) can be prescribed to aid the body in combating the infection. The depression typically is cured when the virus is eliminated from the body.

Prions

Prions grabbed headlines nearly a decade ago when these rogue proteins were linked not only to *mad cow disease*, but also to a fatal human illness now known as *new variant Creutzfeldt-Jakob disease (nvCJD)*. People can contract the disease by eating meat from an infected cow. This prion-related disease in humans often surfaces first with mood and personality changes such as depression. Diagnosis offers little consolation, because *nv*CJD is rapidly fatal, typically causing death within two years of the diagnosis.

Influenza in Infants

Fetal flu exposure may significantly increase the risk of depression.[146] A woman who contracts the flu while carrying an unborn child can pass it along to the fetus. This increases the child's risk of becoming afflicted with depression later in life. Consequently, even prenatal influences can result in depression.

Conclusion

With all of the many potential root causes of depression, it is truly amazing that even more people do not develop this prevalent mental disorder. I have found that the brain, in most cases, is extremely resilient. It can normally stand up to a combination of three risk factors and root causes and still function in a healthy manner—without depression. But when the fourth factor, depression, is added, even the healthiest brain will often succumb to major depression.

The long list of factors that can cause or contribute to the process of depression underscores the importance of carefully considering multiple causative factors.

Without medical training, like many of my patients, you may be able to determine that you are experiencing depression as described in this book. However, you will need the assistance of a health professional to take the next steps in identifying the causes of depression and determining an appropriate treatment.

The importance of seeking qualified medical care for depression cannot be overemphasized. Ideally, that care should not only include appropriate diagnosis and treatment of the depression, but also a careful search for all underlying factors. The diagnosis and treatment should involve a comprehensive program that addresses as many of these root causes as possible.

BORNA DISEASE VIRUS

- Infects domestic animals including horses, cattle, sheep, and cats

- Infects blood mononuclear cells; may remain dormant for long periods

- Causes behavioral changes

- Can cause severe depression in humans

Figure 28

References—

[1] Gruenberg AM, Goldstein RD. Chapter 54: Depressive Disorders. In: Psychiatry, 1st ed. (Tasman A, editor). 1997 W. B. Saunders Company; P. 996.

[2] Kessler RC, McConagle KA, et al. Lifetime and 12-month prevalence of DSM IIIR psychiatric disorders in the United States. *Arch Gen Psychiatry* 1994;51:8-19.

[3] US Congress, Office of Technology Assessment: Adolescent Health. Washington, US Government Printing Office, 1991 (cited in Post D, Carr C, Weigand J. Teenagers: mental health and psychological issues. *Prim Care* 1998 Mar;25(1):181-192).

[4] Emslie GE, Weinberg WA, et al. Depressive symptoms by self-report in adolescence: Phase I of the development of a questionnaire for depression by self-report. *J Child Neurol* 1990;5:114-121.

[5] Rao U, Hammen C, Daley S. Continuity of depression during the transition to adulthood: a 5-year longitudinal study of young women. *J Am Acad Child Adolesc Psychiatry* 1999 Jul;38(7):908-915.

[6] Emslie GE, Weinberg WA, et al. Depressive symptoms by self-report in adolescence: Phase I of the development of a questionnaire for depression by self-report. *J Child Neurol* 1990;5:114-121.

[7] Weissman MM, Bruce ML, et al. Affective disorders. Robins LN, Regier DA (eds): Psychiatric Disorders in America. New York: Free Press, 1991:53-80.

[8] Weissman MM, Bruce ML, et al. Affective disorders. Robins LN, Regier DA (eds): Psychiatric Disorders in America. New York: Free Press, 1991:53-80.

[9] Depression Guideline Panel: Depression in Primary Care, Volume 1, Detection and Diagnosis. Clinical Practice Guideline, Number 5. Rockville, MD: U.S. Department of Health and Human Services, Agency for Health Care Policy and Research, 1993. AHCPR publication 93-0550.

[10] Weissman MM, Bland RC, et al. Cross-national epidemiology of major depression and bipolar disorder. *JAMA* 1996;276:293.

[11] Weissman MM, Wolk S, et al, Depressed adolescents grown up. *JAMA* 1999 May 12;281(18):1707-1713.

[12] Warner V, Weissman MM, et al. Grandparents, parents, and grandchildren at high risk for depression: a three-generation study. *J Am Acad Child Adolesc Psychiatry* 1999 Mar;38(3):289-296.

[13] Weissman MM, Kidd KK, Prusoff BA: Variability in rates of affective disorders in relatives of depressed and normal probands. *Arch Gen Psychiatry* 1982;39:1397.

[14] Biederman J, et al. Patterns of psychopathology and dysfunction in high-risk children of parents with panic disorder and major depression. *Am J Psychiatry* 2001;158:49-57.

[15] Smith KA. Relapse of depression after rapid depletion of tryptophan. *Lancet* 1997 Mar 29;349(9056):915-919.

[17] Hibbeln JR. Fish consumption and major depression. *Lancet* 1998 Apr 18;351(9110):1213.

[18] Hibbeln JR, Umhau JC, et al. Do plasma polyunsaturates predict hostility and depression? *World Rev Nutr Diet* 1997;82:175-186.

[19] Fava M, Borus JS, et al. Folate, vitamin B_{12}, and homocysteine in major depressive disorder. *Am J Psychiatry* 1997 Mar;154(3):426-428.

[20] Snowdon DA, Tully CL, et al. Serum folate and the severity of atrophy of the neocortex in Alzheimer disease: findings from the Nun study. *Am J Clin Nutr* 2000 Apr;71(4):993-998.

[21] Penninx BW, Guralnik JM, et al. Vitamin B_{12} deficiency and depression in physically disabled older women: epidemiologic evidence from the Women's Health and Aging Study. *Am J Psychiatry* 2000 May;157(5):715-721.

[22] Coppen A, Bailey J. Enhancement of the antidepressant action of fluoxetine by folic acid: a randomised, placebo controlled trial. *J Affect Disord* 2000 Nov;60(2):121-130.

[23] Bottiglieri T, Laundy M, et al. Homocysteine, folate, methylation, and monoamine metabolism in depression. *J Neurol Neurosurg Psychiatry* 2000 Aug; 69(2):228-232.

[24] Hayward C, Killen JD, et al. Psychiatric risk associated with early puberty in adolescent girls. *J Am Acad Child Adolesc Psychiatry* 1997 Feb;36(2):255-262.

[25] Herman-Giddens ME, Slora EJ, et al. Secondary sexual characteristics and menses in young girls seen in office practice: a study from the Pediatric Research in Office Settings network. *Pediatrics* 1997 Apr;99(4):505-512.

[26] Berkey CS. Relation of childhood diet and body size to menarche and adolescent growth in girls. *Am J Epidemiol* 2000;152:446-452.

[27] Azzena A, Zen T, et al. Risk factors for breast cancer. Case-control study results. *Eur J Gynaecol Oncol* 1994;15(5):386-392.

[28] Campbell TC. Muscling out the meat myth. *New Century Nutrition* 1996 Jul;2(7):1-2.

[29] Lucca A. Neutral amino acid availability in two major psychiatric disorders. *Prog Neuropsychopharmacol Biol Psychiatry* 1995 Jul;9(4):615-626.

[30] Lucca A. Plasma tryptophan levels and plasma tryptophan/neutral amino acids ratio in patients with mood disorder, patients with obsessive-compulsive disorder, and normal subjects. *Psychiatry Res* 1992 Nov;44(2):85-91.

[31] Armstrong B, Doll R. Environmental factors and cancer incidence and mortality in different countries, with special reference to dietary practices. *Int J Cancer* 1975 Apr 15;15(4):617-631.

[32] Nedley N. *Proof Positive: How to Reliably Combat Disease and Achieve Optimal Health through Nutrition and Lifestyle.* Ardmore, OK: Nedley Publishing, 1999 p. 147.

[33] Christensen L, Somers S. Adequacy of the dietary intake of depressed individuals. *J Am Coll Nutr* 1994 Dec;13(6):597-600.

[34] Trimble MR. The role of toxins in disorders of mood and affect. *Neurol Clin* 2000 Aug;18(3):649-664.

[35] White RF, Feldman RG, Proctor SP. Behavioral Syndromes in Neurotoxicology in Fogel BS, Schiffer RB, Rao SM (eds): *Neuropsychiatry*. Baltimore, Williams and Wilkins, 1996, pp. 959-969.

[36] Baker EL, Feldman RG, et al. Occupational lead neurotoxicity: A behavioral and electrophysiological evaluation. Study design and one year results. *Br J Indust Med* 1984;41:352-361.

[37] Baker EL, White RF, et al. Occupational lead neurotoxicity: Improvement in behavioral effects following exposure reduction. *Br J Indust Med* 1985;42:507-516.

[38] Needleman HL. The neurobehavioral consequences of low lead exposure in childhood. *Neurobehav Toxicol Teratol* 1982;4:729-732.

[39] Adler R, Moore C. Herbal vitamins: lead toxicity and developmental delay. *Pediatrics* 2000 Sep;106(3):600-602.

[40] Ross EA. Lead content of calcium supplements. *JAMA* 2000 Sep 20;284(11):1425-1429.

[41] Lucas SR, Sexton M, et al. Relationship between blood lead and nutritional factors in preschool children: a cross-sectional study. *Pediatrics* 1996 Jan;97(1):74-78.

[42] Ambrose TM, Al-Lozi M, Scott MG. Bone lead concentrations as-

sessed by in-vivo X-ray fluorescence. *Clin Chem* 2000 Aug; 46(8 Pt 1):1171-1178.

[43] Schwartz B. Associations of Blood Lead, Dimercaptosuccinic Acid-Chelatable Lead, and Tibia Lead with Polymorphisms in the Vitamin D Receptor and Aminolevulinic Acid Dehydratase Genes. *Environmental Health Perspectives* 2000 Oct;108(10):949-954.

[44] Hanninen H: The behavioral effects of occupational exposure to mercury and lead. *Acta Neurol Scand* 66(suppl 92):167-175, 1982.

[45] Lishman WA: Organic Psychiatry, 3rd ed. Blackwell Scientific as quoted by Trimble MR, In: The role of toxins in disorders of mood and affect. *Neurol Clin* 2000 Aug;18(3):649-664.

[46] Adler R, Moore C. Herbal vitamins: lead toxicity and developmental delay. *Pediatrics* 2000 Sep;106(3):600-602.

[47] McRill C, Boyer LV, et al. Mercury toxicity due to use of a cosmetic cream. *J Occup Environ Med* 2000 Jan;42(1):4-7.

[48] Summary of the joint statement on thimerosal in vaccines. American Academy of Family Physicians, American Academy of Pediatrics, Advisory Committee on Immunization Practices, Public Health Service. *MMWR Morb Mortal Wkly Rep* 2000 Jul 14;49(27):622,631.

[49] Egeland GM, Middaugh JP. Balancing fish consumption benefits with mercury exposure. *Science* 1997 Dec 12;278(5345):1904-1905.

[50] Sorensen N, Murata K, et al. Prenatal methylmercury exposure as a cardiovascular risk factor at seven years of age. *Epidemiol* 1999;10:370-375.

[51] Nierenberg DW, Nordgren RE, et al. Delayed cerebellar disease and death after accidental exposure to dimethylmercury. *N Eng J Med* 1998;338(23):1672-1676.

[52] Kulig K. A tragic reminder about organic mercury. *N Eng J Med* 1998;338(23):1692-1693.

[53] Trimble MR. The role of toxins in disorders of mood and affect. *Neurol Clin* 2000 Aug;18(3):649-664.

[54] Gorell JM, Johnson CC. Occupational exposures to metals as risk factors for Parkinson's disease. *Neurol* 1997 Mar;48(3):650-658.

[55] Trimble MR. The role of toxins in disorders of mood and affect. *Neurol Clin* 2000 Aug;18(3):649-664.

[56] Trimble MR. The role of toxins in disorders of mood and affect. *Neurol Clin* 2000 Aug;18(3):649-664.

[57] Hartmann DE: Neuropsychological Toxicology: Identification and assessment of human neurotoxic syndromes. New York, Plenum Press, 1995, pp. 79-148. As quoted by Trimble MR, In: The role of toxins in disorders of mood and affect. *Neurol Clin* 2000 Aug;18(3):649-664.

[58] Trimble MR. The role of toxins in disorders of mood and affect. *Neurol Clin* 2000 Aug;18(3):649-664.

[59] Trimble MR. The role of toxins in disorders of mood and affect. *Neurol Clin* 2000 Aug;18(3):649-664.

[60] Kendler KS, Kessler RC, et al. The prediction of major depression in women: Toward an integrated etiologic model. *Am J Psychiatry* 1993;150:1139-1147.

[61] Minkler M, Fuller-Thomson E. The health of grandparents raising grandchildren: results of a national study. *Am J Public Health* 1999 Sep;89(9):1384-1389.

[62] Cheasty M. Relation between sexual abuse in childhood and adult depression: case-control study. *BMJ* 1998 Jan 17;316(7126):198-201.

[63] Harlow HF, Harlow MK. Social deprivation in monkeys. *Sci Am* 1962;207:136-146.

[64] Peirce RS, Frone MR, et al. A longitudinal model of social contact, social support, depression, and alcohol use. *Health Psychol* 2000 Jan;19(1):28-38.

[65] Sullivan HS. *The Interpersonal Theory of Psychiatry*. New York: Norton, 1953.

[66] Lewinsohn PM. A behavioral approach to depression. In: Friedman RJ, Katz MM (eds): *The Psychology of Depression: Contemporary Theory and Research*. New York: John Wiley & Sons, 1974 p. 157-178.

[67] Klerman GL, Weissman MM, et al. *Interpersonal Psychotherapy of Depression*. New York: Basic Books, 1984.

[68] Post RM. Transduction of psychosocial stress into the neurobiology of recurrent affective disorder. *Am J Psychiatry* 1992;149:999-1010.

[69] Kendler KS, Kessler RC, et al. The prediction of major depression in women: Toward an integrated etiologic model. *Am J Psychiatry* 1993;150:1139-1147.

[70] Mausner-Dorsch H, Eaton WW. Psychosocial Work Environment and Depression: Epidemiologic Assessment of the Demand-Control Model. *Am J Pub Health* 2000;90(11):1765-1770.

[71] Genesis 2:18. *The Holy Bible*. New American Standard Version.

[72] Hemfelt R, Minirth F, Meier P. *Love Is A Choice*, copyright 1989, Thomas Nelson Publishers, Nashville, TN, p. 13.

[73] Fuller JA. Family stressors as predictors of codependency. *Genet Soc Gen Psychol Monogr*, 2000 Feb;126(1):5-22.

[74] Hemfelt R, Minirth F, Meier P. *Love Is A Choice*, copyright 1989, Thomas Nelson Publishers, Nashville, TN, p. 13.

[75] Lindley NR. Codependency: predictors and psychometric issues. *J Clin Psychol*, 1999 Jan;55(1):59-64.

[76] Martsolf DS. Codependency and related health variables. *Arch Psychiatr Nurs*, 2000 Jun;14(3):150-158.

[77] *Scientific American Medicine* May 2000

[78] Milani RV, Lavie CJ, Cassidy MM. Effects of cardiac rehabilitation and exercise training programs on depression in patients after major coronary events. *Am Heart J* 1996;132(4):726-732.

[79] Frasure-Smith N, Lesperance F, Talajic M. Depression following myocardial infarction. *JAMA* 1993;270:1819-1825.

[80] Czeisler CA: Human circadian physiology: Internal organization of temperature, sleep-wake and neuroendocrine rhythms monitored in an environment free of time cues (dissertation). Stanford, CA, Stanford University, 1978.

[81] Harrington JM. Shift work and health: A critical review of the literature on working hours. *Ann Acad Med Singapore* 1994 Sep;23(5):699-705.

[82] Boivin DB, Czeisler CA, et al. Complex interaction of the sleep-wake cycle and circadian phase modulates mood in healthy subjects. *Arch Gen Psychiatry* 1997 Feb;54(2):145-152.

[83] Riemann D, Hohagen F. Advanced vs. normal sleep timing: effects on depressed mood after response to sleep deprivation in patients with a major depressive disorder. *J Affect Disord* 1996 Apr 12;37(2-3):121-128.

[84] Faedda GL, Tondo L, et al. Seasonal mood disorders: patterns of seasonal recurrence in mania and depression. *Arch Gen Psychiatry* 1993;50:17.

[85] Lam RW, Gorman CP, et al. Multicenter, placebo-controlled study of fluoxetine in seasonal affective disorder. *Am J Psychiatry* 1995;152:1765.

[86] Terman M, Terman JS, Ross DC. A controlled trial of timed bright light and negative air ionization for treatment of winter depression. *Arch Gen Psychiatry* 1998;55:875.

[87] Breslau N, Peterson EL, et al. Major depression and stages of smoking. A longitudinal investigation. *Arch Gen Psychiatry* 1998 Feb;55(2):161-166.

[88] Brown RA, Lewinsohn PM, et al. Cigarette smoking, major depression, and other psychiatric disorders among adolescents. *J Am Acad Child Adolesc Psychiatry* 1996 Dec;35(12):1602-1610.

[89]Harlow BL, Cohen LS, et al. Prevalence and predictors of depressive symptoms in older premenopausal women: the Harvard Study of Moods and Cycles. *Arch Gen Psychiatry* 1999 May;56(5):418-424.

[90] Jacobsen BK, Hansen V. Caffeine and health. *BMJ* (Clinical Res Ed) 1988 Jan 23;296(6617)291.

[91] *Physician's Desk Reference, 55th edition.* Montvale, NJ: Medical Economics Company, Inc., 2001, p. 2721.

[92] Gruenberg AM, Goldstein RD. Chapter 54: Depressive Disorders. In: *Psychiatry*, 1st ed. (Tasman A, editor). 1997 W. B. Saunders Company; p. 994.

[93] Binder LM. Persisting symptoms after mild head injury: A review of the post concussive syndrome. *J Clin Exp Neuropsychol* 1988;8:323.

[94] Evans RW. The post concussion syndrome and the sequelae of mild head injury. *Neurol Clin* 1992;10:815.

[95] Collins MW, Grindel SH, et al. Relationship between concussion and neuropsychological performance in college football players. *JAMA* 1999 Sep 8;282(10):964-970.

[96] Powell J, Barber-Foss K. Traumatic brain injury in high school athletes. *JAMA* 1999 Sep 8;282(10):958-963.

[97] DH Smith, Chen X-H, et al. Accumulation of amyloid B and tau and the formation of neurofilament inclusions following diffuse brain injury in the pig. *J Neuropathol Experim Neurol* 1999;58(9):982-992.

[98] Plassman BL, Harlik RJ, et al. Documented head injury in early adulthood and risk of Alzheimer's disease and other dementias. *Neurol* 2000 Oct;55(8):1158-1166.

[99] Depression Guideline Panel: Depression in Primary Care, Volume 1, Detection and Diagnosis. Clinical Practice Guideline, Number 5. Rockville, MD: U.S. Department of Health and Human Services, Agency for Health Care Policy and Research, 1993. AHCPR publication 93-0550.

[100] Kessler RC, McGonagle KA, et al. Lifetime and 12-month prevalence of DSM-III-R psychiatric disorders in the United States. *Arch Gen Psychiatry* 1994;51:8-19.

[101] Steffens DC, Helms MJ, et al. Cerebrovascular disease and depression symptoms in the cardiovascular health study. *Stroke* 1999 Oct;30(10):2159-2166.

[102] Pohjasvaara T, Leppavuori A, et al. Frequency and Clinical Determinants of Poststroke Depression (Helsinki Univ Central Hosp; Univ of Helsinki). *Stroke* 1998;29:2311-2317.

[103] Gonzalez MB, Snyderman TB, et al. Depression in patients with coronary artery disease. *Depression* 1996;4(2):57-62.

[104] Frasure-Smith N, Lesperance F, et al. Gender, depression, and one-year prognosis after myocardial infarction. *Psychosom Med* 1999;61:26.

[105] Nedley N, Chapter 3 through Chapter 6, Chapter 16 In: *Proof Positive: How to Reliably Combat Disease and Achieve Optimal Health through Nutrition and Lifestyle.* Ardmore, OK: Nedley Publishing, 1999.

[106] Hyman SE, Rudorfer MV. Depressive and Bipolar Mood Disorders; Depression in the Medically Ill. *Scientific American* May 2000.

[107] Hyman SE, Rudorfer MV. Depressive and Bipolar Mood Disorders; Depression in the Medically Ill. *Scientific American* May 2000.

[108] Singer EJ. Headache in ambulatory HIV-1-infected men enrolled in a longitudinal study. *Neurol* 1996 Aug;47(2):487-494.

[109] Cote TR, Biggar RJ, Dannenberg AL. Risk of suicide among persons with AIDS. A national assessment. *JAMA* 1992 Oct 21;268(15):2066-2068.

[110] Nedley N, *Proof Positive: How to Reliably Combat Disease and Achieve Optimal Health through Nutrition and Lifestyle.* Ardmore, OK: Nedley Publishing, 1999 p. 347-368.

[111] Pezzoli G. Hydrocarbon exposure and Parkinson's disease. *Neurology* 2000 Sep 12;55(5):667-673.

[112] Racette, BA, et al. Welding-related parkinsonism: Clinical features, treatment, and pathophysiology. *Neurology* 2001 Jan 9;56(1):8-13.

[113] Betarbet R, et al. Chronic systemic pesticide exposure reproduces features of Parkinson's disease. *Nat Neurosci* 2000 Dec;3(12):1301-1306.

[114] Gorell JM, et al. Occupational exposures to metals as risk factors for Parkinson's disease. *Neurology* 1997 Mar;48(3):650-658.

[115] Prusiner S, Nobel Prize winner addressing the annual meeting of the American Neurological Association.

[116] LaVaute T, Smith S, et al. Targeted deletion of the gene encoding iron regulatory protein-2 causes misregulation of iron metabolism and neurodegenerative disease in mice. Nature Genetics 2001;27(2):209-214.

[117] Sveinbjornsdottir, S, et al. Familial aggregation of parkinson's disease in Iceland. *N Engl J Med* 2000 Dec 14;343(24):1765-1770.

[118] Gruenberg AM, Goldstein RD. Chapter 54: Depressive Disorders. In: *Psychiatry*, 1st ed. (Tasman A, editor). W. B. Saunders Company, 1997 p. 993.

[119] Cummings JL. Depression and Parkinson's disease: a review. *Am J Psychiatry* 1992;149:443-454.

[120] Sclar DA, Robison LM, et al. Depression in diabetes mellitus: a national survey of office-based encounters, 1990-1995. *Diabetes Educ* 1999 May-Jun;25(3):331,332,335,340.

[121] Stowe AN. Women at risk for postpartum-onset major depression. *Am J Obstet Gynecol* 1995 Aug;173(2):639-645.

[122] Kendell RE, Chalmers JD, Platz C. Epidemiology of puerperal purposes. *Br J Psychiatry* 1987;150:662-673.

[123] Pop VJ. Prevalence of postpartum depression—or is it post-puerperium depression? *Acta Obstet Gynecol Scand* 1993 Jul;72(5):354-358.

[124] Stowe AN. Women at risk for postpartum-onset major depression. *Am J Obstet Gynecol* 1995 Aug;173(2):639-645.

[125] Stowe AN. Women at risk for postpartum-onset major depression. *Am J Obstet Gynecol* 1995 Aug;173(2):639-645.

[126] Stern G. Multi-disciplinary perspectives on postpartum depression: an anthropological critique. *Soc Sci Med* 1983;17(15):1027-1041.

[127] Rees WD, Lutkins SG. Parental depression before and after childbirth: An assessment with the Beck Depression Inventory. *J R Coll Gen Practice* 1971;21:26-31.

[128] Stowe AN. Women at risk for postpartum-onset major depression. *Am J Obstet Gynecol* 1995 Aug;173(2):639-645.

[129] Pearlstein TB. Symposium—Women and Depression: Who is at risk? *Am J Obstet Gynecol* 1995 Aug;173(2):646-653.

[130] Pearlstein TB. Symposium—Women and Depression: Who is at risk? *Am J Obstet Gynecol* 1995 Aug;173(2):646-653.

[131] Pearlstein TB, Frank E, et al. Prevalence of axis I and axis II disorders in women with late luteal phase dysphoric disorder. *J Affective Disord* 1990;20:129-134.

[132] Pearlstein TB. Symposium—Women and Depression: Who is at risk? *Am J Obstet Gynecol* 1995 Aug;173(2):646-653.

[133] Wilson CA, Turner CW, Keye WR Jr. Firstborn adolescent daughters and mothers with and without premenstrual syndrome: a comparison. *J Adolesc Health* 1991;12:130-137.

[134] Wyatt KM. Efficacy of vitamin B-6 in the treatment of premenstrual syndrome: systematic review. *Br Med J* 1999 May

22;318(7195):1375-1381.

[135] Bendich A. The potential for dietary supplements to reduce premenstrual syndrome (PMS) symptoms. *J Am Coll Nutr* 2000 Feb;19(1):3-12.

[136] Thys-Jacobs S. Calcium carbonate and the premenstrual syndrome: effects on premenstrual and menstrual symptoms. *Am J Obstet Gynecol* 1998 Aug;179(2)444-452.

[137] Bendich A. The potential for dietary supplements to reduce premenstrual syndrome (PMS) symptoms. *J Am Coll Nutr* 2000 Feb;19(1):3-12.

[138] Barnard ND. Diet and sex-hormone binding globulin, dysmenorrhea, and premenstrual symptoms. *Obstet Gynecol* 2000 Feb;95(2):245-250.

[139] Leigh H, Kramer SI. The psychiatric manifestation of endocrine disorders. *Adv Intern Med* 1984;29:413-445.

[140] Gruenberg AM, Goldstein RD. Chapter 54: Depressive Disorders. In: *Psychiatry*, 1st ed. (Tasman A, editor). W. B. Saunders Company, 1997 p. 994.

[141] Cummings JL. Frontal-subcortical circuits and human behavior. *Arch Neurol* 1993 Aug;50(8):873-880.

[142] Burbeau J, Brisson C, Allaire S. Pevalence of the sick building syndrome symptoms in office workers before and six months and three years after being exposed to a building with an improved ventilation system. *Occup Environ Med* 1997 Jan;54(1):49-53.

[143] Menzies D, Pasztor J, et al. Germicidal ultraviolet irradiation in air conditioning systems: effect on office worker health and wellbeing: a pilot study. *Occup Environ Med* 1999 Jun;56(6):397-402.

[144] Nedley N. *Proof Positive: How to Reliably Combat Disease and Achieve Optimal Health through Nutrition and Lifestyle.* Ardmore, OK: Nedley Publishing, 1999 p. 33,34,226,243,250,251,383,540,542.

[145] Chen CH. High seroprevalence of Borna virus infection in schizophrenic patients, family members and mental health workers in Taiwan. *Mol Psych* 1999 Jan;4(1):33-38.

[146] Machon RA, Mednick SA, Huttunen MO. Adult major affective disorder after prenatal exposure to an influenza epidemic. *Arch Gen Psych* 1997 Apr;54(4):322-328.

DEPRESSION

HEALTHY FOOD, BETTER MOOD:
Nutritional Treatments for Depression

Misty Lamberton, an excellent registered nurse, was in charge of the afternoon shift of the Intensive Care Unit at Mercy Hospital. She is one of those nurses who is well liked by physicians, fellow workers, and patients alike. But then tragedy struck her home. Her husband was killed suddenly in an auto accident.

In the aftermath, Misty made a poor decision and landed a boyfriend who dumped her within a few weeks. Her associate nurses noticed that even one year after her husband's death she was not eating much and losing weight, yet talking about how fat she was, even though she had become very thin. Her nursing friends were so concerned that they insisted on taking her to Dr. Baxter, a respected psychiatrist in town.

Not surprisingly, she was diagnosed with major depression and anorexia nervosa, which can be a lethal combination. When she did not get better with medications and counseling, he hospitalized her and even placed a tube going from her nose to her stomach (nasogastric tube) to feed her. After 10 days in the hospital she improved enough to go home. But soon after discharge she relapsed and began losing weight while feeling very depressed. Dr. Baxter consulted me, simply because an internist and psychiatrist working together will often accomplish more by managing the case together than separately. It was agreed that Dr. Baxter would manage her medications, while I would manage her nutrition and lifestyle issues.

Within a few days Misty began to improve, slowly at first, and then rather dramatically. She felt happier and began to look to the future with hope and positive excitement. She actually felt hungry again and began gaining weight. What made the difference? Misty attributes her turn-around to the nutritional program outlined in this book. Within a month after feeling better, Misty went back to her "old ways" of eating, and within a week she was down in the dumps again.

She returned to the nutritional program and has stayed with it since. It has now been six months since that last relapse. Misty has been back to work for the last four months and she is cheerful again. She proved to herself that her diet change was the key to her good health. She is looking good, and again she is the same excellent nurse she used to be.

Many Patients Improve Their Mood With Diet Changes

I have had many patients, all with different backgrounds and stories, respond with an improved mood simply by changing their eating habits. Even though I base each part of the program on good science, I must tell you that a lifestyle approach to mental disease *is not in common use for treating depressed or anxious patients*. It is my hope that there will soon be large, controlled clinical trials run on the lifestyle approach, and that it will become the standard everywhere if it is confirmed in the trials, as I expect it would be. Until that happens, I am not the least bit hesitant to put patients on this program since (1) it is based on good nutritional science, (2) I have repeatedly seen it work, and (3) it has no potential adverse health effects.

Having said that, I must hasten to add that this is by no means the only treatment a depressed patient should be on. I hope I have made it abundantly clear by now that depression is almost always a multi-factorial disease, meaning that it has many potential causes. Nutritional concerns are usually only one of several causes that act together to bring about mental illness. We must search for and deal with as many causes as possible to bring about complete and lasting cures. Unfortunately, *nutritional counseling* for depressed, anxious, or bipo-lar individuals is *almost never done*. I believe this leaves a gaping hole in the treatment approach to mental illness.

The Importance of Serotonin

Serotonin is an important neurotransmitter in the brain, particularly in the frontal lobe. This is an area that needs to be vitally enhanced in depressed patients. The brain can make no serotonin unless tryptophan is first present. Most depressed patients have a loss of appetite (appetite *increase* occurs in only a minority of the depressed)[1]. Thus, the foods that they do eat should have an abundance of tryptophan. Foods that are high in tryptophan are listed in **Figure 1**[2].

Note that whole milk has the lowest amount of tryptophan on the list, though many people believe that milk is one of the best sources of tryptophan. Fortunately, there are better sources, with tofu (soybean curd) being the best source in this list.

As the previous chapter stated, some depressed individuals are *very sensitive to even a small, temporary reduction in tryptophan,* and missing just one day of moderate to high tryptophan intake can send them into a relapse of depression. Misty is one of my patients who noticed that she *had to get enough tryptophan* to stay mentally healthy.

Meat in the Diet Blocks Tryptophan Flow to the Brain

Getting enough tryptophan is not the only nutritional factor in serotonin production. As stated in the preceding chapter, five large amino acids compete against tryptophan in traveling to the brain. A food that contains a large total amount of these five amino acids will reduce the flow of tryptophan to the brain[3]. Thus, if our diet is moderate in tryptophan but high in those five amino acids, we may still develop a tryptophan deficiency in the frontal lobe of the brain. The amount of tryptophan compared to the amount of the five amino acids is the critical yardstick.

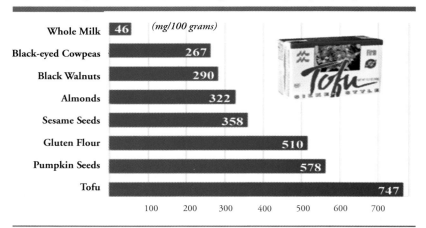

TRYPTOPHAN CONTENT OF FOODS

Food	mg/100 grams
Whole Milk	46
Black-eyed Cowpeas	267
Black Walnuts	290
Almonds	322
Sesame Seeds	358
Gluten Flour	510
Pumpkin Seeds	578
Tofu	747

Figure 1

Foods with high ratios of tryptophan to these five competitors are shown in **Figure 2.**[4]

Figure 2 shows that whole milk has a low amount of tryptophan compared to the five amino acids. It also contains a very little quantity of tryptophan, as shown in **Figure 1.** These factors work together to render milk of less value in supplying the brain with tryptophan.

Tofu, however, is in sharp contrast to whole milk. It has a high amount of tryptophan relative to the five amino acids, and a high quantity of tryptophan. This makes it an excellent food for supplying a high quantity of tryptophan to the brain, which enhances the production of serotonin, which in turn combats depression.

Once sufficient tryptophan is in the brain, other lifestyle issues are crucial in the production of serotonin. Lifestyle Treatments are outlined in the next chapter.

Importance of Omega-3 in Combating Depression

Omega-3 fats are emerging as an important nutritional element in brain science.[5] There are actually two types of fat that are absolutely essential in our diets—omega-6 and omega-3 fats. The omega-6 fats are abundant in many foods, so it is extremely rare to see mental or physical problems develop due to a shortage of omega-6. Omega-3 fats are not so abundant, so it is more common to see adverse effects from a diet too low in omega-3.

Tryptophan tends to be low in the diet when calorie intakes are low, but omega-3 can be too low in the diet even if calorie intakes are more than adequate.[6] Even a high fat diet can be too low in omega-3, particularly when the ratio of omega-3 to omega-6 in the diet is low. Interestingly, the ratios of these two fats in the blood do have a direct relationship to rates of depression.[7] The lower the omega-3 to omega-6 ratio, the higher the rate of depression. Recent research demonstrates that *bipolar disorder* (manic-depression) in addition to *major depression* (unipolar disorder) can be helped by a *diet high in omega-3*.[8]

Most people increase their omega-3 fat intake by eating fish. Most fish, however, are not good sources of omega-3 fats. Cold water ocean fish are good sources, not because their bodies manufacture omega-3, but because they eat a lot of cold saltwater

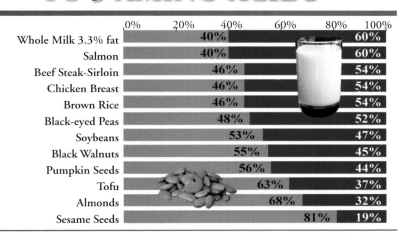

RATIO OF TRYPTOPHAN TO 5 AMINO ACIDS

Whole Milk 3.3% fat	40%	60%
Salmon	40%	60%
Beef Steak-Sirloin	46%	54%
Chicken Breast	46%	54%
Brown Rice	46%	54%
Black-eyed Peas	48%	52%
Soybeans	53%	47%
Black Walnuts	55%	45%
Pumpkin Seeds	56%	44%
Tofu	63%	37%
Almonds	68%	32%
Sesame Seeds	81%	19%

Figure 2

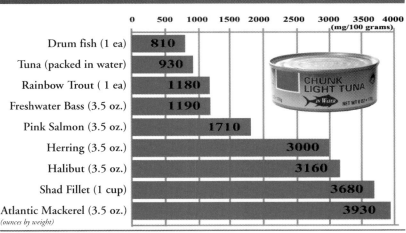

OMEGA-3 CONTENT OF FISH

(mg/100 grams)

Drum fish (1 ea)	810
Tuna (packed in water)	930
Rainbow Trout (1 ea)	1180
Freshwater Bass (3.5 oz.)	1190
Pink Salmon (3.5 oz.)	1710
Herring (3.5 oz.)	3000
Halibut (3.5 oz.)	3160
Shad Fillet (1 cup)	3680
Atlantic Mackerel (3.5 oz.)	3930

(ounces by weight)

Figure 3

seaweed, which is very high in omega-3 fats. It is important to note that the original sources of omega-3 fats are plant sources, and when we obtain our omega-3 from fish *we are getting the nutrients second-hand.* The omega-3 content of certain fish is listed in **Figure 3**.[9]

Note the wide variation in omega-3 content from one kind of fish to another. For example, drum fish, which has the lowest omega-3 content, has only 25 percent as much as Atlantic mackerel.

There are many benefits of a diet with adequate omega-3 fat, but there is a downside in getting it from fish. I list six major health problems of getting omega-3 fats from fish in the book **Proof Positive**.[10] For the sake of brevity I will elaborate on only one of these concerns here.

Fish Are Contaminated

Fish collect and concentrate *toxins* in their fatty tissues. These toxins include pesticides, chlorinated hydrocarbons, dioxin, chlordane, and mercury. As of 1996, 47 states had fish consumption advisories that *warn against eating certain species.* They cover *1,740 rivers and lakes* (including all of the Great Lakes) and large chunks of coastal areas.[11] The most common reason for consumption advisories is mercury, which can cause brain and nerve damage especially to fetuses and young children. Large fish like fresh tuna, swordfish, and shark contain the highest levels of mercury.[12]

Despite the popular belief that fruits and vegetables have the greatest risk of pesticide contamination, FDA research reveals that *domestic fish products contain significantly more pesticide residues than domestic fruits, grains, or vegetables.*[13] Bluefish, along with lake trout and other freshwater fish caught in inland lakes, are most likely to be contaminated with carcinogens like dioxin or PCBs (polychlorinated biphenyls).[14]

Contaminated Fish from Contaminated Waters

Pesticides are an extremely important issue. Worldwide, there are more than 900 different active pesticides in some 40,000 different chemical formulations.[15] In the U.S., about 600 pesticide ingredients are used, accounting for some 800 million to 1 billion pounds per year.[16] Huff and Haseman reviewed some 200 rodent studies. They concluded that "there is considerable evidence that exposure to certain pesticides may present *real carcinogenic hazards to humans.*"[17]

How do fish become exposed to pesticides? One major cause is agricultural run-off. When a farmer sprays his fields, a portion of the chemicals run off into neighboring creeks and streams, and ultimately into rivers and oceans. Overflows of sewage, faulty septic systems, boating wastes, and poisonous run-off from city streets have also contributed to the pollution of waters. These waters are sometimes considered so dangerous that signs like the one shown in **Figure 4**, "Swimming Prohibited," are erected on some beaches.

If *swimming in the water is hazardous* for humans, it is ironic that *people still go*

SWIMMING PROHIBITED HAZARDOUS TO YOUR HEALTH

Gastroenteritis, dysentery, hepatitis and other illnesses occur due to:
- Sewage overflows
- Faulty septic systems
- Boating waste
- Poisonous run-off from farms and city streets

DANGER
NO SWIMMING
HAZARDOUS TO
YOUR HEALTH

Figure 4

fishing in these areas. The signs are not "crying wolf." Illnesses such as gastroenteritis, dysentery, hepatitis, and more have resulted from swimming in contaminated water.

Cancer in Fish is Increasing

The risk of spending time in bodies of water on our globe is highlighted by a disturbing trend among fish. Fish are found with more cancer now than 50 years ago.[18] A Canadian biologist, Ron Sonstegard, has examined bottom-dwelling fish in the Great Lakes and the rivers that feed them. He has found *tumors in every fish species—often malignant.*[19] For example, *30 percent of the bullheads in Lake Erie had liver cancer.*

The Ph.D. nutritionist and author, Dr. Winston Craig, in commenting on these findings, added three more sobering facts: (1) the Great Lakes situation is not unique—cancerous fish turn up from Puget Sound to the Gulf of California and from the Hudson River to the Florida Keys; (2) National Cancer Institute data show an increased death rate from cancer among people living in areas where fish have exceptionally large amounts of tumors; (3) the toxic nature of what is found in some of our waterways is astonishing. When sediments from the bottom of Lake Erie were painted on the skin of mice, the mice developed skin cancers.[20]

Although Craig's insights may not necessarily prove human risk, they surely raise serious concerns about the human health hazards related to the "epidemic" of cancers in fish.

Possible links to cancer from contaminated fish are summarized in **Figure 5**.

Rather large amounts of fish die in droves every year throughout our country due to pollution. The Environmental Protection Agency (E.P.A.) of the U.S. government has attempted to trace the amount of fish kills due to pollution as well as other causes. **Figure 6** reports by state the number of fish kills caused by pollution in 1993.[21]

Each fish kill in the figure can represent literally thousands of fish. The E.P.A. admits that these statistics greatly underestimate the actual number of fish kills, since 15 states did not report or keep track of their fish kills. Also, many fish kills occur that cannot be definitely proven to be due to pollution.[22] Pesticides were the most frequently identified toxic pollutant causing fish kills, followed by oil and gasoline products, chlorine, ammonia, heavy metals, and other toxic substances. Unfortunately, many ill fish that are suffering from these pollutants are caught by fisherman, taken to market, and consumed by humans who think they are eating healthy food.

EVIDENCE LINKING FISH CONTAMINATION TO CANCER

- Elevated levels of pesticide compounds have been found in the tissue of breast-cancer patients.

- National Cancer Institute data show an increased death rate from cancer among people living in areas where fish have exceptionally large amounts of tumors.

- Fish have more cancer now than 50 years ago. Example: 30 percent of the bullheads in Lake Erie were found with liver cancer.

Figure 5

NUMBER OF REPORTED FISH KILLS CAUSED BY POLLUTION

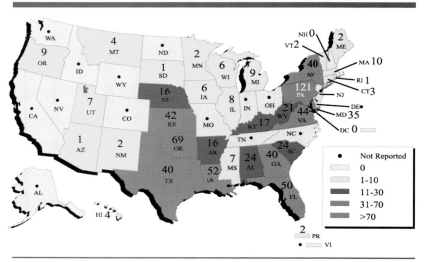

Figure 6

No Mandatory Inspection of Fish

Dr. Craig has pointed out another serious concern with fish safety. There is *no government mandatory inspection program for fish or fish products* at this writing. Craig states that only about 10 percent of fish undergo any type of inspection, and this is through a voluntary program.[23] Obviously, there is need for a well-ordered fish inspection system.

If we could find non-fish sources of the beneficial omega-3 fats, wouldn't it be more sensible from all that we have learned, to set fish aside? Such foods would not provide a potential reservoir for cancer, infectious diseases, and other ailments. Foods of this kind do exist, as we shall see later.

Mildly-polluted Water Produces Super-polluted Fish

With cancer being the greatest concern regarding exposure to pesticides and other toxins, we must recognize which toxins pose the greatest long-term exposure risk. Poi-

sons that present the greatest long-term threats to humans have two natural characteristics—a tendency toward both *bioaccumulation* and *biomagnification*. Both of these processes cause fish from *mildly polluted waters* to have *large concentrations of toxins* in their tissues.

Bioaccumulation is the process by which *toxins gradually build up* in certain organs of humans or other target organisms. Biomagnification refers to a process where toxins become progressively *more concentrated as they move up the food chain.*[24]

A classic example of biomagnification was discovered in Clear Lake, California, about 90 miles north of San Francisco.[25] The lake had been sprayed several times with an insecticide called DDD to control the insect population. (DDD, a less potent cousin of the infamous DDT, is technically referred to as a halogenated hydrocarbon.) The results of spraying this insecticide are shown in **Figure 7**.

Notice that the lake water revealed barely detectable levels of this pesticide, at .02 parts per million (2 drops of DDD in every 100 million drops of lake water). Biomagnification, however, caused a dramatic increase in the tissue levels of organisms that lived in the lake. The concentration of DDD in the phytoplankton in the lake measured 5 ppm, which is 250 times the concentration in the lake water. In progressing up the food chain, the concentration of DDD approached 2,500 ppm—a whopping 125,000 times the concentration in the water.

One of the most common questions I receive after giving a public health presentation involves the quality of household water. Many people are very concerned about what toxins might be in their tap water. They should be much more concerned about the quality of water in the rivers, lakes, streams, and oceans where the fish that they are eating come from. Low levels of toxins, such as in Clear Lake, California, result in high levels of toxins in the fish that humans consume every day.

Such examples of biomagnification are not the exception; they are the rule. The EPA has gone on record saying, "Aquatic organisms may bioaccumulate environmental contaminants to *more than 1 million times the concentrations detected in the water. . . .*"[26]

Cancer and Heart Disease from Fish are Suspect

Evidence is mounting that there may be a relationship between toxins and chronic human diseases such as cancer and heart disease that affect the developed nations in epidemic proportions. One piece of evidence involves the halogenated hydrocarbons, which is one class of compounds known to be biomagnified through the food chain.

Halogenated hydrocarbons also bioaccumulate in humans. Elevated levels of these compounds have been found in the tissue of breast cancer patients.[27] The researchers who identified this breast cancer linkage concluded, "These results, although preliminary, suggest a role for environmentally derived suspect carcinogens in the genesis [origin] of mammary [breast] carcinoma."

But the problems do not stop with cancer. One investigator, in his review of the literature, found a "correlation between DDT plus DDE [two other halogenated hydrocarbons] in the blood and subjects who reported hypertension, arteriosclerosis, and diabetes during subsequent years. . . ."[28]

Fish present some of the greatest concerns from the standpoint of biomagnification and bioaccumulation. They are not only contaminated with PCBs and various heavy metals such as mercury, but also with petroleum hydrocarbons and halogenated organic compounds.[29,30] In a prominent medical textbook on environmental medical issues, Dr. Kenneth Rosenman of Michigan State University stated, "The major ongoing source of PCB exposure for the general population is the consumption of fish."[31] Along with concerns about causing cancer, there is preliminary evidence linking both PCBs and dioxins with elevated blood cholesterol and triglycerides.[32] Other data indicate that PCBs may affect male sperm counts and fertility.[33]

Research suggesting that these contaminants can harm the developing fetus has increased the stakes in the PCB issue even further. Dr. Theo Colborn has pointed out that the research literature suggests that PCB present in the womb can "affect the developing nervous system of the embryo, fetus, and newborn."[34] Recently, the *New England Journal of Medicine* grabbed headlines when Drs. Joseph and Sandra Jacobsen further determined the developmental risks of PCB exposure.[35] At 11 years of age, children with higher exposures to PCBs before birth showed impaired intellectual development. Although the children were not

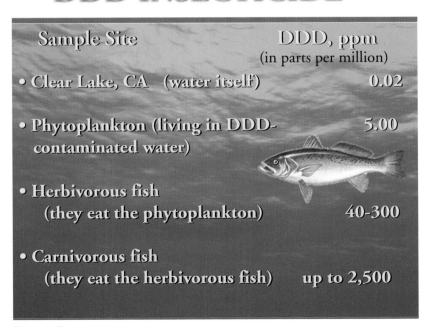

BIOMAGNIFICATION OF DDD INSECTICIDE

Sample Site	DDD, ppm (in parts per million)
• Clear Lake, CA (water itself)	0.02
• Phytoplankton (living in DDD-contaminated water)	5.00
• Herbivorous fish (they eat the phytoplankton)	40-300
• Carnivorous fish (they eat the herbivorous fish)	up to 2,500

Figure 7

retarded, those with the highest PCB exposures were three times more likely to have low IQs and twice as likely to be at least two years behind in their reading comprehension.

Acid Rain—A Pollution Agent for Toxic Metals

Accumulation of toxic metals in fish has recently caused particular concern in light of the problem of acid rain. Acid rain leads to acidified waters. This chemically altered water can then leach aluminum, manganese, lead, zinc, cadmium, and mercury out of bottom sediments or soil and into the water. Once these toxic metals are liberated, they find their way into the food chain and tend to bioaccumulate in fish tissues.

Warnings Advise Limited Fish Consumption

Even in scenic Maine, women of childbearing age and children under eight are being urged not to eat fish from any pond or lake in Maine. Others are advised to restrict their annual consumption to no more than six large fish or 22 small ones, all due

to the mercury content of the fish.[36] Mercury ingestion in high levels can harm the development of human fetuses and children, and cause nervous system disorders and kidney damage in children and adults.

Michigan is the only other state to issue such a statewide warning. However, according to Martha Keating, an EPA staff scientist, other U.S. lakes and streams are just as hazardous as Maine's. The Boston-based Clean Water Action group has even gone on record stating that 90 percent of freshwater fish caught in New England waters have contamination levels of mercury, lead, PCBs, or dioxin that are unsafe when consumed more that once a week. Although the group had collected significantly less data on saltwater fish, (so could not make a similarly sweeping statement), they did warn that the saltwater fish that were tested had high levels of PCB and mercury.

Probably the most widely publicized case of fish-related heavy metal poisoning had nothing to do with acid rain. It involved the tragic methyl mercury poisoning that resulted from eating fish from Japan's Minamata Bay. Japanese factory discharges of methyl mercury into the bay laid the foundation for the problem. The biomagnification that occurred through the food chain exposed humans who ate the fish to dangerous organic mercury levels.[37]

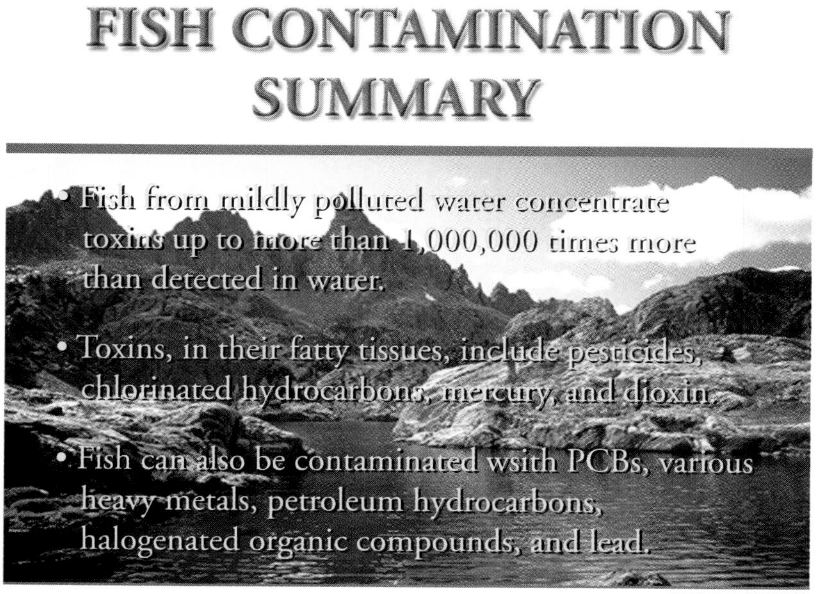

Known Health Problems from Contaminated Fish

Perhaps nursing infants face the greatest danger from fish. One study found that pregnant mothers who consumed contaminated Great Lakes fish experienced complications with their newborns. These included alterations in birth size, gestational age, changes in neonatal health status, and effects that persisted into early infancy.[38] As a result of these risks, some have suggested that infants should not be breastfed because of the cancer risk. Although this may seem to make sense in our toxin-contaminated

FISH CONTAMINATION SUMMARY

- Fish from mildly polluted water concentrate toxins up to more than 1,000,000 times more than detected in water.

- Toxins, in their fatty tissues, include pesticides, chlorinated hydrocarbons, mercury, and dioxin.

- Fish can also be contaminated with PCBs, various heavy metals, petroleum hydrocarbons, halogenated organic compounds, and lead.

Figure 8

world, a better alternative may be to avoid the major sources of those toxins. Other research suggests that the bottle-feeding strategy may backfire. There is evidence that breastfeeding in and of itself decreases breast cancer risk. A 1994 study found that daughters who were breast fed by their mothers had 25 percent less breast cancer.[39] Breastfeeding has many other benefits as well.

For the reader's convenience, a summary of previously mentioned contamination compounds found in fish is shown in **Figure 8**.

Benefits versus Risk Of Eating Fish

Some nutritionists would say that in certain individuals, risks of consuming fish are outweighed by the benefits of a diet high in omega-3 fats, particularly the mental and heart benefits. A diet high in omega-3 may also help rheumatoid arthritis and ulcerative colitis.[40]

Happily, there is a way to have the benefits of the omega-3 fatty acids without the risk of eating fish, fish oil, or expensive supplements. There is a way to bypass the cholesterol and toxins that come with the animal-derived omega-3. The way is so simple, yet it is not getting the publicity it deserves. We can obtain the benefits of omega-3 fatty acids from a plant fat called "linolenic acid." A certain variety of plant foods are high in omega-3 and can supply all of the body's needs for this essential fat. A list of plant foods high in omega-3 is provided in **Figure 9**.

It is possible for both meat-eaters and vegetarians to have a diet too low in omega-3 fats. For individuals who have depression or bipolar disorder, I recommend that each day they consume dishes that include some foods high in omega-3. In addition, I recommend a home remedy that has helped a number of mentally ill patients to recover. A favorite recipe of many is included in **Figure 10**.

PLANT FOODS CONTAINING OMEGA-3
(Linolenic Acid)

Food Item	Amount	Omega-3(mg)
Flaxseed/Linseed oil	1 Tbs.	7520
Walnuts, English (chopped)	¼ cup	2043
Canola oil	1 Tbs.	1267
Walnuts, Black (chopped)	¼ cup	1031
Wheat Germ oil	1 Tbs.	938
Soybean oil Crisco/Wesson	1 Tbs.	927
Green Soybeans/w salt	1 cup	637
Spinach (canned)	1 cup	353
California Avocado (pureed)	½ cup	132
Almonds (dry roasted)	¼ cup	127
Safflower oil	1 Tbs.	55
Turnips	1 cup	50
Banana (medium)	1 each	39
Sweet Potatoes (mashed)	1 cup	36
Apple (medium w/peel)	1 each	25
Roasted Potato (medium)	1 each	17
Cucumber (slices w/peel)	½ cup	16
Whole Wheat Bread	1 slice	14

Figure 9

FLAX-NUT SPRINKLE RECIPE
(High Omega-3 Content)

¼ cup   walnuts, ground

¼ cup   flax meal

1 Tbsp. date sugar

⅛ tsp.   salt

Mix and serve over toast, cereal, etc.

Figure 10

Note the high content of omega-3 fats in the recipe. This is nearly equal to the daily amount consumed in fish oil by bipolar disorder patients that produced promising results in a Harvard Medical School study (9.6 g/day).[41] Commenting on this study, Dr. Joseph Calabrese and colleagues at Case Western Reserve University in Cleveland, Ohio, call the trial a "landmark attempt in drug development for bipolar disorder." I would agree that it is a landmark study. However, no drugs were used, but omega-3 supplements only.

I recommend that at least one meal a day include foods high in omega-3. I also recommend a minimum *supplementation of 9 grams of omega-3 fats per day*—ideally from plant sources.

Some nutritionists believe that it is not only important for the diet to contain sufficient omega-3 but to also emphasize foods that have a higher omega-3 to omega-6 fatty acid *ratio*. The average American consumes a diet many times higher in omega-6 than omega-3. Appendix VIII lists foods with a more favorable omega-3 to omega-6 ratio.

Improved Learning Capability with Breast Feeding, Polyunsaturated Fats, and Vitamins.

Regardless of how strong a case I make for proper eating habits in relation to mental health, depression treatment, and depression prevention, I am confronted with a sobering reality. Our earliest dietary choices are not really ours to make. Those who were fortunate enough to have mothers who chose to *breast feed* them were bequeathed a *precious frontal lobe legacy*. Research shows that children who are breast-fed have a *mental edge* that persists at least for a number of years and probably for a lifetime.[42,43]

A recent analysis of 20 different studies on the subject confirmed the connection between breast-feeding and subsequent mental advantage.[44] Of note, the mental benefits accruing from breast-feeding appear to be even more important for premature and/or low-birth weight infants when compared to full term, normal weight babies.

Failure to breast-feed may also predispose a child to social and emotional problems later in life. In a classic European study, girls who were exclusively *bottle-fed* were assessed at 16 years of age. They demonstrated not only significant *decreases in learning capacity and school achievements* but also in *social adaptability*.[45] Although such research does not confirm a link between failure to breast-feed and future depression, it certainly raises the question.

All of the reasons for the superiority of breast milk regarding brain function are not clear. However, one factor appears to be the fat content of breast milk. Dr. Yokota of Japan showed that newborn rats need adequate amounts of omega-3 fats in their diet. Without those fats, *learning is impaired*.[46] Other international research teams such as Bourre and his French colleagues[47] have made similar discoveries in animal studies. All have demonstrated the vital need for the omega-3 fats in the developing mammalian brain.

It is well recognized in research circles that a traditional *infant formula provides substandard amounts of omega-3 fats* when compared to breast milk.[48] Supplementing the child's diet with foods other than formula cannot reasonably make up the omega-3 deficit. One group of researchers came to this stunning conclusion: "It is concluded that it is virtually *impossible to supplement the diet of formula-fed infants* to match the long-chain polyunsaturated fatty acids intake of breast-fed infants with currently available whole foods."[49]

Vegetable Fat is Superior to Animal Fat for Enhanced Learning

The superiority of breast feding is obviously inportant information for expectant parents. However, the proper type of fat also seems to be necessary for *short-term learning in adults*. Dr. Coscina and colleagues demonstrated this fact some 15 years ago.[50] They fed two groups of adult rats foods that had identical amounts of fat. However, the fat came from different sources.

After only three weeks, rats given a diet based on a moderate amount of *vegetable fat* (20 percent polyunsaturated soybean oil) exhibited *improved learning skills* compared to those fed a diet based on 20 percent saturated fat (lard). The authors saw this as solid evidence that "short-term variations in the quality of dietary fat can enhance mammalian learning." Israeli researchers also found that animals on a diet adequate in such plant fats as alpha linolenic acid and linoleic acid can *improve memory* and help the brain tolerate pain better.[51]

Dr. Bernell Baldwin has offered one explanation for why the type of fat may make a difference. The saturated fats typically found in animal products may make brain nerve communication more difficult. His hypothesis is that the brain's synapses are rendered more rigid by a diet rich in saturated fat, while unsaturated fats from vegetables, seeds, and nuts create more flexible membranes that promote greater communication efficiency.[52] Another possibility is that some of the unsaturated fats actually have beneficial effects that may be blocked by their saturated cousins. If this is true, unsaturated fats like the omega-3 fats may be especially important for adult learning as well.

Fortunately for adults there are other sources of high quality fat besides breast milk. Many readers may immediately think "fish." It is true that cold-water fish tend to be rich in omega-3 fats. However, fish have a number of undesirable characteristics from a health standpoint. In fact, in ***Proof Positive*** I devote an entire chapter to "The Truth About Fish." My recommendation remains the same, namely, that we can obtain the benefits of omega-

3 fatty acids from a plant fat called *linolenic acid.*

Ingestion of polyunsaturated fat is not the only nutritional key to optimal brain function. Adequate vitamin and mineral intake also appears to be essential for human brain performance. Some of the micronutrients that have a role in improving our brain's achievements include thiamin, riboflavin, niacin, B_6, B_{12}, folic acid, the antioxidant vitamins A, C, and E, and iron.[53,54,55] The growing list of such nutrients supports the adoption of a well-balanced diet rich in a broad array of these compounds.

Folic Acid Deficiency Causes Depression

A *folic acid (or folate) deficiency* can be a *direct cause of depression.*[56] I have found this a *much more common cause of depression in meat-eaters* than in vegetarians. (People with an *omega-3 deficiency* seem to have similar depression rates *whether they are meat-eaters or vegetarians*). The RDA (recommended daily allowance) for folate is 400 micrograms. As you can see in **Figure 11**, which lists the folate con-

SOURCES OF FOLATE

Food Item	Amount	Folate (mcg)
Chickpeas	1 cup	1114
Black-eyed Cowpeas	1 cup	1057
Lentils	1 cup	831
Red Kidney Beans	1 cup	725
Okra Pods	1 cup	269
Navy Beans	1 cup	255
Spinach	1 cup	109
Mustard Greens	1 cup	105
Spanish Peanuts	¼ cup	88
Fresh Orange Juice	1 cup	75
Sirloin Steak, broiled	5 ½ oz.	16

Figure 11

tent of foods, it would require an enormous quantity of meat to obtain 400 micrograms. On the other hand, it is very easy to obtain a minimum of 400 micrograms with a diet based on plant foods, as the figure demonstrates.[57]

Patients who are depressed due to a folate deficiency *tend not to improve at all with standard antidepressants.* The real treatment is simple—foods high in folate.

Vitamin B12 linked to Depression

Another nutrient that is vital for optimal brain functions, including avoidance of a depressed mood, is Vitamin B_{12}.[58] Plant sources that are not fortified do not contain B_{12} unless they are grown in soils with organic fertilizers that are very rich in B_{12}.[59] Food sources of B_{12} are listed in **Figure 12**.[60]

I recommend the fortified plant sources of B_{12} as the best way to obtain B_{12}. If a vegetarian does not have access to regular use of the fortified plant sources or B_{12} supplements, then I recommend the regular use of skim milk.

SOURCES OF B12

Food Item	Amount	B12 (mcg)
Dry Cereal (Total)	3 oz.	6.00
Steak ¼" lean	3 oz.	2.85
Egg Whole	1 lg.	1.00
Soy Milk (Soy Dream)	8 oz.	1.00
Soy Milk (EdenSoy Extra)	8 0z.	1.00
Milk Skim	8 oz.	0.38
Milk Whole	8 oz.	0.36
Chicken Breast	1 lg.	0.32
Egg White	1 lg.	0.20
Spinach Organic	1 cup	0.02
Soybean Organic	1 cup	0.01
Fruits, Vegetables, Nuts, Grains		0.00

Figure 12

Vegetarian Diet and Depression

When Dr. Dean Ornish began to study how coronary artery disease (the disease that leads to the leading cause of death in America) can be reversed by a healthy vegetarian diet, many people thought that such a diet could easily bring about depression or anxiety. Since only a minority of Americans are vegetarian, it was thought that adherence to such a diet would decrease social affiliations, increase anxiety over a "strict regimen," and be less tasty or satisfying. To help determine whether these assumptions were valid, Dr. Ornish's research group surveyed both the vegetarian-treatment group as well as the non-vegetarian control group. Each participant was asked to fill out a questionnaire before and after the study regarding his or her psychological distresses. They were asked to rate their degree of anxiety, depression, insomnia, and their inability to experience pleasure (anhedonia). These four distresses were totaled to yield a distress index level for each participant. The average levels are shown in **Figure 13**.

It came as a surprise to many that after one year it was the vegetarian group that not only felt better *physically*, but *mentally as well.* They had a decrease in depression and anxiety, fewer problems with stress, and improved interpersonal relationships.[61] Many mistakenly believe that their overall enjoyment of life will deteriorate if they change to a healthy lifestyle, especially if they become vegetarians. To the contrary, evidence continues to accumulate showing that *vegetarians tend to enjoy life more and even have a better social life than before becoming vegetarians.* Moreover, the incidence of both depression and anxiety has been found to be lower in vegetarians when compared to non-vegetarians.[62]

Conclusion

Our example patient in this chapter, Misty Lamberton, learned the value of nutrition in combating depression. Nutrition's importance became even clearer to her after she abandoned her nutrition program and found herself sliding back into depression. We learned from Misty that depression can cause anorexia, which depletes the body of needed nutrients and intensifies the cycle of depression. Like Misty, almost everyone with depression can improve their circumstance by following the simple rules outlined in this chapter. A variety of simple foods from plant sources provide the nutrition needed for a healthy, functioning brain.

CHANGES IN PSYCHOLOGICAL DISTRESS IN THE LIFESTYLE HEART TRIAL

Anxiety, depression, insomnia, & anhedonia index

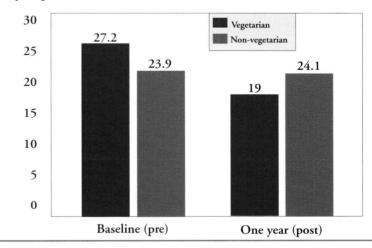

Figure 13

References—

[1] Hyman S, Rudorfer M. Depressive and bipolar mood disorders. *Scientific American Medicine* May 2000.

[2] ESHA Research. 2nd edition. 1990.

[3] Lucca A. Plasma tryptophan levels and plasma tryptophan/neutral amino acids ratio in patients with mood disorder, patients with obsessive-compulsive disorder, and normal subjects. *Psychiatry Res* 1992 Nov;44(2):85-91.

[4] *ESHA Research*. 2nd edition. 1990.

[5] Hibbeln JR, Fish consumption and major depression. *Lancet* April 18;351:1213.

[6] Edwards R, Peet M, et al. Omega-3 polyunsaturated fatty acid levels in the diet and in red blood cell membranes of depressed patients. *J Affect Disord*. 1998 Mar;48(2-3):149-155.

[7] Adams PB, Lawson S, et al. Arachidonic to eicosapentaenoic acid ratio in blood correlates positively with clinical symptoms of depression. *Lipids* 1996;31:S-167-176.

[8] Stoll AL, Severus WE, et al. Omega 3 fatty acids in bipolar disorder: a preliminary double-blind, placebo-controlled trial. *Arch Gen Psychiatry* 1999 May;56(5):407-412.

[9] *ESHA Research*. 2nd edition. 1990.

[10] Nedley N, *Proof Positive: How to Reliably Combat Disease and Achieve Optimal Health through Nutrition and Lifestyle*. Ardmore, OK: Nedley Publishing, 1999 p. 116.

[11] Schardt D, Schmidt S. fishing for safe seafood. *Nutrition Action Health Letter* 1996 Nov;23(9):1,3-5.

[12] Schardt D, Schmidt S. fishing for safe seafood. *Nutrition Action Health Letter* 1996 Nov;23(9):1,3-5.

[13] Food and Drug Administration Pesticide Program. Residue Monitoring 1992. *J Assoc Off Anal Chemists*. 1993 Sep/Oct;76.

[14] Schardt D, Schmidt S. fishing for safe seafood. *Nutrition Action Health Letter* 1996 Nov;23(9):1,3-5.

[15] Waxman MF. When pest control gets out of control. *Occ Health Safety* May 1993:81-87.

[16] Schneider K. New pesticide plan puts safety first. *The New York Times* 143:49,461 (September, 21, 1993), p. A19.

[17] Huff JE, Haseman JK. News Forum. Risk assessment of pesticides. Exposure to certain pesticides may pose real carcinogenic risk. *Engineering News* 1991;69(1):33-36.

[18] Morell V. Fishing for trouble. A cancer epidemic in fish is warning us: You may be next. *Intl Wildlife* 1984 Jul/Aug;14(4):40-43.

[19] Morell V. Fishing for trouble. A cancer epidemic in fish is warning us: You may be next. *Intl Wildlife* 1984 Jul/ Aug;14(4):40-43.

[20] Craig WJ. Fishing for Trouble. In: *Nutrition For The Nineties*. Eau Claire, MI: Golden Harvest Books, 1992 p. 76-84.

[21] Environmental Protection Agency (EPA). National Water Quality Inventory. 1994 Report to Congress. p. 141.

[22] Environmental Protection Agency (EPA). National Water Quality Inventory. 1994 Report to Congress. p. 143.

[23] Craig WJ. Fishing for trouble. In: *Nutrition for the Nineties*. Eau Claire, MI: Golden Harvest Books, 1992 p. 76-84.

[24] Nadakavukaren A. Pests and pesticides. In: *Man and Environment*, A Health Perspective, Third Edition. Prospect Heights, IL: Waveland

[25] Nadakavukaren A. Pests and pesticides. In: *Man and Environment, A Health Perspective*, Third Edition. Prospect Heights, IL: Waveland

Press, 1990.

[26] U.S. EPA. Office of Science and Technology. Office of Water. Guidance for assessing chemical contaminant data for use in fish advisories. Volume 1: *Fish Sampling and Analysis-Second Edition*. September 1995; EPA 823-R-95-007; p. 1.

[27] Falck F Jr, Ricci A Jr, et al. Pesticides and polychlorinated biphenyl residues in human breast lipids and their relation to breast cancer. *Arch Environ Health* 1992 Mar-Apr;47(2):143-146.

[28] Igbedioh SO. Effects of agricultural pesticides on humans, animals and higher plants in developing countries. *Arch Environ Health* 1991 Jul-Aug;46(4):218-224.

[29] Nicola RM, Branchflower R, Pierce D. Chemical contaminants in bottomfish. *J Environ Health* 1987;49(6):342-347.

[30] Hovinga ME, Sowers M, Humphrey HE. Environmental exposure and lifestyle predictors of lead, cadmium, PCB, and DDT levels in Great Lakes fish eaters. *Arch Environ Health* 1993 Mar-Apr;48(2):98-104.

[31] Rosenman KD. Dioxin, polychlorinated biphenyls, and dibenzofurans in *Environmental and Occupational Medicine-2nd edition* (editor: WN Rom). Boston MA: Little Brown and Co, 1992 p. 927-933.

[32] Rosenman KD. Dioxin, polychlorinated biphenyls, and dibenzofurans in *Environmental and Occupational Medicine-2nd edition* (editor: WN Rom). Boston MA: Little Brown and Co., 1992 p. 927-933.

[33] Colborn T. Animal/Health Connection. In: *Proceedings of the US Environmental Protection Agency's* National Technical Workshop "PCBs in Fish Tissue." September 1993. EPA/823-R-93-003; p. 2-27 to 2-30.

[34] Colborn T. Animal/Health Connection. In: *Proceedings of the US Environmental Protection Agency's* National Technical Workshop "PCBs in Fish Tissue." September 1993. EPA/823-R-93-003; p. 2-27 to 2-30.

[35] Jacobson JL, Jacobson SW. Intellectual impairment in children exposed to polychlorinated biphenyls in utero. *NEJM* 1996 Sept 12;335(11):783-789.

[36] Maine issues mercury warning reported June 29, 1994.

[37] Rosenman KD. *Chemical Contamination Episodes in Environmental and Occupational Medicine-2nd edition* (editor: WN Rom). Boston, MA: Little Brown and Co., 1992 p. 935-940.

[38] Swain WR. Effects of organochlorine chemicals on the reproductive outcome of humans who consumed contaminated Great Lakes fish: an epidemiologic consideration. *J Toxicol Environ Health* 1991 Aug;33(4):587-639.

[39] Freudenheim JL, Marshall JR, et al. Exposure to breast milk in infancy and the risk of breast cancer. *Epidemiology* 1994 May;5(3):324-331.

[40] Nedley N. *Proof Positive: How to Reliably Combat Disease and Achieve Optimal Health through Nutrition and Lifestyle*. Ardmore, OK: Nedley Publishing, 1999 p. 115.

[41] Stoll AL, Severus WE, et al. Omega-3 fatty acids in bipolar disorder: a preliminary double-blind, placebo-controlled trial. *Arch Gen Psychiatry* 1999 May;56(5):407-412.

[42] Rogan WJ, Gladen BC. Breast-feeding and cognitive development. *Early Hum Dev* 1993 Jan;31(3):181-193.

[43] Lucas A, Morley R, et al. Breast milk and subsequent intelligence quotient in children born preterm. *Lancet* 1992 Feb 1;339(8788):261-264.

[44] Anderson JW, Johnstone BM, Remley DT. Breast-feeding and cognitive development: a meta-analysis. *Am J Clin Nutr* 1999 Oct;70(4):525-35.

[45] Dorner G, Grychtolik H. Long-lasting ill-effects of neonatal qualitative and/or quantitative dysnutrition in the human. *Endokrinologie* 1978 Feb;71(1):81-88.

[46] Yokota A. Relationship between polyunsaturated fatty acid (PUFA) and learning ability in the brain of rat fetus and newborn. *Nippon Sanka Fujinka Gakkai Zasshi* 1993 Jan;45(1):15-22.

[47] Bourre JM, Bonneil M, et al. Function of dietary polyunsaturated fatty acids in the nervous system. *Prostaglandins Leukot Essent Fatty Acids* 1993 Jan;48(1):5-15.

[48] Makrides M, Neumann MA, et al. Erythrocyte fatty acids of term infants fed either breast milk, standard formula, or formula supplemented with long-chain polyunsaturates. *Lipids* 1995 Oct;30(10):941-948.

[49] Jackson KA, Gibson RA. Weaning foods cannot replace breast milk as sources of long-chain polyunsaturated fatty acids. *Am J Clin Nutr* 1989 Nov;50(5):980-982.

[50] Coscina DV, Yehuda S. Learning is improved by a soybean oil diet in rats. *Life Sci* 1986 May 12;38(19):1789-1794.

[51] Yehuda S, Carasso RL. Modulation of learning, pain thresholds, and thermoregulation in the rat by preparations of free purified alpha-linolenic and linoleic acids: determination of the optimal omega-3-to-omega-6 ratio. *Proc Natl Acad Sci USA* 1993 Nov 1;90(21):10345-10349.

[52] Baldwin BE. Diet and the brain. *Ministry Magazine* 1990 Mar:25-27.

[53] Rosenberg IH, Miller JW. Nutritional factors in physical and cognitive functions of elderly people. *Am J Clin Nutr* 1992 Jun;55(6 Suppl):1237S-1243S.

[54] Tucker DM, Penland JG, et al. Nutrition status and brain function in aging. *Am J Clin Nutr* 1990 Jul;52(1):93-102.

[55] La Rue A, Koehler KM, et al. Nutritional status and cognitive functioning in a normally aging sample: a 6-yr reassessment. *Am J Clin Nutr* 1997 Jan;65(1):20-29.

[56] Fava, Maurizio. Folate, vitamin B12, and homocysteine in major depressive disorder. *Am J Psychiatry* 1997;154:426-428.

[57] ESHA Research. 2nd edition. 1990.

[58] Penninx BW, Guralnik JM, et al. Vitamin B12 deficiency and depression in physically disabled older women: epidemiologic evidence from the Women's Health and Aging Study. *Am J Psychiatry* 2000 May;157(5):715-721.

[59] Mozafar A. Enrichment of some B-vitamins in plants with application of organic fertilizers. *Plant and Soil* 1994;167:305-311.

[60] *ESHA Research*. 2nd edition. 1990.

[61] Ornish D, Brown SE et al. 1990. Can lifestyle changes reverse coronary heart disease? The lifestyle heart trial. *Lancet* Jul21,336(8707):129-133.

[62] Rodriguez Jiminez J, Rodriguez JR, Gonzalez MJ. [indicators of anxiety and depression in subjects with different kinds of diet: vegetarian and omnivores] Bol Assoc Med PR 1998 Apr-Jun; 90(4-6):58-68.

CHAPTER FIVE

LIFESTYLE
TREATMENTS
for DEPRESSION

Amanda had experienced rectal bleeding and severe abdominal cramps for four weeks. She had waited for her symptoms to go away with medication, but instead she was feeling worse and the bleeding was becoming more severe. She had been diagnosed a few years earlier with ulcerative colitis, had undergone treatment with medication, and her symptoms had gradually abated. She had encountered several minor episodes of pain and bleeding since, and each time returned to her medication with resulting improvement. When it became clear that the medication was not working, she was referred to me for further evaluation. During the interview, Amanda stated that she had been suffering from depression for more than ten years and if it weren't for Prozac® and now Zoloft® (antidepressant medications), she didn't know how she could have made it. She was taking Advil® almost continuously for various muscle aches and severe headaches, which she did not recognize were complications of depression. There were times when she had felt reasonably happy and had attempted to wean herself from the antidepressants, but within days she would have uncontrolled crying spells that her husband "could not tolerate" and she would have to resume the drugs.

She was overweight, but said that she had never been overweight until she became depressed and placed on Prozac.® She put on 20 pounds within a few months and continued to put on a few more over the years. Going through several medication changes did not improve her weight. Now her abdominal pain had worsened significantly over the last month to the point that even narcotic pain medication was not controlling it.

As I examined her, I found that the left and lower portions of her abdomen were exquisitely tender to the point that tears quickly came to her eyes. She almost jumped off the exam table during slight hand pressure on the abdomen.

I chose to deal first with her most severe and acute symptoms, the bleeding and abdominal pain. Amanda's blood work revealed she was quite anemic, although not yet in need of a blood transfusion. She underwent a bowel cleanse that day and I performed a colonoscopy the following day. It revealed severe, large ulcers with redness and swelling of the non-ulcerated colon tissues. Her colon biopsies revealed severe active ulcerative colitis. I placed her on the appropriate medical therapy and on a diet higher in omega-3 fat (which can help both depression and ulcerative colitis), and had her stop the Advil® and similar pain and anti-inflammatory medications.

Two weeks later her ulcerative colitis symptoms had improved significantly, but Amanda was having a very hard time dealing with headaches, especially without the Advil.® It became clear that we needed additional ways to treat Amanda's depression beyond her antidepressant medications. I put her on the lifestyle approach outlined in this chapter and in the previous chapter of this book.

Within one month Amanda was feeling so much better that she stopped her antidepressant medications. Usually I wait for four to six months after instituting lifestyle treatments before attempting to withdraw most mental medications that have been used for years. Amanda was aware of this, but on her own she decided to experiment and stopped taking the drugs.

One year later, Amanda is still free from antidepressants and is feeling better than she has "her entire adult life." She is almost down to her ideal weight and no longer feels a need for Advil® or other over-the-counter head and muscle ache remedies. She still requires mild medications to keep her ulcerative colitis from flaring up. But her doctor bills are much less, and she is elated over being mentally healthy without the drugs she had previously thought she had to take for the rest of her life. Her only regret is that she did not understand earlier that *depression could actually be treated by nutrition and lifestyle measures.*

Treating Depression via Lifestyle

As important as nutrition is in treating depression, my experience has demonstrated that in most people, other lifestyle treatments for depression are even more important. There are many safe lifestyle treatments that will benefit anyone who practices such an approach, whether or not they are depressed. These lifestyle changes I advocate for almost anyone, but I insist upon them for my depressed patients. They are outlined in **Figure 1**.

I will explore each of these seven general lifestyle treatments listed in **Figure 1**, followed by six other lifestyle treatments for depression that I prescribe for specific cases.

Regular Physical Exercise

It should not be surprising that exercise can help manage depression. Since it helps improve so many body functions, why shouldn't we expect it to improve the function of the mind as well?

Even if you are not depressed, physical exercise is good for the mind. A very large study from the National Institutes of Health looked at 1,900 healthy subjects. It showed that women who exercise only occasionally or not at all have twice the risk of developing major depression within eight years

GENERAL LIFESTYLE TREATMENTS FOR DEPRESSION

• Bright light therapy

• Avoid negative thinking

• Regular, restful sleep

• Daily spiritual exercises

• Regular physical exercise

• Deep breathing exercises

• Classical music therapy

Figure 1

compared with those that exercised moderately at least several times a week.[1]

Physical activity not only prevents depression, but it is also good treatment for those who are depressed. Further, it is useful in treating other mental illnesses including episodes of anxiety, ongoing anxiety, and panic disorder.[2] New evidence indicates that *regular workouts may help soothe deep sadness as effectively as antidepressant medications.*[3]

What kind of exercise and how much is needed? **Figure 2** describes it.

Researchers at Duke University tested people with major depression and found that a moderate exercise program (30 minutes three times per week) reduced depression as well as antidepressant medication. The medications produced results more quickly, but after 16 weeks the exercise effect caught up according to the study. At least a partial explanation of the mental benefits is that exercise causes the brain to produce more serotonin and norepinephrine, which are neurotransmitters in the brain that can reduce depression.[4]

After reviewing all the studies published since 1981 on exercise and mental health, Canadian researchers found that exercise—whether it is strength training, running, walking, or other forms of aerobic exercise—helps to alleviate mild to moderate depression. It also helps in the treatment of other mental disorders including anxiety, substance abuse disorders, body image disorders, and even attention deficit hyperactivity disorder (ADHD).[5] The amount of exercise varied in these studies from 20 minute sessions to up to 60 minute sessions at least three times a week.

Physical exercise brings about better results than most counseling approaches and is certainly much more cost effective.[6] Another study showed that as little as eight minutes of daily vigorous exercise on an inclined treadmill to the point of exhaustion reduced symptoms of depression as well as tension, anger, and fatigue.[7] A summary of the benefits of regular aerobic exercise in combating mental disorders is shown in **Figure 3**.

It is important for the *depressed patient* to realize that they likely will not feel any

EXERCISE—WHAT KIND AND HOW MUCH?

Aerobic exercise:

- Requires rhythmic motion of large muscle groups.
- Examples: walking, jogging, swimming, cycling
- At least 30 min 3x/wk
- 30 minutes 6x/wk is better

Figure 2

AEROBIC EXERCISE COMBATS DEPRESSION

Regular aerobic exercise:

- increases serotonin levels in the brain

- is as good as medicine for reducing depression

- is better than counseling for reducing depression

- alleviates anxiety, substance abuse disorders, and ADHD

- prevents and treats depression

Figure 3

81

better after their first few exercise sessions. This is in contrast to those who are suffering from *tension, anxiety, anger, or fatigue.* Exercise will tend to improve their symptoms even after the first session. Not so with people suffering from *major depression.* Thus, a depressed person will often stop their recently started exercise routine, thinking that it is not doing them any good. In my experience, it takes *at least a week of daily exercise before depressive symptoms begin to improve* in most individuals. There is more good news. Once the symptoms begin to improve they usually continue to gradually improve over the course of four to six months, during which the maximum effect is finally achieved.

There are additional mental benefits associated with exercise. Researchers who discovered that exercise counteracted depression also found that after four months of regular aerobic exercise, memory and other mental abilities were improved.[8]

ADDITIONAL BENEFITS OF ENDURANCE TRAINING

- Increases HDL cholesterol
- Decreases blood pressure
- Improves insulin sensitivity
- Strengthens bones
- Helps control obesity
- Decreases risk of gallstones
  - Helps control osteoarthritis
  - Improves fibromyalgia
  - Decreases risk of certain cancers

All these benefits are not limited to the young. A study followed more than 900 older adults (average age of 70) for 11 years, and found that those who exercised regularly at the start of the study but later quit were more likely to develop depression compared with those who stayed active. The quitters and those who never exercised during the study had the highest scores on a depression test at the end of the study.[9] Specifically, mood benefits were seen in those whose regular exercise caused them to break a sweat. Even those who did any kind of exercise just three times a week were less likely to have depressed moods. Interestingly, the older participants who took up exercising during the study got a mood boost similar to those who had exercised throughout the study. In other words, no matter how old you are, you will benefit by starting a good exercise program.

I tell my depressed patients that they need to commit themselves to a regularly scheduled (not haphazard) exercise program for life. They can vary the type of exercise so that it does not become monotonous. For instance, one of my patients does brisk walking on Tuesdays, Thursdays, and Saturdays; runs on Mondays and Fridays; swims on Wednesdays; and lifts weights on Sundays.

If you want to bring a friend along and socialize during exercise sessions, do so. But do not depend on a friend in order to exercise; otherwise, you will eventually stop exercising. Choosing pleasant surroundings to exercise helps maintain a program.

Fortunately, the benefits of physical exercise do not stop with improved mental health. **Figure 4** lists additional benefits of endurance training.[10,11,12,13]

More complete information on these and other benefits of physical exercise is found in the book *Proof Positive.*

Figure 4

Deep Breathing Exercises

Exercising muscles requires an abundant supply of oxygen. For this reason, maximal physical performance necessitates deep breathing.[14] However, most people don't think it is obvious that deep breathing has profound effects on *mental* performance. This section, however, deals with the *benefits of deep breathing* apart from physical exercise.

A simple, readily available test in many doctors' offices is an oxygen saturation test. A probe is placed on a finger or earlobe and a blood oxygen saturation is measured. A blood oxygen saturation of less than 95 percent is associated with decreased ability to perform complex mental tasks.[15] When a person is sitting in a classroom, in church, or even on the sofa socializing or watching television, the blood oxygen saturation often drops to levels less than 95 percent. This can happen even though they may have a completely healthy pair of lungs. Why does it occur? Because of shallow breathing, which in turn is often associated with poor posture.

One study showed that lower oxygen levels adversely affect mood, and also have several other consequences as outlined in **Figure 5**.[16]

Another study examined blood oxygen levels in cardiac patients and normal subjects during both spontaneous breathing and periods of controlled breathing to determine the effect of respiratory rate on arterial oxygen saturation.[17] Controlled breathing at a rate from 3 to 15 breaths per minute improved blood oxygen levels, but ideal oxygen levels were reached during deep breathing at *3 to 6 breaths per minute.* To prevent shortness of breath while breathing only three times a minute, it is imperative that the breaths be *very deep.*

Since maintaining three breaths a minute throughout a normal day's activities seems unrealistic, Dr. Bernardi, the study's lead author, had participants do slow, deep breathing at *six breaths per minute for one hour a day.* This not only improved blood oxygen levels during the exercises but also throughout the entire day. It also had a pleasant side effect of improved exercise tolerance in patients with a heart condition. This improvement was additive to other forms of treatment.

Interestingly, the value and importance of deep breathing given by modern researchers was recognized 100 years ago by Ellen White. She wrote, "The one who sits and stands erect is more likely than others to breathe properly. But the teacher should impress upon his pupils the importance of deep breathing. Show how the healthy action of the respiratory organs, assisting the circulation of the blood, invigorates the whole system. [It] excites the appetite, promotes digestion, and induces sound, sweet sleep, thus not only refreshing the body, but soothing and tranquilizing the mind. And while the importance of deep breathing is shown, the practice should be insisted upon. Let exercises be given which will promote this, and see that the habit

EFFECTS OF LOW OXYGEN LEVEL

Low blood oxygen level:

• impairs muscle function

• impairs metabolic function

• leads to muscle atrophy

• leads to exercise intolerance

Figure 5

becomes established."[18]

It is important to maintain proper posture, especially for people who are depressed or are not handling stress well. I encourage my patients to utilize deep breathing techniques during their physical exercise session. Throughout the rest of the day, when conscious of their breathing, they are to attempt to breathe deeply six breaths per minute. At first it will require the use of a watch and taking a breath every ten seconds, but after some practice they will be able to do this without looking at a watch. I also encourage deep breathing while performing the next lifestyle measure, "classical music therapy."

Classical Music Therapy

Music therapy to improve mood and mental function is not a new practice. Thousands of years ago King Saul had a problem with depression. It even got in the way of his ability to function as king. His physician advisors recommended, "Let our lord now command thy servants, which are before thee, to seek out a man, who is a cunning player on an harp: and it shall come to pass, when the evil spirit from God is upon thee, that he shall play with his hand, and thou shalt be well."[19]

The historical record goes on to say, "And it came to pass, when the evil spirit from God was upon Saul, that David took an harp, and played with his hand: so Saul was refreshed, and was well, and the evil spirit departed from him."[20]

Facts about the benefits of music in combating mental disorders are cited in **Figure 6**.

Not all music will improve mood. Each person tends to have musical preferences, but even listening to these musical favorites will not always improve mood after the music stops.

Music psychotherapy, in which people are encouraged to associate mental images with classical music, can improve mood and reduce stress. After six sessions of guided imagery and music (GIM) therapy held over a 12-week period, 14 healthy adult volunteers, ages 23 to 45, showed improved scores on tests of overall mood, and reported feeling less fatigue and depression.[21] The improvement was more than just subjective. The patients' blood levels of the steroid hormone cortisol, which elevates during stress, also fell significantly.

In the GIM therapy sessions, volunteers listened to specific, selected sequences of classical music, including portions from the music of Respighi, Ravel, Bach, and Brahms. To encourage introspection while listening, they were asked to identify one to three areas of concern in their lives. They then shared and discussed with a therapist the spontaneous images that came to mind during the music selections.

Thirteen weeks into the study, test scores on mood disturbance, fatigue, and depression were significantly decreased, compared with pre-GIM therapy test scores. The changes persisted at a follow-up six weeks later. However, no significant changes in test scores or cortisol levels were found among 14 volunteers (control subjects) who did not undergo classical GIM therapy.

MUSIC THERAPY FACTS

- The mental health benefits of music have been well proven.

- Not all kinds of music are beneficial.

- Classical music has been found to be most effective, even among those who do not know it or even prefer it.

Figure 6

This study did not allow people to choose their own musical preference. Most people in the 23 to 45-year-old age group have never been seriously exposed to enough classical music to choose it as a preference. Yet, *traditional classical music is the only style of music that has been demonstrated to improve mental health both subjectively and objectively to date.*[22]

I recommend that individuals listen intently to classical music no less than one hour every two weeks. This can take place in a live concert or in church (if traditional classical hymns and other classical musical numbers are performed), on your living room stereo system, or in your automobile. The only requirement is that the individuals think of areas of concern in their life and keep their imagination active during the performance.

Regular Restful Sleep

Another general lifestyle treatment for depression is regular restful sleep. As mentioned in *Chapter 4*, a continual lack of adequate sleep can lead to depression. In turn, depression in and of itself can then lead to insomnia. Fortunately, many of the general lifestyle measures that I recommend are related to each other and can often be practiced together.

Sleepless nights and feelings of despair are very closely linked, according to a study conducted by the National Institute of Mental Health. The Institute compared various sleep complaints and symptoms of depression in about 8,000 subjects. The results are stated in **Figure** 7.

Note in the figure that mental disorders are strongly linked to insomnia. In this study, a sleep problem that continued for at least one year was defined as insomnia. The risk of *new major depression was extremely high*—a whopping 40 times more likely in those with chronic insomnia than those who typically get a good night's sleep. But notice that even among those

experiencing a temporary bout with sleeplessness there was a 60 percent greater likelihood that they would also fall prey to a depressive episode.[23]

An even greater percent of those with hypersomnia (excessive sleep) developed a mental disorder compared with 16 percent of those with normal sleeping habits.

It has also been discovered that women are about 30 percent more likely to be insomniacs than men, and the prevalence of problems with sleep increases as people age.[24] In older adults, insomnia not only contributes to depression but also to memory impairment.

According to Dr. Peter Hauri and his colleagues at the Mayo Sleep Disorders Center, being physically fit can prevent spasmodic sleep. People who exercise fall asleep more easily, awaken less during the night, and sleep more efficiently than those

SLEEP COMPLAINTS AND DEPRESSION

- Insomnia was reported by 10% of the subjects.

- About 40% of those with insomnia developed a mental disorder.

- Risk of major depression among insomniacs was 40 times higher than those who had no insomnia.

- Those experiencing temporary sleeplessness had a 60% greater likelihood that they would fall prey to a depressive episode.

Figure 7

who do not.[25] This may be associated with what is called circadian cycling, which is explained in *Chapter 3*. An increased metabolism, faster heart rate, and elevated body temperature are associated with poor sleep.[26]

Initially, exercise increases the metabolism, but a few hours after completing the exercise session the body temperature and metabolism drop to a lower level than if the person had not exercised. This is why exercise just before retiring should be avoided, especially if it is possible to exercise in the late afternoon or early evening, which helps to induce sleep.[27] The form of exercise can be as simple as a brisk walk several times around the block. Exercising outdoors in sunshine is advisable whenever possible.

One factor in the inability to sleep well is that as we get older there is a steady, sharp decline in the production of melatonin, a hormone that helps induce sleep.[28] The decline begins before age 10 and continues through age 70, at which time it is reduced to only about two percent of the amount that a youth produces.

This decline is partly due to lifestyle practices that interfere with the production of this important sleep aid. Some people make the mistake of staying up late with the idea of getting tired enough to fall asleep more easily, but exposure to artificial light when burning the midnight oil actually interferes with melatonin production. Failing to get adequate sunlight during waking hours may also diminish melatonin production. For more information on this subject, see the chapter entitled "Melatonin" in the book *Proof Positive.*[29]

Nicotine withdrawal makes sleeping difficult for many individuals, but this should last only two to three weeks after quitting smoking.[30] Sleeping and waking at irregular times may cause insomnia in some people. Others may use stimulants such as coffee or other caffeine drinks to stay awake during the day, and alcohol to later fall asleep, but these artificial means of encouraging alertness or sleep have been found to compound the problem.[31]

A host of medications can also cause insomnia. Just about any medication that has an effect on the brain can cause or aggravate insomnia in some people.[32] This list includes anti-anxiety, antidepressants, anti-seizure, stimulants, and anti-psychotic medications.

Many other medications that are not designed to affect the mind can cause insomnia. This list would include certain antibiotics such as Cipro® and Floxin,® hormones such as Prednisone,® breathing medications such as theophylline, antihistamines, and many other drugs.

Eating just before retiring or eating a heavy meal in the evening often contributes to heartburn or acid reflux, and insomnia can result. Simply going to bed with a full stomach will cause less than a restful night. *When the evening meal is eaten three to four hours before retiring*, digestion will usually be completed, and superior, more efficient rest will be experienced.

Insomnia will improve when the order of meals is reversed, *shifting the bulk of the day's calories to the breakfast and lunch meals, and choosing light and easily digested foods for the evening meal.* A simple fruit meal is an excellent choice for the third meal. For some individuals, cutting out the evening meal altogether may prove to be a very helpful sleep aid. If there is a feeling of hunger, try drinking 8 to 12 ounces of cool water. With the stomach resting through the night, both mind and body will be more rested in the morning.

When a person is stressed and over-committed with a full schedule of activity until just before bedtime, it is difficult to fall asleep and sleep well. Often excessive stress and pressure are self-imposed, and are driven by feelings of insecurity and inferiority.[33] In this case, a healthy spiritual focus is often what is needed, although it may not be as simple as "counting your blessings instead of sheep." Personal issues may need to be examined in the light of God's love and care for us, which may be accomplished through personal study or counseling. *Chapter 8* elaborates on this subject. When individuals develop a healthier perspective, reprioritize duties, relax, and experience inner peace, they usually fall asleep more easily.

It is interesting that a workaholic may have difficulty sleeping, but an inactive and bored person can have the same problem. It is true that anxiety and hyperactivity make it difficult to fall asleep. But on the other end of the spectrum, boredom, such as is often experienced following retirement, may also result in nights of "tossing and turning."[34] Taking up a new hobby or volunteering for a church ministry or a service organization may help restore a sense of worth and purpose. *Filling the day with interesting and profitable activities can also combat sleep disorders.*

Sometimes a very simple adjustment can be helpful in relieving insomnia, such as creating a dark, quiet room, and being as still as possible after going to bed. Eliminating the clock in the bedroom to avoid focusing on how long the time of wakefulness may be helpful.[35] This may not be practical for those with time-sensitive commitments, but if feasible, may prove to be beneficial.

Another means of inducing sleep is to engage in a calming activity such as reading spiritual material or listening to soothing music for 15 to 30 minutes before retiring. A season of prayer, though certainly not recommended solely for the purpose of inducing sleep, may also have a calming effect. These activities will not only be relaxing, but may help by providing a distraction from trying intently to fall asleep. A summary of the sleep aids mentioned in this section is listed in **Figure 8**.[36]

Sleep disturbances can be either a cause or a result of depression. In either case, treating the sleep disorder is a key to preventing depression. Several lifestyle measures that may ensure a good night's rest also offer other health benefits as well, including weight loss and increased energy. Improved sleep habits in combination with these other enhancements to overall health could be powerful aids in relieving depression.

Bright Light Therapy

Seasonal Affective Disorder (SAD) is a common condition in Northern Latitudes like the Scandinavian countries and Alaska. It occurs most often in winter when there is little or no sunlight, even at noon. The condition has identical symptoms to depression and resolves when individuals are exposed to bright light (2,000 to 10,000

SUMMARY OF SUGGESTED SLEEP AIDS

- Afternoon or early evening exercise, outdoors in daylight
- Early, light supper, if supper is eaten at all
- Avoid caffeine, alcohol, nicotine
- Avoid "burning the midnight oil"
- Effective stress management
- Schedule reasonable work hours
- Eliminate the bedroom clock
- Fall asleep in a dark, quiet room
- Lie still shortly after going to bed
- Use regular sleep/wake scheduling
- Avoid excessive daytime boredom
- Soothing music, reading spiritual materials, prayer

Figure 8

lux) for at least 30 minutes a day. This amount of brightness can be achieved indoors by being exposed to a special bright light (such as the Hap-E light)[37] or by being outdoors in the United States (at similar latitudes) at least 30 minutes after sun-up and at least 30 minutes before sundown. The only mandatory exposed human surface to the light is the eyes.

Outdoor light is amazingly more intense than the normal indoor variety. Outdoor light can reach 3000 lux on a bright sunny day.[38] A bright indoor environment may provide only 400 lux, less than 15 percent of daylight brightness.[39] *Bright light, such as sunlight, increases serotonin production in the daytime, which can in turn treat depression and fatigue.*[40] Bright light exposure in the day may also increase blood melatonin levels at night, which can create more restful and efficient sleep.[41]

Bright light therapy can also help restore the normal daily body rhythm called the *circadian rhythm.* If a person has problems with early morning awakening (3 to 5 a.m.) but needs more sleep, exposure to bright light in the early evening for 30 minutes can restore the normal sleep pattern. For the more common problem of not being able to fall asleep at bedtime (insomnia), combined with awakening too late in the morning, exposure to early morning bright light (6 to 8 a.m.) can restore the normal sleep cycle.[42] Utilizing morning-light therapy for depression brings superior results to evening-light therapy, although evening therapy is better than no light therapy at all.[43]

I usually recommend an exercise program that is outdoors in the morning sun. This is not possible for everyone to do in winter when the sun comes up later. For these people I recommend a lunch time outdoor exercise period such as a brisk walk for 30 minutes. Others who are fortunate enough to have a south side office window that brightens their room enough that indoor light is unnecessary, can often get by without taking the afore-mentioned outdoor exercise precautions. However, there is one additional important benefit of outdoor exercise to consider—negative ions. *Fresh country air has negative ions* that have been demonstrated to both treat and prevent depression.[44]

AVOID PESSIMISM

"While the 'power of positive thinking' is encouraged as a way to improve health and well-being, this study shows it is more important to avoid negative thinking."

Avoid Negative Thinking

This particular lifestyle measure cannot be over-emphasized. I have had many patients, including Amanda, point to this particular lifestyle measure as perhaps the most important in leading them to success in depression-free living without the use of medications.

Researchers at Ohio State University in Columbus studied 224 middle-aged and older adults who were already dealing with significant stress in their lives. At one-year intervals for three years, participants reported their degree of optimism and pessimism, negative life events, depression, stress, anxiety, and other issues. The researchers found that optimism and pessimism, previously thought to be linked, are actually independent factors that

Figure 9

individually influence stressed and non-stressed people. One factor is more influential than the other. Specifically, pessimism predicted anxiety, perceived stress, and self-rated lack of physical health for the next year. An optimistic attitude did not predict anything. **Figure 9** demonstrates the impact of this study.[45]

This requires a retraining of the thought processes. I have found that many depressed individuals have a tendency to look at the down side of life. We are all well aware that there always will be things in this imperfect world to complain about. We are helpless to personally do anything about many of these negative things or events. In contrast, focusing the mind on *enjoying the wonderful blessings of life* is not only uplifting but also therapeutic. As soon as conscious awareness of an unconstructive negative thought is realized, a *positive thought* should immediately replace it. This means that the person should plan ahead as to what positive thought to contemplate so that no delay in *thought-shifting* occurs. The human brain is both flexible and trainable and as positive thoughts become habitual, depression will likely become a thing of the past.

One religious author stated, "It is a positive duty to resist melancholy, discontented thoughts and feelings—as much a duty as it is to pray."[46] If negative-thinking people visited the setting portrayed in **Figure 10** and saw the low clouds and dead leaves, they would complain that they did not choose another day to be there. Others would revel in seeing the grand mountains, the valley clothed with living green, and the beautiful flowers.

Incidentally, this may be one of the reasons that country music (now the most listened-to music in the U.S.) does not come out on top in uplifting the mood. Melancholic guitars accompanying voices and lyrics combine to complain about a wrecked pick-up, lost dog, or missed ex-spouse. Even though the rhythm may be classified as *upbeat*, the effect does not truly

uplift the thoughts.

IT IS A POSITIVE DUTY . . .

. . to resist melancholy, discontented thoughts and feelings . .

Figure 10

BENEFITS OF AN INNER RELIGIOUS EXPERIENCE

- Several studies show that depressed patients with high inner religiosity recover sooner than non-religious patients.

- Going through the forms of religion without firm belief is of little benefit.

- Daily reading of scripture is recommended for improved mental health.

Figure 11

Daily Spiritual Exercises

An inner religious experience has been found to be effective in recovery from depression, according to several studies. The results are cited in **Figure 11**.

For just under a year, researchers from Duke University in North Carolina used diagnostic interviews to track the emotional well-being of 94 individuals, each of whom was more than 60 years of age. They all had been diagnosed as suffering from depression upon discharge from a hospital.[47]

Some of their tests and questions focused on the study participant's level of inner religiosity. To ascertain this level of inner faith, researchers used a ten-question evaluation test that had been developed with the help of Christian ministers and Jewish rabbis. They also established the level of each participant's external religious practice—activities such as service attendance and involvement in church-related clubs and activities. During the course of the study 54 percent of the participants recovered from their depression.

Religion helped in that recovery. "Depressed patients with *higher intrinsic (inner) religiosity scores had more rapid remissions than patients with lower scores,*" according to the study. In fact, patients recovered from depression 70 percent sooner with every ten-point increase in the religiosity evaluation test score. But the researchers found that *external religious activity had much less of an impact.*

The Duke team urges psychiatrists to initiate inquiries into a patient's religious faith, especially when patients are depressed, since "these beliefs may bring comfort and facilitate coping."

Other studies have found that strong religious faith is not only helpful in treating depression, but also in preventing it.[48,49,50]

Many studies have suggested that going through the forms of religion without firm belief does little if any good to overall mental health.[51] Thus, I do not emphasize a casual reading of the Bible, but a serious study that contemplates the themes of scripture. Reading and meditating on a chapter of the book of Proverbs each day (with the chapter number corresponding to the day of the month—there are 31 chapters) has been helpful for many of my depressed patients. Memorizing and reciting a text a week that summarizes or succinctly states a beautiful Scriptural idea is also very helpful. One new program that has met with wonderful worldwide success in accomplishing these objectives is called FAST.[52]

This concludes the presentation of the seven general lifestyle elements listed in **Figure 1**. We will now look at several lifestyle treatments that will not apply in general, but will be helpful to certain people with specific needs.

Six Selective Lifestyle Treatments

So far, I have discussed general lifestyle principles that will be of benefit to practically every depressed person. Even

SIX SELECTIVE LIFESTYLE TREATMENTS FOR DEPRESSION

- Social support
- Cognitive behavioral therapy
- Codependency therapy
- Owning a pet
- Hydrotherapy
- Stress control measures

Figure 12

those who are not depressed can decrease their risk of ever contracting depression as well as improve their own mood and outlook on life by following such a program.

Now we will explore lifestyle measures that can be of benefit to selected individuals, and arguably could be of benefit to most depressed patients. These particular lifestyle measures are outlined in **Figure 12**.

The Importance of Social Support

In animals and in humans, isolation leads to depression and withdrawal, while social support and a sense of belonging leads to improved mood and improved mental and physical health.[53] The importance of strong social support should not be underestimated. The benefits are stated in **Figure 13**.

One study showed that good support of families and friends can be lifesaving. After suffering a heart attack, 887 patients were followed for a year.[54] Researchers evaluated the patients for depression soon after they were transferred out of intensive care units. The patients were asked questions about the support they receive from family, friends, or a "special person."

Soon after having the heart attack, about a third of the patients were mildly or moderately depressed. Patients who were depressed were more than three times as likely to die during the year after having the heart attack. But the effect of depression on survival varied depending on a person's *perceived social support.*

The odds of dying were highest in depressed people who felt that they did not get enough support from their friends, families, and loved ones. In contrast, the depressed patients who felt the strongest support by friends and family were not any more likely to die than non-depressed people. In addition, symptoms of depression were much more likely to improve in depressed patients who felt well supported.

Another study suggested that there is something even more important than perceived social support. This particular study sent questionnaires to 31 patients with major depression and to 379 community college students in Ann Arbor, Michigan.[55] Questions focused on issues such as a psychological sense of belonging, the extent of one's social network and social activities, and feelings of conflict and loneliness. The study showed that from all social factors considered, a sense of belonging is the best predictor of what an individual might experience in terms of depressive symptoms.[56] The point is that many friends and a busy social life do not necessarily equate with a strong sense of belonging. An individual may have friends that he does not feel belong to him.

I recommend that individuals who do not have a close family or close friends, especially if they have a low sense of belonging, involve themselves in certain community or church projects that are consistent with their own goals. They will often form close relationships in the process, and with a sense of common purpose will soon feel truly "belonged."

SOCIAL SUPPORT IS VITAL

- A sense of belonging improves mood and mental health

- Social support reduces risk of death following a heart attack.

- A busy social life does not guarantee a sense of belonging.

- The need is for close family and/or close friends.

Figure 13

Cognitive Behavioral Therapy

For many years, *psychotherapy* (counseling), as practiced by most mental health professionals, was an open-ended, unstructured process aimed at uncovering so-called "unconscious" reasons for depression. A lot of time was spent on how the individual was raised as a child, and other past events that may have shaped the person's feelings and behavior. This lengthy, intensive effort has never been proven effective in the treatment of depression or any other mood disorder.

Even though this type of counseling has never been shown to be better than taking a placebo pill for depression, it is still practiced by many mental health professionals today. Fortunately, a relatively new form of psychotherapy is emerging that has been shown to be superior—*cognitive-behavioral therapy*.

Dozens of controlled clinical trials during the past 20 years have established the effectiveness of cognitive-behavioral therapy in the treatment of major depression and dysthymic disorder.[57,58,59,60,61] This particular type of therapy is focused, time-limited, and directed at the specific needs of the depressed individual. It aims at identifying and correcting erroneous interpretations of events and negative automatic thoughts that may initiate or perpetuate a depressed mood. The focus is very much on the depressed individual and *what he can do differently*—not on finding circumstances or others to blame.

Chronic depression has an earned reputation of being very difficult to treat. By definition, chronic depression has to have lasted for greater than two years. Often the depressed individual has not responded to medication, counseling, or other therapy. A recent landmark study showed that a combination of the antidepressant drug nefazodone (Serzone®) and intensive psychotherapy effectively reduces or eliminates chronic depression in a record 85 percent of patients.[62] No other study had ever shown such a dramatic response. Not surprisingly, the type of psychotherapy used was the cognitive-behavioral analysis system.

"We were stunned," said lead investigator Martin Keller of Brown University. "None of us had anticipated we'd show anything close to an 85 percent response rate for the combination." Patients on the combination did significantly better than those undergoing the counseling or the medication by themselves. The study highlights the importance of using a combination of successful approaches to more effectively combat depression. The conclusions of these studies are summarized in **Figure 14**.

Therapy for Codependency

Chapter 3 describes the unhealthy mental condition and causes of codependency. Therapy that works for codependency should be directed toward the primary cause of the condition—low self-worth.[63] Low self-worth is primarily a spiritual problem in my view—a lack of perception of the

COUNSELING COMBINED WITH DRUG THERAPY

- Traditional counseling that focuses on the victim's life events has proven to be ineffective.

- Counseling that seeks what the victim can do differently reduces or eliminates depression.

Figure 14

value of each of us in the sight of our Maker.

How Much is a Person Worth?

What someone else thinks or even what you think of your own personal worth sinks into insignificance when compared with what God, the Ruler of the universe, thinks of you. Our Creator loves you so much that He gave His only beloved Son to save you—even though you did not love Him.[64] The scriptures cited at the previous endnote imply that for one person, "Christ would, to save … one, have chosen His life of toil and humiliation and His death of shame."[65]

Thus, one person is worth what the Son of God is worth—infinite value! No wonder the apostle Paul asked, "Who shall separate us from the love of Christ? Shall tribulation, or distress, or persecution, or famine, or nakedness, or peril, or sword?[66] He answered his own question with a resounding no, then continued with a declaration of the strength of God's love that is recited in **Figure 15**.[67]

The love of God for one person is a wonderful, exhaustless subject. Once studied, one begins to realize that one person is worth more in God's sight than the entire physical world. For those who are suffering from love hunger or codependency, I recommend that they spend a thoughtful half-hour a day contemplating and reading about the life of Christ—especially the last 24 hours before His cruel death. Two books, along with the Bible that have helped many people accomplish this are the *Desire of Ages* and *The Story of Redemption*.[68]

Self-worth vs. Self-esteem

There is a difference between *self-worth* (infinite value) and what is usually referred to as *self-esteem*. Webster's definitions are shown in **Figure 16**.[69] Codependents often have low self-esteem[70,71] (as well as low self-worth). As a result, many therapists try to build up self-esteem by reciting the client's

DECLARATION OF PAUL THE APOSTLE

"For I am persuaded, that:
neither death,
nor life,
nor angels,
nor principalities,
nor powers,
nor things to come,
nor height,
nor depth,
nor any other creature,
shall be able to separate us from the love of God, which is in Christ Jesus our Lord."

Romans 8:38,39

Figure 15

SELF-ESTEEM vs. SELF-WORTH

As defined in Webster's New World Dictionary:

- **Self-esteem:** pride, conceit, self-love

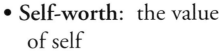

- **Self-worth:** the value of self

Figure 16

93

wonderful, positive traits, which naturally tend to result in an inflated ego. This sometimes appears to benefit clients in the short term, but I have found that it often fails in the long term. The apostle Paul, who understood the *infinite self-worth* of every individual, also stated, "Let nothing be done through selfish ambition or conceit, but in lowliness of mind let each *esteem others better than himself*."[72]

I have found that many codependents make poor decisions based on pride and what others might think of them, instead of determining first what the right decision is, and then following through on the decision. The dual concepts of *infinite self-worth*—based on the Everlasting Father's infinite love and what He has done for the individual—and *humility*, are usually necessary for the person to break free from the cycle of poor decisions that often permeate the codependent's life.

The psychology literature correctly speaks of self-esteem as pride. Unfortunately, it also speaks of self-esteem as self-worth; the two terms are used interchangeably. The only way to detect the difference in the literature is by the context, or how "self-esteem" was determined in the study.

Doing the Right Thing

Love needs law to guide it. For instance, the Ten Commandments are often referred to as the law of God. Yet, these same commandments are referred to in both the Old and New Testaments of Scripture in terms of deep and lasting love and are summarized as "love to God and love to man."[73] Christ said if we love Him we will keep His law.[74] Love without law (not based on principle), is not true love at all.

Consider a woman whose husband is an alcoholic. She may often try to "protect" him. The reasons can stem from "this is what is expected," to "he might lose his job if I turn him in," to "he might decide to leave me if I do what is best for him." Because the perceived consequences of doing what

is right seem rather troublesome, the codependent wife often unwittingly assists the codependent addict to continue the addiction. What follows is a litany of unforeseen consequences that are worse than what would have happened if the "right thing" had been done originally.

It is crucial for a codependent wife to ask, "What is the right decision?" If she doesn't know, then she should seek counsel specifically to determine what is right. Then she should carry out that decision. For instance, the addicted loved one must undergo an "intervention." This means that those who care about him must converge on him simultaneously to help him admit his problem so that he can get the help he needs to overcome the addiction. To carry out such a decision, counseling from a person experienced in helping addicts admit their true condition so that the addict is willing to seek essential help, is often necessary to perform the intervention successfully.

Instead of living life based on feelings and emotions, it is important for the codependent wife to surrender those feelings to principle, strong as they may be. The result will be a life lead by true love guided by principle, instead of a life guided by pride, infatuation, fear, and a train of unpleasant results.

Owning a Pet

One basic human adult need is to be needed. Pets are loving toward humans as well as dependent upon them. Elderly depressed patients have had their moods improved by owning a pet.[75] A recent study also showed that depressed AIDS patients who owned a pet reduced their risk of contracting depression.[76] The benefit is especially pronounced when people are strongly attached to their pets and have few close confidants. I recommend pets for those who do not have close, caring friends or family and who are unable to successfully implement the recommendations under the social support section.

Hydrotherapy

For more than 100 years, mental illness has occasionally been treated with warm baths utilizing natural hot springs or other sources. Before the 1950s, special showers, baths, wet sheet wraps, and other forms of hydrotherapy were routinely used in psychiatric hospitals throughout the United States and Europe. These approaches were not only used to treat depression, but were also used to treat delirium, agitation, insomnia, gastrointestinal disturbances, and pain syndromes.

Recent research now confirms that normal subjects who are passively warmed just before going to bed have an improved quality of sleep, as measured by brain wave analysis (EEG). Since sleep disturbance occurs in as many as 90 percent of individuals with major depression, could warm baths actually assist in treating depression?

Warm baths can help, according to a recent preliminary study conducted at Michigan State University.[77] More than 40 patients ranging from 18 to 62 years of age who were admitted to a hospital psychiatry unit with an episode of major depression were given a warm, 30-minute bath (102 to 106 degrees Fahrenheit, or 39 to 41 degrees Celsius) just before going to bed. Improvements occurred in tension, anxiety, anger, hostility, confusion, bewilderment, and depression. The findings were the same for men and women.

Stress Combined with Depression

Stress coexists with depression so frequently that this combination is the rule rather than the exception. Often the same medications are used to treat each one alone.[78] Many of the remainder of depressed patients feel stressed-out, unable to cope

effectively with the stress in their lives. If stress is a significant component that appears related to their depression, I encourage them to also *adopt the stress control program outlined in Chapter 8.*

Conclusion

Lifestyle changes need to take place if the person is to break free from depression and the complications of medications that come with it. Amanda's experience of being able to live happily without the use of anti-depressant medications is not unique. Countless others have found the way to lasting happiness and meaning by changing their lifestyle for the better. Three steps that will lead to a happier and healthier life are listed in **Fig. 17**.

Although some of the changes may seem hard at first, the end result will be a life that is much more pleasant, meaningful, and uncomplicated.

THREE STEPS TO A HAPPIER LIFE

1. An analysis of your life

2. A desire to change

3. The courage to embark on a new plan for your life.

Figure 17

References—

[1] Farmer ME, Locke BZ, et al. Physical activity and depressive symptoms: the NHANES I Epidemiologic follow-up study. *Am J Epidemiol* 1988 Dec;128(6):1340-1351.

[2] Paluska SA, Schwenk TL. Physical activity and mental health: current concepts. *Sports Med* 2000 Mar;29(3):167-180.

[3] Blumenthal JA, et al. Effects of exercise training on older patients with major depression. *Arch Intern Med* 1999 Oct 25;159(19) 2349-56.

[4] Blumenthal JA, Babyak MA, et al. Effects of exercise training on older patients with major depression. *Arch Intern Med* 1999 Oct 25;159(19):2349-2356.

[5] Tkachuk GA, Martin GL. *Professional Psychology: Research and Practice* 1999;30:275-282.

[6] Tkachuk GA, Martin GL. *Professional Psychology: Research and Practice* 1999;30:275-282.

[7] Moore KA, presented by Duke University at the Society of Behavioral Medicine, San Francisco, California, April 17, 1997.

[8] Blumenthal J, et al. *J of Aging and Physical Activity* 2001;9.

[9] Kritz-Silverstein D, Barrett-Connor E, Corbeau C. Cross-sectional and prospective ptudy of exercise and depressed mood in the elderly: the rancho bernardo study. *Am J Epidemiol* 2001 Mar 15;153:596-603.

[10] Physical activity and cardiovascular health. NIH Consensus Development Panel on Physical Activity and Cardiovascular Health. *JAMA* 1996 Jul 17;276(3):241-246.

[11] Surgeon General's report on physical activity and health. From the Centers for Disease Control and Prevention. *JAMA* 1996 Aug 21;276(7):522.

[12] Leitzmann MF, Rimm EB, et al. Recreational physical activity and the risk of cholecystectomy in women. *N Engl J Med* 1999 Sep 9;341(11):777-784.

[13] Nedley N. Chapter 20 Beyond the leading causes of death, In: *Proof Positive: How to Reliably Combat Disease and Achieve Optimal Health through Nutrition and Lifestyle.* Ardmore, OK: Nedley Publishing, 1998, p. 492-496.

[14] Bernardi L, Spadacini G, Bellwon J, Hajric R, Roskamm H, Frey AW. Effect of breathing rate on oxygen saturation and exercise performance in chronic heart failure. *Lancet* 1998 May 2;351 (9112):1309-11.

[15] Author's Clinical Experience.

[16] Munger MA, Stanek E, et al. Arterial oxygen saturation in chronic congestive heart failure. *Am J Cardiol* 1994;73:180-185.

[17] Bernardi L. Effect of breathing rate on oxygen saturation and exercise performance in chronic heart failure. *Lancet* 1998 May;35:1308-1311.

[18] White EG. *Child Guidance.* Hagerstown, MD: Review and Herald Publishing Association, 1954, p. 364-365.

[19] 1 Samuel 16:15. *The Holy Bible.* KJV.

[20] 1 Samuel 16:23. *The Holy Bible.* KJV.

[21] McKinney CH, Antoni MH, et al. Effects of guided imagery and music (GIM) therapy on mood and cortisol in healthy adults. *Health Psychology* 1997; 16:390-400.

[22] McCabe P, et al. Effects of guided imagery and music (GIM) therapy on mood and cortisol in healthy adults. *Lancet* 1998:351:1308-1311.

[23] Ford DE, Kamerow DB. Epidemiologic study of sleep disturbances and psychiatric disorders. An opportunity for prevention? *JAMA* 1989 Sept 15;262(11):1479-1484.

[24] Mellinger G, Balter M, Uhlenhuth E. Insomnia and its treatment: Prevalence and correlates. *Arch Gen Psychiatry* 1985;42:225-232.

[25] Edinger JD, Morey MC, et al. Aerobic fitness, acute exercise and sleep in older men. *Sleep* 1993;16:351-359.

[26] Bonnet MH, Arand DL. Twenty-four-hour metabolic rate in insomniacs and matched normal sleepers. *Sleep* 1995;18:581-588.

[27] Hauri, P. Sleep disorders, insomnia. From the Mayo Sleep Disorders Center, Mayo Clinic, Rochester, Minnesota. *Clinics in Chest Med* 1998 Mar;10(1):157. Copyright 1998 W. B. Saunders Company.

[28] Reiter RJ, Robinson J. The best antioxidant. In: *Melatonin: Your Body's Natural Wonder Drug.* New York, NY: Bantam Books, 1995 p. 20.

[29] Nedley N. Chapter 9. Melatonin. In: *Proof Positive: How to Reliably Combat Disease and Achieve Optimal Health through Nutrition and Lifestyle.* Ardmore, OK: Nedley Publishing, 1999, p. 193.

[30] Glynn TJ, Manley MW. *How to Help Your Patients Stop Smoking: A National Cancer Institute Manual for Physicians.* National Institutes of Health Publication Number 92-3064. Revised Nov. 1991 p. 37.

[31] Hauri, P. Sleep disorders, insomnia. From the Mayo Sleep Disorders Center, Mayo Clinic, Rochester, Minnesota. *Clinics in Chest Med* 1998 Mar;10(1):157. Copyright 1998 W. B. Saunders Company.

[32] Nakajima T, Nippon Drug-induced sleep disorders. *Rinsho Hyoka* 1998 Feb;56(2):469-74.

[33] Hauri, P. Sleep disorders, insomnia. From the Mayo Sleep Disorders Center, Mayo Clinic, Rochester, Minnesota. *Clinics in Chest Med* 1998 Mar;10(1):163. Copyright 1998 W. B. Saunders Company.

[34] Hauri, P. Sleep disorders, insomnia. From the Mayo Sleep Disorders Center, Mayo Clinic, Rochester, Minnesota. *Clinics in Chest Med* 1998 Mar;10(1):163. Copyright 1998 W. B. Saunders Company.

[35] Hauri, P. Sleep disorders, insomnia. From the Mayo Sleep Disorders Center, Mayo Clinic, Rochester, Minnesota. *Clinics in Chest Med* 1998 Mar;10(1):163. Copyright 1998 W. B. Saunders Company.

[36] Harrington ME, Rusak B, et al. Anatomy and physiology of the mammalian circadian system. In Kryger MH, Roth T, Dement WC (eds): *principles and practice of sleep medicine*, ed 2. Philadelphia, WB Saunders Company, 1994, pp. 286-300.

[37] Terman M: Light treatment. In Kryger MH, Roth T, Dement WC (eds): *principles and practice of sleep medicine*, ed 2. Philadelphia, WB Saunders Company, 1994, pp. 1012-1029.

[38] Reiter RJ, Robinson J. Back in Sync. In: *Melatonin: Your Body's Natural Wonder Drug.* New York, NY: Bantam Books, 1995 p. 161.

[39] Reiter RJ, Robinson J. Back in Sync. In: *Melatonin: Your Body's Natural Wonder Drug.* New York, NY: Bantam Books, 1995 p 161.

[40] Rao ML, Muller-Oerlinghausen B, et al. The influence of photo-therapy on serotonin and melatonin in non-seasonal depression. *Pharmacopsychiatry* 1990 May;23(3):155-158.

[41] Laakso ML, Porkka-Heiskanen T, et al. Twenty-four-hour patterns of pineal melatonin and pituitary and plasma prolactin in male rats under 'natural' and artificial lighting conditions. *Neuroendocrinology* 1988 Sep;48(3):308-313.

[42] Wagner DR. Sleep disorders; disorders of the circadian sleep-wake cycle. *Neurologic Clinics* 1996 Aug;14(3):651.

[43] Terman M. A controlled trial of timed bright light and negative air ionization for treatment of winter depression. *Arch Gen Psychiatry* 1998 Oct;55(10):875-882.

[44] Terman M. A controlled trial of timed bright light and negative air ionization for treatment of winter depression. *Arch Gen Psychiatry* 1998 Oct;55(10):875-882.

[45] Robinson-Whelen S. *J Personality and Social Psychology* 1997;73:1345-1353.

46 White, EG. *Ministry of Healing*, Hagerstown, MD: Review and Herald Publishing Association, 1905, p. 251.

47 Koenig HG, George LK, et al. Religiosity and remission of depression in medically ill older patients. *Am J Psychiatry* 1998 Apr;155(4):536-542.

48 Miller L, Warner V, et al. Religiosity and depression: ten-year follow-up of depressed mothers and offspring. *J Am Acad Child Adolesc Psychiatry* 1997 Oct;36(10):1416-1425.

49 McCullough ME, Larson DB. Religion and depression: a review of the literature. *Twin Res* 1999 Jun;(2):126-136.

50 Koening HG, Smiley M, Gonzales JA: *Religion, health and aging: a review and theoretical integration.* New York, Greenwood Press, 1988.

51 McCullough ME, Larson DB. Religion and depression: a review of the literature. *Twin Res* 1999 Jun;(2):126-136.

52 www.fast.st based in Ann Arbor, Michigan.

53 Kaufman IC, Stynes AJ. Depression can be induced in a bonnet macaque infant. *Psychosom Med* 1978 Feb;40(1):71-75.

54 Frasure-Smith N. Circulation. *J Am Heart Association* 2000;101:1919-1924.

55 Hagerty BM, Williams RA. The effects of sense of belonging, social support, conflict, and loneliness on depression. *Nurs Res* 1999 Jul-Aug;48(4):215-219.

56 Hyman S, Rudorfer M. Depressive and bipolar mood disorders. *Scientific American Medicine* May 2000.

57 Thase ME, Greenhouse JB, et al. Treatment of major depression with psychotherapy-pharmacotherapy combinations. *Arch Gen Psychiatry* 1997;54:1009.

58 Gloaguen V, Cottraux J, et al. A meta-analysis of the effects of cognitive therapy in depressed patients. *J Affect Disord* 1998;49:59.

59 Schulberg HC, Pilkonis PA, Houck P. The severity of major depression and choice of treatment in primary care practice. *J Consult Clin Psychol* 1998;66:932.

60 DeRubeis RJ, Gelfand LA, et al. Medications versus cognitive behavior therapy for severely depressed outpatients: mega-analysis of four randomized comparisons. *Am J Psychiatry* 1999;156:1007.

61 Katon W, Robinson P, et al. A multifaceted intervention to improve treatment of depression in primary care. *Arch Gen Psychiatry* 1996;53:924.

62 Keller MB, McCullough JP, et al. A comparison of nefazodone, the cognitive behavioral-analysis system of psychotherapy, and their combination for the treatment of chronic depression. *N Engl J Med* 2000 May 18;342(20):1462-1470.

63 Lindley NR. Codependency: predictors and psychometric issues. *J Clin Psychol,* 1999 Jan;55(1):59-64.

64 Rom 5:8. *The Holy Bible.* Authorized King James Version
    But God commendeth his love toward us, in that, while we were yet sinners, Christ died for us.

Eph 2:4-5. *The Holy Bible.* The New American Standard Version
But God, being rich in mercy, because of His great love with which He loved us, even when we were dead in our transgressions, made us alive together with Christ (by grace you have been saved).
1 John 4:9-10. *The Holy Bible.* KJV.
In this was manifested the love of God toward us, because that God sent his only begotten Son into the world, that we might live through him. Herein is love, not that we loved God, but that he loved us, and sent his Son to be the propitiation for our sins.
John 3:16. *The Holy Bible.* KJV.
For God so loved the world, that he gave his only begotten Son, that whosoever believeth in him should not perish, but have everlasting life.

65 White, EG. *Ministry of Healing,* p. 135. (1905).

66 Rom 8:35. *The Holy Bible.* KJV.

67 Rom 8:38-39. *The Holy Bible.* KJV.

68 White EG. *Desire of Ages.* Public domain book. 1898. White EG. *The Story of Redemption.* 1947. Both books an be ordered from www.adventistbookcenter.com.

69 *Webster's New World Dictionary,* 2nd College edition, 1984.

70 Lindley NR. Codependency: predictors and psychometric issues. *J Clin Psychol* 1999 Jan;55(1):59-64.

71 Cook DL. Relationship between social support, self-esteem and codependency in the African American female. *J Cult Divers* 1997 Spring;4(1):32-38.

72 Phil 2:3 *The Holy Bible.* KJV.

73 Deut 6:5 and Matthew 22:37-40. *The Holy Bible.* KJV.

74 John 14:15. *The Holy Bible.* KJV.

75 Raina P, Waltner-Toews D, et al. Influence of companion animals on the physical and psychological health of older people: an analysis of a one-year longitudinal study. *J Am Ger Soc* 1999 Mar;47(3):323.

76 Siegel JM, Angulo FJ, et al. AIDS diagnosis and depression in the Multicenter AIDS cohort study: the ameliorating impact of pet ownership. *AIDS Care* 1999 Apr;11(2):157-170.

77 Meyers JA. Depression may respond to a warm bath. *Internal Medicine World Report* 1996 Jul;11(13):32.

78 Mental Health: A Report of the Surgeon General Department of Health and Human Services, National Institutes of Health, National Institutes of Mental Health, 1999 p. 253.

79 Mental Health: A Report of the Surgeon General Department of Health and Human Services, National Institutes of Health, National Institutes of Mental Health, 1999 p. 252,253.

CHAPTER SIX

HERBS *and* MEDICATIONS

After attending a local community college for her freshman year, Angela decided to leave home to attend the University of Oklahoma for her sophomore year. During her first year of college, she had felt "down" at times to the point of crying herself to sleep. The summer before Angela left for O.U., her parents noticed that she would have sporadic spells of impatience, followed by apologies. She would then admit to not knowing why little things would get on her nerves.

She also regularly complained of being tired, sometimes to the point of being too tired to eat. Angela was excited to be enrolling in a large university with the possibility of getting to know new friends with interests similar to hers. The success of her educational plan was dependent upon making excellent grades in her science major.

Within a week of arriving at the University, Angela was calling home almost every night. Since this was the first time she had been away from home for any extended period, her parents chalked it up to homesickness. Angela's roommate had a different schedule and stayed up until after midnight. Angela had to get up at 6 a.m. every morning to make her 7 a.m. class. She felt she was not getting the sleep she needed. Even after her roommate went to bed, Angela would often suffer from insomnia. She felt she was not able to accomplish as much during her study time as she did previously, and almost always felt exhausted.

As the fall break neared, Angela looked forward to being home, where she knew she was loved and where she could sleep in her own bed and perhaps catch up on some sleep. When Angela came home, she had a great evening with her family, filled with much laughter. When her mother came into her bedroom to say goodnight, she found Angela crying with heartfelt sobs. Mother thought that maybe she had said something to offend Angela. It was then that Angela admitted that she had cried every night at school.

Her parents noticed that just making simple decisions, like what to wear for church, would turn her into an emotional basket case—turning the simplest decisions into major events. Angela's parents wisely insisted that she see me during her fall break. At first Angela refused, but when she realized that her emotional state was jeopardizing her academic success, she came.

Yes, Angela was suffering from major depression. But in just a few days Angela no longer had any crying spells, she slept better, had much more energy, and most important for her, she was concentrating better and studying more efficiently. Her treatment regimen included nutritional changes, lifestyle measures, and a medication.

Philosophy on Herbs and Medications

In many cases of depression, some type of medication may initially be necessary to successfully treat and prevent further complications. I will examine for you, not only pharmaceutical remedies, but also herbal treatments that are becoming quite popular with the general public.

Whether pharmaceutical or herbal, if medication is appropriate, I usually advise using it for less than six months. When my patients begin treatments that include medications, I recommend specific nutritional and lifestyle therapies that are targeted to wean them from the medication within a five-to-six-month time frame. Herbs and medications do have potential side effects and are expensive; thus, I treat the root cause of depression so that results are long-term and drug-free.

Herbs for Depression—"Natural" Agents

Not too long ago, the mention of herbal remedies might have conjured up pictures of grandma mixing up a special potion to cure a cold or flu, or concocting a smelly ointment to soothe and cure a stubborn rash. Not as warmly nostalgic are images of a primitive witch doctor dancing around a magic potion he brewed from leaves and roots in the jungle. Even today, some people see herbal medicine strictly belonging to the realm of new age gurus.

During the past half century, modern pharmaceuticals had nearly obliterated the use of herbs as remedies, but the last decade has seen a tremendous resurgence in their popularity. The increase in the use of herbs and supplements is shown in **Figure 1**.

This trend began its re-emergence in the '70s and '80s, followed by the use of herbal medicines increasing a whopping 380 percent between 1990 and 1997. During this short period, the therapeutic use of herbs among the general population increased from 2.5 percent to 12.1 percent.[1]

In the treatment of depression, many herbs have been reported to "lift the spirits." None require a prescription. Several are

GROWTH OF SUPPLEMENT AND HERB USAGE

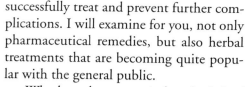

- 40% of Americans take supplements.
- Usage increased by 380% in a recent seven-year period.
- Expenditures are $1.5 billion annually.
- Future sales growth projected at 15%/yr.
- Therapeutic uses of herbs increased by 400% in a seven-year period.

Figure 1

HERBS THAT MAY LIFT THE SPIRITS

- Lemon Balm
- Oat Straw
- Chamomile
- Valerian
- Feverfew

- Kava-Kava
- Borage
- St. John's Wort
- SAMe
- 5-HTP

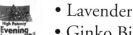

- Evening Primrose Oil
- Lavender
- Ginko Biloba
- Blue Vervain

Figure 2

listed in **Figure 2.**

Some of these herbs may bring relief to causative factors or complications of depression such as anxiety, insomnia, and memory impairment. The frustrating downside is that there has been little or no research done to back the claims of benefits attributed to the many herbs and preparations now for sale on the shelves of even your grocery store. Unfortunately, the claims made for herbal treatment are mostly based on anecdotal evidence instead of statistical studies.

St. John's Wort—An Herb to Combat Depression

For the treatment of depression there is one herb that has been substantially tested with results showing significant benefit — St. John's wort or Hypericum perforatum. Used for centuries as a therapy for insomnia and nervous conditions, this common weed is indigenous to much of the United States. Wort is the Old English word for plant, and the yellow flowers of the hypericum herb were traditionally gathered for a feast held in honor of John the Baptist—hence, its unusual name.[2] The history of its usage is recited in **Figure 3.**

Though St. John's wort has been a leading antidepressant in Germany for years, this herbal remedy has seen an astounding rise in popularity in the U.S. only since the late 90s. Between 1995 and 1997, annual sales increased from $20 million to $200 million.[3]

Numerous studies demonstrate that in mild to moderate major depression, symptoms improve as much as 40 to 55 percent, compared to 15 percent improvement with a placebo.[4,5,6] Other studies have shown St. John's wort to be as effective in many cases as synthetic chemical pharmaceuticals like Prozac®[7] and Imipramine.®[8]

Though the results of these studies appear promising, the use of this antidepressant herb remains controversial. The critics' greatest argument is that St. John's wort studies have been too short with too much variation in the dosage of the commercially-prepared products that were used. Also, some claim that the studies are invalid and unfair because a low dosage of the particular standard medication was compared to the herbal preparation. A summary of its effectiveness is shown in **Figure 4.**

HISTORY OF ST. JOHN'S WORT

- It has been used for centuries to treat "insomnia and nervous conditions."

- It has been a leading antidepressant in Germany for years.

- In a recent two-year period, annual sales in the U.S. have increased ten-fold.

Figure 3

BENEFITS OF ST. JOHN'S WORT

- Positive results in patients with mild depression

- Side effects are rare and mild.

- Effective as Prozac® or Imipramine® in some cases

- Symptoms of mild to moderate major depression improve about 50%

- Benefits are controversial; more statistical studies are needed.

Figure 4

One high profile study of St. John's wort involved 200 depressed patients at 11 major medical centers. [9] It fueled skepticism reguarding this touted anti-depressant herb when the authors claimed that "St. John's wort was not effective for treatment of major depression." However, lost in the fine print was the fact that depression remission occurred nearly three times more frequently in St. John's wort users. Furthermore, the herb had amazingly few side effects. In addition to all this, I have seen favorable results in some of my own mildly depressed patients who have used St. John's wort. Therefore, I believe this herb is still worthy of consideration.

How St. John's wort fights depression is not yet clear, though some researchers believe it inhibits MAO (monoamine oxidase), which allows more serotonin and epinephrine to collect in the central nervous system, giving an increased sense of well-being. As with most herbals, the effect is gentler than pharmaceuticals, and the side effects are much milder. *Reported side effects are rare* but include nausea, rash, fatigue, and restlessness. Photosensitivity, or the skin burning more easily when exposed to ul-tra-violet rays (sunlight), has occurred when taken in high doses. [10,11]

Prescription drugs used to treat depression have the potential to interact negatively with numerous other drugs. This makes it essential for any patient being treated for depression to *inform their doctor of any and every substance they take*. Even St. John's wort can interact with certain medications. Since it is often used without the benefit of physician consultation, it is important to note some of the potential hazards of using the herb in combination with prescription medications. [12]

Initial studies indicate that St. John's wort seems to stimulate enzymes in the liver which inactivate drugs and help to remove them from the body. In some cases this would be desirable. The National Institutes of Health reported that when eight men and women were given a protease inhibitor called indinavir (Crixivan), which combats the HIV virus, along with St. John's wort, the HIV drug was rendered virtually useless. [13]

Other drugs that have diminished effectiveness when used in combination with this particular herb are cyclosporine, used to keep the body from rejecting transplanted organs, digoxin or Lanoxin,® (used to treat heart disease), theophylline, (used to treat asthma), and warfarin (Coumadin®), an anti-clotting drug used to prevent strokes and heart attacks. [14] Additional prescription drugs that may be weakened by St. John's wort include oral contraceptives and medications used to treat seizures, certain cancer chemotherapy drugs, and antidepressant medications. [15]

The result could be devastating, however, when taken with antidepressant drug medicines. The combination may cause what is called serotonin syndrome, which is an over-accumulation of serotonin in the neuronal junctions. Plainly stated, serotonin is not absorbed as it should be, and the neurons become over-saturated. This causes *serious physical and mental symptoms that can come on quite suddenly*, and may involve

CAUTIONS FOR ST. JOHN'S WORT

- May weaken the effect of some drug medications
- Should not be taken with antidepressant drugs
- Sun exposure may cause sunburn or rash
- May be sedating

Figure 5

confusion, agitation, sluggishness, fever, rapid heartbeat, nausea, vomiting, diarrhea, dilated pupils, and even coma.[16]

If you are considering taking St. John's wort for depression, note the cautions listed in **Figure 5**. The usual dosage of St. John's wort is 900 mg two or three times a day.

"Sammy"—Another Herb for Combating Depression

Another natural therapy for depression, which is claimed to bring relief with minimal side effects, was approved for use in the United States in the spring of 1999. Sometimes referred to as "Sammy," SAMe, or S-adenosyl-methionine is a naturally occurring brain chemical that provides a significant boost in mood and outlook. The mechanism by which SAMe actually works is unclear; it is thought to increase the brain's production of neurotransmitters such as serotonin and norepinephrine.[17] Initially used to treat major depression in patients who had not responded to other treatments or who had a history of being antidepressant resistant, SAMe has now been used successfully as a primary treatment of depression.[18]

SAMe has several pluses and minuses. Numerous trials have shown SAMe to be effective in reducing depressive symptoms, but in almost every study it was administered by injection.[19] Results involving oral doses of this mood enhancer have been inconclusive, possibly due to the fact that the chemical stability of oral SAMe has not been good, meaning its shelf-life is rather short. SAMe is generally very well tolerated, with nausea, gas, headache, and anxiety occasionally reported. An additional concern is the fact that SAMe is transformed into homocysteine, which has been associated with heart disease.[20]

SAMe is not advised for those with a history of mania or bipolar disorder as it can trigger mania and agitation in some individuals. Four trials have reported this effect in up to 30 percent of subjects, none of whom even had a history of mania.[21]

SAMe, like all other herbs mentioned in this chapter, is not considered a prescription drug, so is not covered by insurance, neither is it regulated by the FDA (U.S. Food and Drug Administration).

Unfortunately, some of the formulations sold have been found to contain no SAMe at all.[22] Three separate tests conducted by Consumer Reports, Consumerlab.com, and Pharmavite found only four brands that passed all three tests, by containing at least 90 percent of the ingredients listed on the label. Those four were *GNC*,® *Natrol*,® *Nature Made*,® and *TwinLab*.® [23] A summary of facts about SAMe is shown in **Figure 6**.

I have a number of patients who experienced dramatic improvement in their depression with the use of SAMe. Often it will only take 400 mg a day to produce this change for the better. At a cost of about $50.00 a month (for 400 mg a day), it is significantly more expensive than St. John's wort. SAMe can be dosed from 200 mg to 1600 mg a day.

FACTS ABOUT SAMe

- A natural treatment for depression
- Fewer side effects than drug medicines
- Provides a significant boost in mood and outlook
- Not advised for those with a history of mania or bipolar disorder
- Can occasionally trigger mania or agitation

Figure 6

Like the use of prescription medication, I have found that unless the underlying causes of depression are not found and addressed, the patient will experience a sudden relapse of their depression once SAMe is discontinued.

5-HTP Increases Serotonin Levels

Another herb that may have antidepressant properties is 5-HTP. It comes from the African plant Griffonia simplicifolia, and is metabolized into serotonin in the small bowel, thereby increasing serotonin levels in the brain. The benefits of high levels of serotonin in the brain are mentioned in several other chapters. See "serotonin" in the index for more information on this important hormone. Studies with 5-HTP have been positive, though limited because of inconsistent standards of testing.[24] Facts about 5-HTP are listed in **Figure 7**.

On the positive side, tests that have been run suggest that it is as effective as several antidepressant drugs. Side effects are minimal with the most common complaint being mild digestive distress. On the negative side, people with peptic ulcer disease, plate-let disorders, or renal disease should not take it. It also should not be taken with the class of antidepressant medications known as MAO inhibitors, as toxicity can occur since both increase serotonin levels.[25]

Another concern is the fact that some of the 5-HTP products have contained "Peak X," an impurity that is associated with more than 1,500 cases of eosinophilia-myalgia syndrome (severe muscle pain), and 38 deaths in 1991. All things considered, *I do not recommend taking 5-HTP* until further studies show its effectiveness and safety, and the purity of ingredients issue is resolved.[26]

Let us look at some of the other herbs listed in **Figure 2**. They all have been subjected to only a limited amount of research, but *some appear to have therapeutic effects that can be helpful to alleviate certain symptoms of those with mild to moderate depression.*

Chamomile is for depressed mood and loss of appetite. There are no known hazards. The dosage is 4.5 grams daily.[27]

Feverfew can be helpful for migraine. It may interact with aspirin or arthritis medicine. Dosages range from 50 mg to 1.2 grams a day.[28]

Ginkgo Biloba claims to provide improvement of organic brain dysfunction, loss of concentration, and memory.[29] *I have noticed that my depressed patients who are also having difficulty in making routine decisions can improve with this remedy.* Adverse reactions can include mild intestinal complaints such as nausea and rarely allergies, spasms, or cramps. It can interact with anti-clotting drug therapy and should not be used with aspirin. Dosage is 120 mg a day.

Kava-kava is helpful for nervousness, stress, and anxiety.[30] It should not be used by people with a biological reason for depression or anyone who is contemplating suicide, as *it may increase the risk of suicide.*[31] *It should not be used by pregnant or nursing moms.* It can cause allergies, yellow skin, gastrointestinal complaints, various eye disorders, and morning fatigue. It also can in-

FACTS ABOUT 5-HTP

- An extract from a natural plant seed

- Raises serotonin levels

- Balances mood, specifically in bipolar behavior

- Should not be used in ulcer patients

- High doses should be avoided

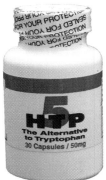

Figure 7

teract with alcohol, barbiturates, and anti-depressants. Dosage ranges from 60 to 100 mg a day. I only recommend Kava-kava if the depression stems wholly from stress and anxiety, and thus *it is rarely used for depression in my practice*. I use it more commonly for those who have *stress and anxiety without depression.*

Lavender is suggested for loss of appetite, nervousness, and insomnia. Dosage is 3 to 5 grams a day.[32] Some of my women patients have reported that the aroma of lavender significantly improves their mood.

Lemon Balm is recommended for nervousness, insomnia, and gastric complaints. The dosage is 8 to 10 grams per day.[33]

Valerian can help nervousness, insomnia, stress, and anxiety. There are rare cases of intestinal or allergy complaints. Long-term use may cause headache, restlessness, and sleeplessness. The recommended dose is 15 grams a day.[34]

If you are considering any herb or medication as a means of alleviating mild to moderate depressive symptoms, please consider that *lifestyle measures should always be your first line of action*. You can encourage your body to fight depression naturally by producing its own mood-enhancers through *proper diet, exercise, moderate sunlight, effective stress management, and other lifestyle measures outlined in Chapters 4 and 5 that have virtually no risk.* Bonus side effects include *improved physical health.* This critical concept is spelled out in **Figure 8**.

So far in this chapter we have looked at herbs, the claims made for them, their effectiveness, their safety, and increased popularity with the public. Now we will examine the different types of prescription drugs that are in use, how they work, their positive effects, and their negative effects.

Drug Medications for Depression

Suffering from depression can be a dark and frightening disorder that can progress into a potentially life-threatening illness. I would emphasize that vigorous treatment should not be delayed for anyone who has moderate to severe depression. Traditional vigorous treatment includes antidepressant drugs and specific short-term psychological counseling.[35,36,37] For people who fail to respond to such treatment, some practitioners will suggest the use of a radical treatment like electroconvulsive therapy (ECT).[38,39] In the conclusion of this chapter, you will see that I recommend a different approach.

Antidepressant drugs come in many different chemical compounds. Most, when properly prescribed, are effective in the treatment of depression. They can also be useful in treating cases of panic disorder, other anxiety disorders, eating disorders, and attention deficit disorder. Some have been successful in the treatment of several types of physical pain.[40,41,42] Even smokers can rejoice if they want to quit. Some newer antidepressant medications have improved the success of smoking cessation efforts.[43]

This amazing spectrum of effectiveness that antidepressant medications provide in all these dissimilar disorders is not because

FUNDAMENTAL PRINCIPLE FOR ATTACKING MILD TO MODERATE DEPRESSION

- In attacking depression, lifestyle measures should be your first line of action.

- Herbs or drug medications should be a secondary line of action.

- A combination of the two may be required.

Figure 8

of physical or mental relationships between the disorders. More accurately, it reflects the many different roles these chemicals play in the human nervous system.

While studies show that certain drugs are effective in fighting depression, patients often make the high-risk mistake of discontinuing them if they do not experience immediate improvement or are experiencing unpleasant side effects.

How Do Antidepressants Work?

Before we answer this question, it will be helpful to briefly review certain activities within the brain. I presented an overview of the brain mechanism in *Chapter 1*. Within the brain, chemicals called *neurotransmitters* send electrical messages from the axons across synapses. It has been discovered that *a deficiency of two neurotransmitter chemicals, serotonin and norepinephrine*, are associated with depression. A *shortage of two additional neurotransmitters, dopamine and epinephrine*, have also been linked to depression. This shortage may occur for several reasons, such as a shortage of their production, or their improper release, or accelerated destruction, accelerated absorption, or impaired receptors (too few receptors, or receptors that are blocked) on the receiving neurons. With a shortage of the neurotransmitters, *the mechanism for transmitting electrical signals is impaired, leading to depressed brain function.*

Antidepressants Correct the Shortage of Neurotransmitters

Antidepressants are aimed at correcting the shortage of neurotransmitters *by increasing the body's supply of one or more of these important brain chemicals.* As you will see by the following information, each type of medication corrects deficiencies in a different way.

Three Main Classes of Antidepressant Drugs

There are three main classes of commonly prescribed synthetic antidepressants. They are listed in **Figure 9** and **Table 1.**

These classifications are based on chemical structures as well as the type of effect the chemicals have on the brain. Each of the three classes deserves a closer examination, which will include an unbiased look at some brand names of these antidepressants.

Tricyclic Antidepressants

Tricyclic antidepressants increase the accullulation of norepinephrine in the brain. Brand names you may have heard of include Tofranil®, Desipramine®, Doxepin®, and Elavil®. Commonly used generic names are imipramine and amitriptyline. There are a

THREE CLASSES OF ANTIDEPRESSANT MEDICINES

Tricyclic Antidepressants—they increase the accumulation of norepinephrine, and in some cases serotonin.

Monoamine Oxidase Inhibitors (MAOIs)—they increase the concentration of serotonin and epinephrine in the central nervous system.

Selective Serotonin Reuptake Inhibitors (SSRIs)—they allow serotonin to selectively accumulate in the space between the neurons of the brain (synapse), where it can be used rather than be reabsorbed.

Figure 9

number of side effects of these drugs. They are listed in **Figure 10**.

The dry mouth and sleepiness occur in most individuals when they begin taking the drugs. This is one reason that I tend to prescribe these drugs to be taken in the evening before bedtime. More grimly, taking tricyclics may be a risk factor for developing an incurable lung disease called idiopathic pulmonary fibrosis. Studies show that the risk of contracting the disease is increased by a factor of two to five times, depending on which tricyclic is being used.[44] Imipramine is associated with the highest risk (five times) of this disease that causes breathlessness and a dry cough. Those who choose to mix marijuana smoking with their tricyclic medicine can look forward to delirium, a racing heartbeat, and loss of the ability to reason.[45]

From the 1960s through the 1980s, tricyclic antidepressants represented the first-line pharmacologic treatment for major depression in the U.S.[46,47] Although they have been mostly replaced by SSRIs, a recent two-decade study showed them to be equally effective during a short period of time, but with more side-effects than SSRIs.[48] *Tricyclics are generally used as a second or third-line effort if the newer antidepressants do not work.* The reason for this is not only their generally worse side-effect profile, but also the fact that they can be lethal if taken in an overdose. For patients that may be suicidal, the medicine should not be dispensed in large quantities because of this possibility.[49]

There is evidence that for the most severely ill (e.g., hospitalized) patients with depression, tricyclic antidepressants may be more effective than SSRIs.[50,51,52,53] Interestingly, tricyclics have been found effective in smoking cessation (in the case of Nortriptyline)[54] and for treatment of pain syndromes[55] such as peripheral neuropathy in diabetics. The other two main classes of antidepressants have not been effective in these conditions.[56]

Patients may favorably respond to tricyclics within the first week, but chronic depression may take more than six weeks to see a significant response.[57] Patients who have not had a history of depression may be able to taper off and completely discontinue the medication after four to nine months of full remission.[58] This particular class of drugs is ordinarily more difficult to wean due to the possibility of more withdrawal symptoms.

Monoamine Oxidase Inhibitors

Monoamine oxidase inhibitors (MAOIs) include brands like Parnate,® Nardil,® and Marplan.® They are designed to improve one's sense of well-being *by increasing the concentration of serotonin and epinephrine in the central nervous system.*[59] A list of the side effects of MAOIs is seen in **Figure 11**.

The MAOIs have been largely replaced by SSRIs, although *many patients with major depression who do not respond to tricyclic antidepressants improve with MAOIs.*[60,61] Depressed patients with unusual symptoms such as sleeping too much, over-eating for

SIDE EFFECTS OF TRICYCLIC ANTIDEPRESSANTS

- Weight gain
- Blurred vision
- Constipation
- Fast or irregular heartbeat
- Bladder weakness

- Tremors
- Dizziness
- Sleepiness
- Dry mouth

Figure 10

long periods of time, rejection sensitivity, and panic attacks, may get the best results with MAOIs.[62,63,64] MAOIs are also effective for the treatment of panic disorder and bipolar depression. Another MAOI (selegiline) has been shown to be effective in the treatment of early Parkinson's disease at doses lower than those that may be effective for depression.

Those taking MAOIs need to be warned. Two forms of monoamine oxidase—types A and B—are present in the brain. Type A is also found in the gut and liver, where it acts to metabolize organic forms of ammonia, like tyramine, that are present in foods like cheese, yogurt, aged and smoked meats, beer, wine, avocado, and sauerkraut.

The three MAOIs mentioned previously inhibit MAO-A and MAO-B nonselectively. Hence, a diet free of foods containing tyramine is essential, since the MAOs will prevent the tyramine from being processed, which can result in *life-threatening hypertension, rapid heartbeat, and at worst, seizures, stroke, coma, or death.*[65] The MAOI selegiline is an exception in that when given at low dosages to treat Parkinson's disease, it selectively inhibits only MAO-B, thereby not requiring patients to follow a tyramine-free diet.

One final warning—mixing an MAOI medication with an SSRI can cause serotonin toxicity, which can precipitate hyperactivity of the central nervous system, delirium, seizures, and even death.[66]

Selective Serotonin Re-uptake Inhibitors (SSRIs)

Selective serotonin re-uptake inhibitors (SSRIs) are the newest main class of antidepressants. They achieve a desired effect by selectively allowing serotonin to accumulate in the space between the neurons of the brain (the synapse) where it can be used, rather than reabsorbed. It has recently been learned that SSRIs affect a newly discovered pathway in the brain where chemicals called neurosteriods play a role in controlling anxiety and depression.[67] This class includes the popular drug Prozac® (fluoxetine), which had sales of about $1.5 billion in 1999, while those of a similar drug, Zoloft® (sertraline), approached $1 billion.[68] Also quickly gaining wide use are Paxil® (paroxetine) and Celexa® (citalopram) the newest of the SSRIs. A new development is a once-per-week dosage of Prozac® that has been approved by the U.S. Food and Drug Administration.[69] It is recommended for patients whose depression symptoms have stabilized, but require continuing treatment to prevent a relapse. Some facts about SSRI medicines are listed in **Figure 12**.

SSRIs tend to be the current "antidepressants of choice" because of their *limited side effects*, though they may cause, insomnia, agitation, headache, nausea, and diarrhea.[70] They also are far *less dangerous when taken as an overdose than the tricyclic antidepressants.* As an added bonus, unlike most tri-

SIDE EFFECTS OF MAOIs

• Tremors

• Edema

• Dizziness

• Constipation

• Sleepiness

• Dry mouth

• Blurred vision

• Weight gain

• Sexual dysfunction

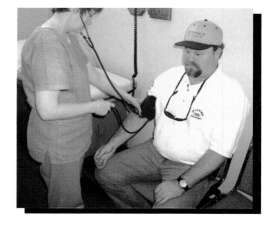

• Increased blood pressure

• Fast or irregular heartbeat

Figure 11

cyclic antidepressants, the SSRIs are not as likely to cause weight gain.[71] SSRIs are also effective in treating obsessive-compulsive disorder, some types of anxiety, and panic disorder.

Conversely, a British study showed that those on SSRIs are more likely to attempt suicide than those on tricyclics, though if they choose to overdose, SSRIs are less toxic.[72] The majority will try a means other than overdose, since only 17 percent of studied suicide attempts try an overdose of their antidepressant.[73]

However, there are serious side effects and interactions to be aware of, making it imperative that you keep your doctor informed of every medication you take. It is important not to combine SSRIs with any other type of serotonin agent like MAOIs, as serotonin toxicity can occur.[74] Combining most SSRIs with other types of drugs can enhance their levels and effects to a dangerous point.[75] As is the case with virtually all antidepressants, SSRIs may precipitate mania in people with a susceptibility for bipolar disorder.

A recent study warns of a *three-fold increased risk of upper GI bleeding* when taking an SSRI. When used in addition to anti-inflammatory medications, which are often used as painkillers, the risk increases even more.[76] Even more seriously, the UK Medicines Control Agency has called for a *suicide warning* to be added to informational materials given to patients taking the medicine. Studies reported that especially during the early stages of treatment, thoughts of suicide and suicidal behavior increase.[77] This is not due to a worsening of the depression, but rather due to an *increase in impulsiveness*—another side effect of SSRIs. Another worrisome mental side effect that can occur when taking an SSRI is an "I don't care" attitude. This effect can be common even when a person *should genuinely care*. I have patients taking SSRIs who stated that they could not cry at a loved one's funeral since they did not feel a sense of deep sadness over the loss. Yet another mental side effect, vivid strange dreams, can occur in those taking SSRIs.

Two other common adverse actions of this class of antidepressants have been the focus of considerable clinical and research interest—sexual dysfunction and withdrawal syndromes. Although depression itself can lower libido (sexual drive) and impair sexual performance, it has been clearly established that SSRIs can cause sexual dysfunction in both men and women independent of their therapeutic activity.[78,79,80,81] The most common problems, which can affect more than half of adults taking SSRIs, are delayed or reversed ejaculation in men and absent or delayed orgasm in women.

Although I prescribe all of the SSRIs, I generally favor Celexa,® since I have found less side effects with it's use, it does not interact with most prescription drugs, and it is at least equally effective as the other SSRIs. I tend to use Paxil® when the patient also has significant anxiety associated with depression.

Wellbutrin (bupropion) for Major Depression

Wellbutrin® (bupropion) is structurally related to amphetamine and has been

FACTS ABOUT SSRIs

- Newest of antidepressants
- Fewer side effects than MAOIs or tricyclic antidepressants
- Less dangerous if overdose
- Weight gain not as prevalent
- Should not be taken with MAOIs

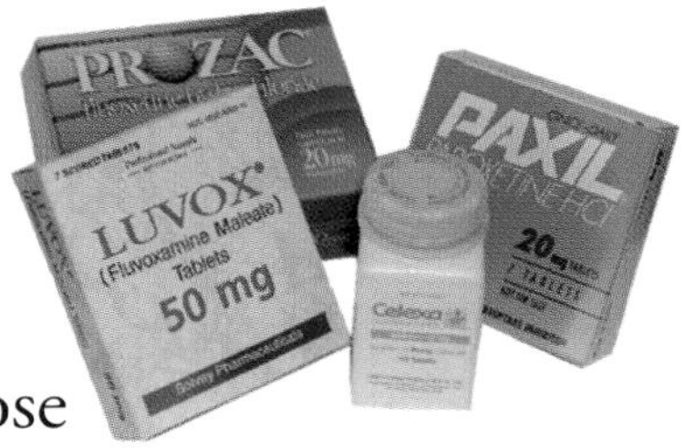

Figure 12

shown to be effective for the treatment of major depression. It blocks the reuptake of dopamine and norepinephrine and is considered appropriate in the event that an SSRI is ineffective or cannot be tolerated.[82] Unlike some antidepressants, it does not cause sedation and may increase the ability to stay alert. It can also help the success rate in people who have chosen to quit smoking.[83] The Zyban® form of bupropion is specifically marketed to smokers because of this effect. Bupropion is also effective in *treating adults and children with attention deficit hyperactivity disorder (ADHD)*.[84]

Bupropion should not be used for patients with anorexia nervosa or bulimia, or for those with an increased risk for seizure. Other than its incompatibility with an MAOI, it does not have significant drug interactions. Another advantage is that it is not associated with sexual dysfunction, a notable distinction from the adverse-effect profile of the SSRIs and tricyclics. I have had some patients state that it actually increased their libido and sexual function. Also, unlike the tricyclics and SSRIs, bupropion is more commonly associated with weight loss than weight gain.[85]

Side effects are common in high doses and include agitation, restlessness, insomnia, and anxiety. Another possible side effect is that the patient's blood pressure may drop upon standing up, which can be associated with standing lightheadedness or dizziness. I have found that these side effects become less common when *I prescribe a low dose at first*, 100 mg twice a day, and increase the dose on the fourth day to 100 mg three times a day. After two to four weeks I may increase the dose to 150 mg three times a day if needed.

Other Antidepressants

Another drug in a new class of antidepressants is reboxetine. It is a selective noradrenaline reuptake inhibitor (SNRI). In two studies released by the American Psy-chiatric Association, patients had a greater reduction in symptoms than those on SSRIs, but had more side effects, resulting in more of them quitting the medication.[86,87] Another SNRI, venlafaxine® (Effexor), appears to be equally effective as the tricylcic antidepressants, but with less side effects. I have found venlafaxine to generally have more side effects than SSRIs.

Trazodone (Desyrel) not only inhibits serotonin reuptake, but through a by-product produced by the liver in metabolizing trazodone it also simulates the action of serotonin itself. It causes significant sedation, however, and is generally taken at bedtime. It can also cause nausea and a drop in blood pressure when standing. In one out of every 6000 men, it can cause an abnormally long and painful erection that can even threaten the blood supply to the penis.[88]

Efforts to improve the side effect profile of trazodone led to the development of nefazodone (Serzone®).[89] Nefazodone also inhibits serotonin reuptake, but in addition blocks a cousin to a serotonin receptor in the brain (called the 5-hydroxytryptamine-2 receptor). It causes less sedation than trazodone and has less risk of painful erections in men.

A relatively new antidepressant, mirtazapine (Remeron®), enhances both norepinephrine and serotonin neurotransmission. How it accomplishes this is quite unique. It blocks a distinctive receptor (called the presynaptic ∝2-adrenergic autoreceptor) which increases the release of norepinephrine. This increase in norepinephrine release stimulates serotonin to also be released. Since this mechanism is unique, the side effect profile of mirtazapine is also unique. The most frequently reported side effect of mirtazapine is sleepiness, experienced by more than 50 percent of patients.[90,91] The other major adverse effect of mirtazapine is increased appetite and considerable weight gain. Fortunately, side effects characteristic of the SSRIs, including nausea, diarrhea, and sexual dysfunction are infrequent with the use of mirtazapine. I will use mirtazapine (Remeron®) for those who suffer from insomnia and anorexia, and will dose it at bedtime once daily.

I have compiled **Table 1** (pages 112,113) for a comparison of the costs, dosages, side effects and my personal clinical experiences using the many antidepressants available today.

Treatment-Resistant Depression

With all of the choices for medicinal treatment, 30 percent of patients with major depression in standard medical or psychiatric practices do not improve at all with the initial medication.[92] What do we do when the treatment does not work? The usual treatment regimen is four to six weeks, and if there is no improvement, another drug may be tried and a thorough re-evaluation of the potential causes of depression should be identified. Unfortunately at this point, most practitioners just try another drug, or perhaps refer the patient for counseling if this has not already been done. They are often *completely unaware of the wonderful nutritional and lifestyle therapies available for depression* and thus do not utilize them.

In my practice, less than 15 percent of my depressed patients do not respond to the initial treatment regimen. The regimen includes changes in their eating and lifestyle habits, as well as a medication for those with at least moderate depression. Many of those who did not respond did not change their lifestyle and only took the medication. For the very few who did follow the treatment regimen but did not improve, I search for a cause of depression that we may have overlooked during the initial evaluation. I might search for uncommon causes such as Vitamin B12 deficiency, an unusual infectious cause, or mercury poisoning.

If no other causes are identified and the nutrition and lifestyle therapies appear to be appropriate for the patient, I will often try a different drug class. Another option would be to maximize the dose of the current antidepressant or use another drug in the same class since it is not uncommon for another drug within the same classification to work.[93] *It is a sad fact that there is actually no research that shows a logical way to choose the type of medication that will work best.*[94]

In situations where a drug has been partially but not completely effective during the initial trial time, it may be appropriate to supplement the treatment with another drug, such as lithium or bupropion. This can be better than trying a different antidepressant drug since improvement may be more rapid than tapering off one drug and starting another. Lithium has proven effective in carefully performed scientific studies and clinical practice.[95] Normal dosages range from 600 to 800 mg a day. The chances of remaining depressed after starting lithium are reduced by 56 to 96 percent.[96]

The adverse effects of lithium with antidepressants are benign, but tend to be seen more in the elderly.[97] Despite its effectiveness, lithium augmentation has become less popular over time, probably since blood levels must be regularly monitored for lithium concentrations to prevent serious toxic effects.

Bupropion (Wellbutrin), which we examined earlier, is another alternative supplement to SSRI medications. As well as enhancing the effect of the SSRI, it can reduce the side effects of sexual dysfunction and apathy that an SSRI may produce. When used in conjunction with an SSRI, blood levels of bupropion should be monitored to prevent toxicity in the patient.

Shock Treatments as a Last Resort

Finally, the standard last resort treatment for patients who face serious incapacitation is often shock treatments. Unfortunately, they are associated with a degree of permanent memory loss of the patient. Some professionals feel that it is now safe enough to be used as an early treatment instead of a

Table 1: Comparison of Antidepressant Medications

Color Code: | TCA Antidepressants | Noval Antidepressants | SSRI Antidepressants | MAOI Antidepressants |

Names (generic)	Daily Dose	Average Monthly Wholesale Price (lowest dose)
Anafranil (clomipramine)	100 to 250 mg	$63.87*
Celexa (citalopram)	20 to 80 mg	$65.93
Desvrel (trazodine)	50 to 600 mg	$60.73
Effexor (venlafaxine)	75 to 375 mg	$41.09
Elavil (amitriptyline)	100 to 300 mg	$13.43*
Luvox (fluvoxamine)	100 to 300 mg	$69.06
Marplan (isocarboxazid)	20 to 60 mg	$22.30
Nardil (phenelzine)	45 to 90 mg	$15.77
Norpramin (deispramine)	100 to 300 mg	$30.10*
Pamelor (nortriptyline)	50 to 200 mg	$46.37*
Parnate (tranylcypromide)	20 to 50 mg	$18.21
Paxil (paroxetine)	20 to 80 mg	$74.49
Prozac (fluoxetine)	10 to 80 mg	$80.40
Remeron (mirtazapine)	15 to 45 mg	$79.56
Serzone (nefazodine)	50 to 660 mg	$38.73
Sinequan (doxepin)	100 to 300 mg	$13.50*
Surmontil (trimipramine)	100 to 300 mg	$61.06
Tofranil (imipramine)	100 to 300 mg	$12.33*
Vivactil (protriptyline)	20 to 60 mg	$38.46*
Wellbutrin SR (bupropion)	150 to 400 mg	$48.12
Zoloft (sertraline)	50 to 200 mg	$70.25

* Generic price

Notable Side Effects	Comments
See TCA side effects at bottom	See TCA comments at bottom
Slightly less sexual dysfunction than other SSRIs. Less nausea, diarrhea, and abdominal pain than most SSRIs.	The "cleanest" SSRI with no serious drug interactions. A common first choice in my practice
High risk of sedation (++++) and nausea. May lower blood pressure significantly when standing.	Rarely causes a prolonged, painful, and dangerous penile erection in men. Some drug interactions can help some anxiety disorders. I tend to use Serzone instead of Desyrel.
Mild sedation common (+). High risk of sexual dysfunction. Nausea, constipation, anorexia, dry mouth, dizziness, sweating.	May cause weight loss. Rarely increases blood pressure by 5 to 15mm. No serious drug interactions.
See TCA side effects at bottom	See TCA comments at bottom
Sedation (++) High risk of sexual dysfunction and gastrointestinal distress.	Useful in obsessive compulsive disorder. Interacts with more drugs than other SSRIs.
Hypotension, impotence, agitation, insomnia	I do not prescribe this medicine unless the patient is under the care of a psychiatrist. Many serious drug and food interactions possible.
Sedation, hypotension, impotence	I do not prescribe this medicine unless the patient is under the care of a psychiatrist. Many serious drug and food interactions possible.
See TCA side effects at bottom	See TCA comments at bottom
See TCA side effects at bottom	See TCA comments at bottom
Hypotension, impotence, agitation, insomnia	I do not prescribe this medicine unless the patient is under the care of a psychiatrist. Many serious drug and food interactions possible.
Sedation (++) High risk of sexual dysfunction, nightmares, nausea, vomiting, headaches.	Effective in many anxiety disorders. Does not last long in bloodstream after stopping. Highest risk of withdrawal symptoms of any SSRI (60%). Few drug interactions.
High risk of sexual dysfunction and gastrointestinal distress.	Effects may last for weeks after stopping; can usually discontinue abruptly without withdrawal symptoms. Interacts with many other drugs. Does not cause sedation.
Quite sedating (++++). Considerable weight gain.	Useful in insomnia and anorexia. Useful in depressed terminal cancer patients. Rare if any sexual dysfunction. Rare gastrointestinal side effects. No serious drug interactions.
Sedation very common (+++). Possible lowering of blood pressure upon standing. Dry mouth, nausea, and dizziness.	Does not cause sexual dysfunction, very effective in chronic depression when combined with lifestyle changes. Start at low dose and increase. Some drug interactions.
See TCA side effects at bottom	See TCA comments at bottom
See TCA side effects at bottom	See TCA comments at bottom
See TCA side effects at bottom	See TCA comments at bottom
See TCA side effects at bottom	See TCA comments at bottom
Headache, dry mouth, nausea, can cause insomnia, shakiness, dizziness, and rare sore throat. Occasional weight loss. Rare spontaneous orgasm.	Start at low dose and increase. Does not cause sedation, no sexual dysfunction, may be energizing, unlike most antidepressant drugs does not cause weight gain, can help in tobacco cessation, can help in adult attention deficit hyperactivity disorder.
May be only mildly sedating (+). High risk of sexual dysfunction, insomnia, nausea, diarrhea, abdominal cramps.	High risk of withdrawal symptoms (60%). Rare drug interactions.

TCA side effects: sedation, weight gain, dry mouth, agitation, restlessness, fast heart rate.

++++ Very sedating
+++ Sedating
++ Somewhat sedating
+ Mildly sedating

TCA comments: High risk of side effects. Should use with caution or not at all in cardiac, glaucoma, thyroid, manic, or schizophrenia patients. Should use with caution or not at all in patients with urinary difficulty.

last ditch effort. I have only utilized it as a last resort measure, having only referred one case in the last 15 years. *Since I started using the specific nutrition and lifestyle therapies presented in Chapters 4, 5, and 9, I have not had to refer any cases for shock treatments.* The therapy is examined in more detail in *Chapter 9.*

The next part of this chapter deals with certain specific groups of patients who require selected treatments tailored to each group.

Treatment of Depression Occurring with Another Illness

When I diagnose a patient with depression, I must carefully evaluate whether the treatment may be complicated by the presence of another mental or physical disorder. Treatment of the primary condition is always the most important focus, but whenever there is a full depressive condition, treatment to help alleviate the depressed symptoms must be considered.

It is important to accurately assess the type and timing of multiple treatments, with care taken to avoid interactions among them. Treating multiple mental disorders can result in increased use of mental health services.[98,99] However, patients with multiple mental illnesses who stick with their antidepressant medications usually end up with lowered healthcare costs, termed a "medical-offset effect."[100,101]

In some cases, the primary consideration in treating depression and another disease simultaneously is the reaction of the body to the drugs. For example, patients with kidney or liver disease often have an accompanying depression. Close attention must be given to the ability of the diseased organ to handle the antidepressant or mood-stabilizing drugs. Diseased livers and kidneys may be unable to process certain antidepressants, causing accumulations of the drugs, or elimination from the body without metabolization.[102,103,104] Treatment of underlying medical conditions with antibiotics[105] or steroids[106] may trigger prominent mental disturbances, and complicate their treatment because of interactions of the antidepressant with the other medications.

Treatment During Pregnancy and the Postpartum Period

Any time a woman is pregnant she should take extra care in deciding what she will take into her digestive system. This is doubly true when using medications, whether they are herbal or prescription. She and her physician should seek to avoid all unnecessary medication during pregnancy. In the case of depression, a pregnant woman should first try counseling, nutrition, and lifestyle therapy. Only if that fails, medications should be used, but with great caution.

Often women with a history of major depression stop their medications when they become pregnant only to have the depression return. Half will restart their medications during pregnancy because of the returning symptoms.[107]

It is not ethically possible to do randomized medication studies on pregnant women and their fetuses. Most of the data gathered on the subject is from experience. These occurrences suggest that many antidepressant medications are relatively safe for pregnant women and the developing fetus. The potential benefits and risks of all available treatment options during and after pregnancy must be reviewed for each woman on an individual basis.[108,109,110]

If it is clear that an expecting mother must take medication for her symptoms, SSRIs appear to be safe for the fetus,[111] and the tricyclics nortriptyline and desipramine cause fewer adverse effects than the other tricyclics. However, blood plasma levels need to be monitored each trimester. MAOIs should be totally avoided. Most importantly, *the lowest possible effective dosage of whatever medication is taken should be used.*[112]

A summary of cautions that should be taken by pregnant women who are taking medicine for depression appears in **Figure 13.**

Depression can also be an issue for the mother after the birth of the baby. Although "the blues" are common after childbirth, true postpartum depression is a serious mental disorder that requires active intervention.[113] In one controlled trial, cognitive behavior therapy was found to be equally effective as limited medication in treating postpartum depression.[114]

Treatment of Depression in the Elderly

With the mean age of the U.S. population steadily increasing, geriatric depression is also increasing, which requires unique attention and treatment. As we grow older, many new and different stresses come into our lives. Losses of loved ones and disruption of familiar situations increase, thereby escalating the chances of depressive symptoms.

Depression need not be feared or a cause for embarrassment. Modern treatment of geriatric depression is safe and effective. With available medicines and cognitive behavioral therapy, at least 70 to 80 percent of older patients with uncomplicated recurrent depression respond to continued treatment.[115,116] Let us review the methods of treatment for older victims of depression.

The overall response rates to SSRIs in geriatric patients appear to be lower than those treated with tricyclic antidepressants. However, the milder side effects of SSRIs often provide an enhanced quality of life during treatment.[117,118] The unique stresses and losses of an older person are often seen as the cause of minor depressive symptoms, but when full-scale depression ensues, treatment is required and is often successful. In one study, the combination of nortriptyline and behavioral therapy produced a 69 percent remission rate in older adults with bereavement-related major depression.[119]

In the senior age group there is considerable frequency, disability, and even risk of death associated with episodes of depression. As with younger patients, seniors should be maintained on treatment for at least four to nine months. Standard long-term drug treatments relieve symptoms as well in the elderly as they do in middle-aged adults.[120,121,122]

Complicated cases of geriatric depression are much harder to treat. Depression caused by a reduced blood supply to certain areas of the brain resists treatment with antidepressants alone, and may require more aggressive treatment. Once again, shock treatments are considered a potentially lifesaving intervention for the geriatric population, with results that decrease the incidence of death in those with severe major depression.[123]

Antidepressant use in elderly nursing home residents has been associated with increases in falls and hip fractures in several case studies.[124,125,126] Surprisingly, SSRIs

CAUTIONS FOR PREGNANT WOMEN

- Avoid all unnecessary medications.

- Counseling, nutrition, and lifestyle therapy are helpful.

- Use the lowest possible dosage of any medication used.

- MAOIs should be totally avoided.

- SSRIs appear to be safe for the fetus.

Figure 13

that tend to have fewer side effects were not consistently better than tricyclic antidepressants in preventing these complications.[127] The impact of the newer antidepressants on these high-risk adverse effects is as yet unknown.

Depression in Children

The 1990s witnessed an increased use of antidepressant medications, singly and in combination, in routine clinical practice dealing with children and adolescents.[128,129] During the same time period, SSRIs replaced the tricyclics as drugs of choice for the treatment of major depression in young as well as adult patients. More than a million prescriptions for these compounds were written annually for young patients, ranking second only to stimulants among brain-affecting drugs prescribed.[130]

Data from controlled trials support the effectiveness of other SSRIs, including fluoxetine, sertraline, and paroxetine in depressed children and adolescents.[131,132,133,134] One study showed that 40 percent of the children and adolescents who improved with SSRIs had experienced a major recurrence of their depression in just one year.[135] This again underscores the importance of finding the real causes of the depression in children and focusing on nutrition and lifestyle changes that can improve their condition long term.

Antidepressant Withdrawal

Once the causes of depression have been found, the appropriate nutrition, social, and lifestyle changes should be implemented. Placing the depressed individual on medication "buys time" for these changes to be fully incorporated into the lifestyle. The changes are made step by step as I describe in detail in *Chapter 10*. Once all of the recommendations are put into practice, I usually have the patient wait another four weeks before withdrawing from the medication.

This not only provides greater assurance that the new lifestyle is enduring, but also gives time for those changes to positively affect the brain.

By the time the withdrawal process begins, the patient has usually been taking the medicine for four to six months. For individuals who have had difficulty implementing the lifestyle, up to a year has transpired. Fortunately, withdrawing from most antidepressants is much safer and less difficult than withdrawing from anti-anxiety medicines. The cravings associated from withdrawing from narcotics, amphetamines, alcohol, or nicotine are not present when stopping SSRIs and tricyclics.

Withdrawal symptoms are more likely with higher doses and greater lengths of treatment. Unfortunately, some patients make a decision to abruptly stop their medication without consulting their physician. This usually happens when unwanted side effects are no longer acceptable to the individual. It can also happen when serious side effects occur, another illness develops such as a heart attack or heart rhythm disturbance, the individual becomes pregnant, or another medication is prescribed that interacts with the existing medication. If the medication has not been effective after a month of use, the patient is often tempted to stop the drug "cold turkey."

There are now many reports of withdrawal symptoms (often referred to in the medical literature as "discontinuation reactions" with tricyclics, SSRIs, and other antidepressants such as Effexor®(venlafaxine). Withdrawal symptoms will occur in 30 to 50 percent of patients suddenly stopping high doses of tricylcic antidepressants.[136,137] Some SSRIs are more likely to produce withdrawal symptoms than others. A well-designed study involving 242 patients was interrupted for five to eight days by placebo substitution, to mimic abruptly stopping an SSRI.[138] The patient and the physician were "blinded", meaning they did not know if or when the placebo would be introduced.

Withdrawal symptoms occurred within 24 to 72 hours and were most likely with Paxil® (66 percent), followed by Zoloft® (60 percent). Only 14 percent of those taking Prozac experienced withdrawal symptoms. Since Prozac® and its active by-products produced by the liver last for weeks, eight-day drug stoppage may not produce withdrawal symptoms. However, a month after discontinuation of Prozac®, the likelihood of withdrawal symptoms occurring may be higher.[139]

The happiest reason for discontinuing antidepressant medication is due to the depression being cured through nutrition and lifestyle and thus it is no longer necessary. In such cases, I rarely abruptly discontinue the antidepressant medication. I first gradually decrease the dosage to the lowest dose that can still be effective, a process that typically takes about 2 weeks. I then recommend that the patient skip a dose every other day, and finally have the patient take the lowest dose of medicine just twice a week before discontinuing the medicine altogether. The entire process from the time weaning begins until the medicine is stopped usually takes about 5 weeks, although there is a lot of variation from patient to patient. The higher the dose the patient is taking, the longer the weaning process; the greater the intensity or number of very troublesome withdrawal symptoms, the slower the process. If the patient has truly incorporated the recommended lifestyle and follows the recommended weaning process, withdrawal symptoms are infrequent. In fact, I have found that most of these patients actually feel better after the medicine is finally stopped, since they are no longer experiencing the mental and physical side effects. If withdrawal symptoms do occur, they usually begin within 48 hours of decreasing or stopping the medicine. Once the medicine is stopped, the withdrawal symptoms will typically disappear within two weeks, although some have reported withdrawal symptoms for up to a month.[140]

Figure 14 lists the possible withdrawal effects of SSRIs.[141,142,143] The more severe effects usually occur when a patient taking a high dose abruptly stops the medicine on his own.

Figure 15 lists the possible withdrawal symptoms of tricyclic antidepressants.[144,145]

Withdrawal from MAOIs is not as easily accomplished as withdrawing from SSRIs and tricyclic antidepressants. In fact, MAOI withdrawal can be such a trying process that it has been likened to withdrawal from opiates and amphetamines. It can be

SSRI Withdrawal Symptoms

abdominal pain	heart palpitations	anxiety
diarrhea	disorientation	apathy
dry mouth	dizziness	aggression
increased appetite	nervousness	impulsiveness
nausea, vomiting	impaired vision	loss of balance
shakiness	chest pain	buzzing in head
confusion	chills	tinnitus
hallucinations	headache	vivid dreams
panic	fatigue	insomnia
return of depression	tingling or shock sensation in the limbs	

Figure 14

117

achieved, but not without some withdrawal symptoms occurring, and sometimes those symptoms can be severe. This is one important reason why I rarely prescribe MAOIs. The most common MAOI withdrawal symptoms are listed in **Figure 16**. [146]

Withdrawal symptoms (occasionally severe) have also been reported after stopping Effexor® (venlafaxine). These symptoms included headache, dizziness, nausea, diarrhea, and shock-like sensations.[147,148] Some antidepressants, such as Wellbutrin® (bupropion), do not seem to be associated with adverse symptoms when the drug is abruptly stopped.

The goal is to use medication as a temporary measure until more permanent lifestyle correcting measures are employed to cure the disease.

Limitations of Medications

A study surveying 1,001 patients taking antidepressants showed that 25 percent of them felt that the medication had not affected their lives in a positive way. About 47 percent reported side effects, and 55 percent of those who had side effects stopped taking the medicine, while another 17 percent skipped doses.

Another survey of nearly 1,400 different patients on long-term antidepressant drug therapy showed that *almost two-thirds were not very satisfied with their treatment*. This does not mean they did not improve with medicine, but that they did not improve as much as they had desired. Between 70 and 80 percent who were taking antidepressants said *depression continued to impair their social life and their work performance, as well as affect family life*.[149]

Sadly, medication is not a cure-all for depression. Yes, about 70 percent of patients will experience some improvement in their mood and other symptoms, with a minority experiencing an apparent "cure" of their condition while taking the medicine. Unfortunately, unless the causes are addressed and the lifestyle changed for the better, either depression will not be treated in a completely satisfactory manner or a relapse into depression will likely occur.

Tricyclic Withdrawal Symptoms

abdominal pain	headache	various sleep disorders
diarrhea	sweating	anxiety
anorexia	heart palpitations	depression
vomiting	dizziness	panic
chills	tremors	fatigue
	impaired mental facilities	

Figure 15

MAOI Withdrawal Symptoms

headache	anxiety	shivering
psychosis	muscle weakness	delirium
hallucinations	tingling or burning of the skin	

Figure 16

Conclusion

In this chapter I have presented much information on medications that needs to be put into perspective. It is important to remember that no matter how effective these drug medications may be, there are many side effects associated with their use—some which can be very serious to your health. If you have ever received the information sheet that comes with a medication, you see that often the side effect list can nearly fill a whole page of fine print.

It is easy to fall into the trap of thinking that taking a pill is the easy way out. While a medication may take away symptoms of a disease—in this case, depression—it does not cure the problem, and often creates a whole new array of side effects. It is important to discover the root of the problem and treat it in a way that can bring lasting relief.

However, medications do have their place if they are not used as an ultimate solution. They should be reserved for moderate to severe depression, and a definite goal should be a discontinuation within six months, and no more than a year in most cases.

When you study the relapse rates of patients who use antidepressant medications, it is not an encouraging picture. Those who discontinued usage after three months had a 77 percent relapse rate within the next two years.[150] Another study found 40 percent relapsed within a year. Even those who continue medication have a relapse rate of 20 to 40 percent.[151]

A review of the main points in this chapter is spelled out in **Figure 17**.

No matter how bleak these facts may sound, I want to leave you with the good news! If you and your doctor take an approach that follows the standards outlined in this chapter, and the lifestyle standards outlined in the rest of the book, the relapse rate for subsequent episodes of depression decreases to about 10 percent. Therein lies the key— putting the body back into the balance God originally outlined, with proper diet and lifestyle choices, and most of all a study of His Word and trust in His leading.

NINE SUMMARY POINTS

1. Herbs and drug medications have their place in treating depression.

2. Herbs and drug medications that are effective are spelled out.

3. Such medications are needed many times at the start of a treatment program.

4. The goal is to discontinue the use of drugs after six months, or at the most one year.

5. Withdrawal from most drugs should be done gradually.

6. Nutrition and lifestyle choices are a key part of the treatment.

7. Without a nutrition and lifestyle approach, relapse is likely when drugs are stopped.

8. Nutrition and lifestyle choices offer a reasonable expectation of a lasting solution.

9. A general improvement in overall health will be a bonus.

Figure 17

119

References—

[1] Gyllenhaal C, Merritt SL, et al. Efficacy and safety of herbal stimulants and sedatives in sleep disorders. *Sleep Med Rev* June 2000;4(3):229-251.

[2] Gaster B, Holroyd J. St. John's wort for depression: A systematic review. *Arch Intern Med* 2000 Jan;160(2):152-156.

[3] Gaster B, Holroyd J. St. John's wort for depression: A systematic review. *Arch Intern Med* 2000 Jan;160(2):152-156.

[4] Meier B, Liske E, Rosinus V. Efficacy and safety of St. John's wort whole extract in patients with depressive symptomatology of different degrees. *Forsch Komplimentarmed* 1997 April;4(2):87-93.

[5] Vorbach EU, Arnoldt KH, Wolpert E. St John's wort: a potential therapy for elderly depressed patients? *Drugs Aging.* 2000 Mar;16(3):189-197.

[6] Schrader E, et al. Hypericum treatment of mild-moderate depression in a placebo-controlled study. A prospective, double-blind, randomized, placebo-controlled, multicentre study. *Human Psychopharmacology* 1998;13:163-169.

[7] Harrer G, et al. Comparison of equivalence between the St. John's wort extract LoHyp-57 and fluoxetine. *Arzneimittelforschung* 1999 Apr; 49(4):289-296.

[8] Philipp M, et al. Hypericum extract versus imipramine or placebo in patients with moderate depression: Randomised multicentre study of treatment for eight weeks. *Br Med J* 1999;319:1534-1539.

[9] Shelton RC, et al. Effectiveness of St. John's wort in major depression: A randomized controlled trial. *JAMA* 2001 Apr 18; 285 (15): 1978-86.

[10] Lieberman S. Nutriceutical review of St. John's wort (Hypericum perforatum) for the treatment of depression. *J Women's Health* 1998;7:177-182.

[11] Miller AL. St. John's wort (Hypericum perforatum): clinical effects on depression and other conditions. Altern Med Rev 1998;3:18-26.

[12] Doraiswamy M. *Public Health Nutr* 2001;3:18-26.

[13] Piscitelli SC, Burstein AH, et al. Indinavir concentrations and St John's wort. *Lancet* 2000;355(9203):547-548.

[14] Schardt D. St. John's Worts and all. *Nutrition Action Healthletter* 2000 Sep;27(7):7-9.

[15] Food and Drug Administration.

[16] Mason PF, Morris VA, Balcezak, TJ. Serotonin syndrome, presentation of 2 cases and review of the literature. *Medicine* July 2000;79(4).

[17] Gaster B. S-adenosylmethionine (SAMe) for treatment of depression. *Alternative Med Alert* 1999 Dec;2(12):133-135.

[18] Rosenbaum JF, Fava M, et al. The antidepressant potential of oral S-adenosyl-l-methionine. *Acta Psychiatr Scand* 1990 May;81(5):432-436.

[19] Bressa GM. S-adenosyl-l-methionine (SAMe) as antidepressant: Meta-analysis of clinical studies. *Acta Neurol Scand Suppl* 1994;154(3):7-14.

[20] Eikelboom JW, et al. Homocysteine and cardiovascular disease: A critical review of the epidemiologic evidence. *Ann Intern Med* 1999 Sep 7;131(5):363-375.

[21] Kagan BL, et al. Oral S-adenosylmethionine in depression: A randomized, double-blind, placebo-controlled trial. *Am J Psychiatry* 1990 May;147(5):591-595.

[22] Schardt D. SAMe SO-SO. *Nutrition Action Healthletter.* 2001 March;28(2):10.

[23] Schardt D. SAMe SO-SO. *Nutrition Action Healthletter.* 2001 March;28(2):11.

[24] Klepser T, Nisly N 5-Hydroxytryptophan (5-HTP) for treatment of depression. *Alternative Med Alert* 2000 Nov;3(11):123.

[25] Klepser T, Nisly N 5-Hydroxytryptophan (5-HTP) for treatment of depression. *Alternative Med Alert* 2000 Nov;3(11):122,123.

[26] Klepser T, Nisly N 5-Hydroxytryptophan (5-HTP) for treatment of depression. *Alternative Med Alert* 2000 Nov;3(11):123.

[27] *Physicians' Desk Reference for Herbal Medicines*, First Edition;1998:961-963.

[28] *Physicians' Desk Reference for Herbal Medicines*, First Edition;1998:1171-1173.

[29] *Physicians' Desk Reference for Herbal Medicines*, First Edition;1998:871-873.

[30] *Physicians' Desk Reference for Herbal Medicines*, First Edition;1998:1043-1045.

[31] *Physicians' Desk Reference for Herbal Medicines*, First Edition;1998:1043.

[32] *Physicians' Desk Reference for Herbal Medicines*, First Edition;1998:929-930.

[33] *Physicians' Desk Reference for Herbal Medicines*, First Edition;1998:967-969.

[34] *Physicians' Desk Reference for Herbal Medicines*, First Edition;1998:1204-1207.

[35] Elkin I, Shea MT, Watkins JT, et al. National Institute of Mental Health Treatment of Depression Collaborative Research Program: general effectiveness of treatment. *Arch Gen Psychiatry* 1989;46:971.

[36] Practice guideline for major depressive disorder in adults. *Am J Psychiatry* 1993;150(suppl):1.

[37] Schulberg HC, Katon W, Simon GE, et al. Treating major depression in primary care practice: an update of the Agency for Health Care Policy and Research practice guidelines. *Arch Gen Psychiatry* 1998;55:1121.

[38] Practice guideline for major depressive disorder in adults. *Am J Psychiatry* 1993;150(suppl):1.

[39] Potter WZ, Rudorfer MV, Manji HK. The pharmacologic treatment of depression. *N Engl J Med* 1991;325:633.

[40] Potter WZ, Rudorfer MV, Manji HK. The pharmacologic treatment of depression. *N Engl J Med* 1991;325:633.

[41] Rudorfer MV, Potter WZ. Antidepressants: A comparative review of the clinical pharmacology and therapeutic use of the 'newer' versus the 'older' drugs. *Drugs* 1989;37:713.

[42] Potter WZ, Manji HK, Rudorfer MV. *Tricyclics and tetracyclics. Textbook of Psychopharmacology*, 2nd ed. Schatzberg AF, Nemeroff CB, Eds. American Psychiatric Press, Washington, DC, 1998, p 199.

[43] Glassman AH. Psychiatry and cigarettes. *Arch Gen Psychiatry* 1998;55:692.

[44] Hubbard R. Exposure to commonly prescribed drugs and the etiology of cryptogenic fibrosing alveolitis: a case-control study. *Am J Respiratory and Critical Care Med* 1998;157(3 Pt 1):743-747.

[45] Wilens TE, Biederman J, Spencer TJ. Case study: Adverse effects of smoking marijuana while receiving tricyclic antidepressants. *J AM Acad Child Adolesc Psychiatry* 1996;36(1):45-48.

[46] Potter WZ, Rudorfer MV, Manji HK. The pharmacologic treatment of depression. *N Engl J Med* 1991;325:633.

[47] Rudorfer MV, Potter WZ. Antidepressants: A comparative review of the clinical pharmacology and therapeutic use of the 'newer' versus the 'older' drugs. *Drugs* 1989;37:713.

[48] Mulrow CD, Williams JW Jr, Trivedi M, et al. Treatment of depression: Newer pharmacotherapies. Evidence-based Practice Center/University of Texas Health Science Center at San Antonio, Agency for Health Care Policy and Research, Evidence Report/Technology Assessment No

7, 1999. *Psychopharmacol Bull* (in press).

49 Schatzberg AF. Antidepressant effectiveness in severe depression and melancholia. *J Clin Psychiatry* 1999;60(suppl 4):14.

50 Schatzberg AF. Antidepressant effectiveness in severe depression and melancholia. *J Clin Psychiatry* 1999;60(suppl 4):14.

51 Danish University Antidepressant Group: Citalopram: Clinical effect profile in comparison with clomipramine: a controlled multicenter study. *Psychopharmacology* 1986;90:131.

52 Danish University Antidepressant Group: Paroxetine: A selective serotonin reuptake inhibitor showing better tolerance, but weaker antidepressant effect than clomipramine in a controlled multicenter study. *J Affect Disord* 1990;18:289.

53 Roose SP, Glassman AH, Attia E, et al. Comparative efficacy of selective serotonin reuptake inhibitors and tricyclics in the treatment of melancholia. *Am J Psychiatry* 1994;151:1735.

54 Hall SM, Reus VI, Munoz RF, et al: Nortriptyline and cognitive-behavioral therapy in the treatment of cigarette smoking. *Arch Gen Psychiatry* 1998;55:683.

55 Smith AJ. The analgesic effects of selective serotonin reuptake inhibitors. *J Psychopharmacol* 1998;12:407.

56 Potter WZ, Manji HK, Rudorfer MV. *Tricyclics and tetracyclics. Textbook of Psychopharmacology*, 2nd ed. Schatzberg AF, Nemeroff CB, Eds. American Psychiatric Press, Washington, DC, 1998, p. 199.

57 Keller MB, Kocsis JH, Thase ME, et al. Maintenance phase efficacy of sertraline for chronic depression: A randomized controlled trial. *JAMA* 1998;280:1665.

58 Smith AJ. The analgesic effects of selective serotonin reuptake inhibitors. *J Psychopharmacol* 1998;12:407.

59 Physicians' Desk Reference 55th Edition 2001 published by Medical Economics Company, Inc. Montavale, NJ 07645-1742.

60 Rudorfer MV: Monoamine oxidase inhibitors: Reversible and irreversible. *Psychopharmacol Bull* 1992;28:45.

61 Thase ME, Trivedi MH, Rush AJ. MAOIs in the contemporary treatment of depression. *Neuropsychopharmacology* 1995;12:185.

62 Nierenberg AA, Alpert JE, et al. Course and treatment of atypical depression. *J Clin Psychiatry* 1998;59(suppl 18):5.

63 Stewart JW, Garfinkel R, Nunes EV, et al. Atypical features and treatment response in the National Institute of Mental Health Treatment of Depression Collaborative Research Program. *J Clin Psychopharmacol* 1998;18:429.

64 Jarrett RB, Schaffer M, et al. Treatment of atypical depression with cognitive therapy or phenelzine: A double-blind, placebo-controlled trial. *Arch Gen Psychiatry* 1999;56:431.

65 Rudorfer MV. Monoamine oxidase inhibitors: Reversible and irreversible. *Psychopharmacol Bull* 1992;28:45.

66 Rudorfer MV, Manji HK, Potter WZ. Comparative tolerability profiles of the newer versus older antidepressants. *Drug Saf* 1994;10:18.

67 Griffin L, Mellon S. Proceedings of the National Academy of Sciences 1999;96:13512-13517.

68 Foster S. *Herbs for Your Health*. Loveland, Colorado:Interweave Press, 1996.

69 *2001 Mosby's Genrx: A Comprehensive Reference For Generic and Brand Prescription Drugs, 11th Edition*. St.Louis, MO:Mosby (Harcourt Health Sciences), 2001.

70 Rudorfer MV, Manji HK, Potter WZ. Comparative tolerability profiles of the newer versus older antidepressants. *Drug Saf* 1994;10:18.

71 Michelson D, Amsterdam JD, et al. Changes in weight during a 1-year trial of fluoxetine. *Am J Psychiatry* 1999;156:1170.

72 Donovan S, et al. Deliberate self-harm and antidepressant drugs: Investigation of a possible link. *Fr J Psychiatry* 2000:177(6):551-556 Lane R, Baldwin D. Selective serotonin reuptake inhibitor-induced serotonin syndrome: review. *J Clin Psychopharmacol* 1997;17:208.

73 Moscicki EK Identification of suicide risk factors using epidemiologic studies. *Psychiatr Clin North Am* 1997 Sep; 20(3): 499-517

74 Lane R, Baldwin D. Selective serotonin reuptake inhibitor-induced serotonin syndrome: review. *J Clin Psychopharmacol* 1997;17:208.

75 Nemeroff CB, DeVane CL, Pollock BG. Newer antidepressants and the cytochrome P450 system. *Am J Psychiatry* 1996;153:311.

76 De Abajo FJ, Rodriguez LA, Montero D. Association between selective serotonin reuptake inhibitors and upper gastrointestinal bleeding: Population based case-control study. *BMJ* 1999 Oct 23;319(7217):1106-1109.

77 Donovan S, et al. Deliberate self-harm and antidepressant drugs: Investigation of a possible link. *Br J Psychiatry* 2000;177(6):551-556.

78 Zajecka J, Mitchell S, Fawcett J: Treatment-emergent changes in sexual function with selective serotonin reuptake inhibitors as measured with Rush Sexual Inventory. *Psychopharmacol Bull* 1997;33:755.

79 Waldinger MD, Hengeveld MW, Zwinderman AH, et al. Effect of SSRI antidepressants on ejaculation: A double-blind, randomized, placebo-controlled study with fluoxetine, fluvoxamine, paroxetine, and sertraline. *J Clin Psychopharmacol* 1998;8:274.

80 Rosen RC, Lane RM, Menza M: Effects of SSRIs on sexual function; a critical review. *J Clin Psychopharmacol* 1999;19:67.

81 Landén M, Eriksson E, Ágren H, et al. Effect of busiprone on sexual dysfunction in depressed patients treated with selective serotonin reuptake inhibitors. *J Clin Psychopharmcol* 1999;19:268.

82 Golden RN, et al. Trazodone, nefazodone, bupropion, and mirtazapine. *Textbook of Psychopharmacology*, 2nd ed. Schartzberg AF, Nemeroff CB, Eds. American Psychiatric Press, Washington, DC, 1998, p. 251.

83 Bupropion to aid smoking cessation. *Drug Ther Bull* 2000 Oct;38(10):73-75.

84 Wilens TE, et al. A Controlled Clinical Trial of Bupropion for Attention Deficit Hyperactivity Disorder in Adults. *Am J of Psychiatry* 2001;158:282-288.

85 Scientific American Medicine May 2000.

86 Kasper S, el Giamal N, Hilger E. Reboxetine: the first selective noradrenaline re-uptake inhibitor. *Expert opin Pharmacother* 200 May; 1(4):771-782.

87 Mucci M. Reboxetine: a review of antidepressant tolerability. *J Psychopharmacol* 1997;11(4 suppl):S33-7.

88 Scientific American Medicine May 2000.

89 Golden RN, Dawkins K, Nicholas L, et al: Trazodone, nefazodone, bupropion, and mirtazapine. Textbook of Psychopharmacology, 2nd ed. Schatzberg AF, Nemeroff CB, Eds. American Psychiatric Press, Washington, DC, 1998, p. 251.

90 Davis JM: Is mirtazapine a better antidepressant than the SSRIs? *Essent Psychopharmacol* 2:309, 1998.

91 Carpenter LL, Jocic Z, Hal JM, et al: Mirtazapine augmentation in the treatment of refractgory depression. *J Clin Psychiatry* 60:45,1999.

92 Depressive and bipolar mood disorders. *Scientific American Medicine* 2000 May:9.

93 Depressive and bipolar mood disorders. *Scientific American Medicine* 2000 May:9.

94 Depressive and bipolar mood disorders. *Scientific American Medicine* 2000 May:9.

[95] Heit S, Nemeroff CB. Lithium augmentation of antidepressants in treatment-refractory depression. *J Clin Psychiatry* 1998;59(suppl 6):28.

[96] Austin PPV, Souza FGM, et al. Lithium augmentation in antidepressant-resistant patients: A quantitative analysis. *Br J Psychiatry* 1991;159:510-514.

[97] Nemeroff CB. Augmentation strategies in patients with refractory depression. *Depress Anxiety* 1996;4:169-181.

[98] Regier DA, Farmer ME, et al. Comorbidity of mental disorders with alcohol and other drug abuse: Results from the epidemiologic catchment area (ECA) Study. *JAMA* 1990;264:2511.

[99] Wu LT, Kouzis AC, Leaf PJ. Influence of comorbid alcohol and psychiatric disorders on utilization mental health services in the National Comorbidity Survey. *Am J Psychiatry* 1999;156:1230.

[100] Panzarino PJ Jr. The costs of depression: Direct and indirect; treatment versus nontreatment. *J Clin Psychiatry* 1998;59(suppl 20):11.

[101] Thompson D, Hylan TR, et al. Predictors of a medical-offset effect among patients receiving antidepressant therapy. *Am J Psychiatry* 1998;155:824.

[102] Rudorfer MV, Manji HK, Potter WZ. Comparative tolerability profiles of the newer versus older antidepressants. *Drug Saf* 1994;10:18.

[103] Rudorfer MV, Potter WZ. The role of metabolites of antidepressants in the treatment of depression. *CNS Drugs* 1997;7:273.

[104] Rudorfer MV, Potter WZ. Metabolism of tricyclic antidepressants. *Cell Mol Neurobiol* 1999;19:373.

[105] Sternbach H, State R: Antibiotics: Neuropsychiatric effects and psychotropic interactions. *Harv Rev Psychiatry* 1997;5:214.

[106] Brown ES, Suppes T. Mood symptoms during corticosteroid therapy: A review. *Harv Rev Psychiatry* 1998;5:239.

[107] Cohen LS, Rosenbaum JF. Psychotropic drug use during pregnancy: Weighing the risks. *J Clin Psychiatry* 1998;59(suppl 2):18.

[108] Cohen LS, Rosenbaum JF. Psychotropic drug use during pregnancy: Weighing the risks. *J Clin Psychiatry* 1998;59(suppl 2):18.

[109] Altshuler LL, Cohen L, et al. Pharmacologic management of psychiatric illness during pregnancy: dilemmas and guidelines. *Am J Psychiatry* 1996;153:592.

[110] Wisner KL, Perel JM, Findling RL. Antidepressant treatment during breast-feeding. Am J Psychiatry 1996;153:1132.

[111] Kulin N. *JAMA* 1998;279:609-610.

[112] Therapeutic Research Center. Preganancy. *Prescriber's Letter* 2000 Nov;7(11):65,66.

[113] Nonacs R, Cohen LS. Postpartum mood disorders: Diagnosis and treatment guidelines. *J Clin Psychiatry* 1998;59(suppl 2):34.

[114] Appleby L, Warner R, et al. A controlled study of fluoxetine and cognitive-behavioural counseling in the treatment of postnatal depression. *BMJ* 1997;314:932.

[115] Little JT, Reynolds CF III, Dew MA, et al. How common is resistance to treatment in recurrent, nonpsychotic geriatric depression? *Am J Psychiatry* 1998;155:1035.

[116] Roose SP, Suthers KM: Antidepressant response in late-lifedepression. *J Clin Psychiatry* 1998;59(suppl 10):4.

[117] Mulrow CD, Williams JW Jr, et al. Treatment of depression: Newer pharmacotherapies. Evidence-based Practice Center/University of Texas Health Science Center at San Antonio, Agency for Health Care Policy and Research, Evidence Report/Technology Assessment No 7, 1999. *Psychopharmacol Bull* (in press).

[118] Roose SP, Suthers KM. Antidepressant response in late-lifedepression. *J Clin Psychiatry* 1998;59(suppl 10):4.

[119] Reynolds CF III, Miller MD, et al. Treatment of bereavement-related major depressive episodes in later life: A controlled study of acute and continuation treatment with nortriptyline and interpersonal psychotherapy. *Am J Psychiatry* 1999;156:202.

[120] Lebowitz BD, Pearson JL, et al. Diagnosis and treatment of depression in late life: Consensus statement update. *JAMA* 1997;278:1186.

[121] Potter WZ, Rudorfer MV, Manji HK. The pharmacologic treatment of depression. *N Engl J Med* 1991;325:633.

[122] Reynolds CF III, Buysse DJ, et al. Maintenance nortriptyline effects on electroencephalographic sleep in elderly patients with recurrent major depression: Double-blind, placebo- and plasma-level-controlled evaluation. *Biol Psychiatry* 1997;42:560.

[123] Rudorfer MV, Henry ME, Sackeim HA. Electroconvulsive therapy. *Psychiatry*. Tasman A, Kay J, Lieberman JA, Eds. WB Saunders Co, Philadelphia, 1997, p. 1535.

[124] Ruthazer R, Lipsitz LA. Antidepressants and falls among elderly people in long-term care. *Am J Public Health* 1993;83:746.

[125] Liu B, Anderson G, Mittmann N, et al. Use of selective serotonin-reuptake inhibitors or tricyclic antidepressants and risk of hip fractures in elderly people. *Lancet* 1998;351:1303.

[126] Thapa PB, Gideon P, et al. Antidepressants and the risk of falls among nursing home residents. *N Engl J Med* 1998;339:875.

[127] Leipzig RM, Cumming RG, Tinetti ME: Drugs and falls in older people: a systematic review and meta-analysis: I. Psychotropic drugs. *J Am Geriatr Soc* 1999;47:30.

[128] Birmaher B. Should we use antidepressant medications for children and adolescents with depressive disorders? *Psychopharmacol Bull* 1998;34:35.

[129] Safer DJ. Changing patterns of psychotropic medications prescribed by child psychiatrists in the 1990s. *J Child Adolesc Psychopharmacol* 1997;7:267.

[130] Jensen PS, Bhatara VS, et al. Psychoactive medication prescribing practices for U.S. children: Gaps between research and clinical practice. *J Am Acad Child Adolesc Psychiatry* 1999;38:557.

[131] Strober M, DeAntonio M, et al. The pharmacotherapy of depressive illness in adolescents: An open-label comparison of fluoxetine with imipramine-treated historical controls. *J Clin Psychiatry* 1999;60:164.

[132] Emslie GJ, Rush AJ, et al. A double-blind, randomized, placebo-controlled trial of fluoxetine in children and adolescents with depression. *Arch Gen Psychiatry* 1997;54:1031.

[133] Alderman J, Wolkow R, et al. Sertraline treatment of children and adolescents with obsessive-compulsive disorder or depression:Pharmacokinetics, tolerability, and efficacy. *J Am Acad Child Adolesc Psychiatry* 1998;37:38.

[134] Ryan ND, Varma D. Child and adolescent mood disorders-experience with serotonin-based therapies. *Biol Psychiatry* 1998;44:336.

[135] Emslie GJ, Rush AJ, et al. Fluocetine in child and adolescent depression: Acute and maintenance treatment. *Depress Anxiety* 1998;7:32.

[136] Dilsaver SC, Greden JF. Antidepressant withdrawal phenomina. *Biol Psychiatry* 1984;19:237-256.

[137] Wolfe RM. Antidepressant withdrawal reactions. *Am Family Phy* 1997 Aug ;56(2):457.

[138] Zajecka J, et al. Discontinuation symptoms after treatment with serotonin reuptake inhibitors: A literature review. *J Clin Psychiatry* 1997 July;58(7):291-297.

[139] Wolfe RM. Antidepressant withdrawal reactions. *Am Family Phy* 1997 Aug;56(2):456.

[140] Wolfe RM. Antidepressant withdrawal reactions. *Am Family Phy* 1997 Aug;56(2):458.

141 *Physicians' Desk Reference* 55th Edition 2001 published by Medical Economics Company, Inc. Montavale, NJ 07645-1742.

142 National Depressive and Manic-Depressive Assoc. 2000 Nov 29.

143 Melfi CA, Chawla AJ, et al. The effects of adherence to antidepressant treatment guidelines on relapse and recurrence of depression. *Arch Gen Psychiatry* 1998;55:1128.

144 Viguera AC, Baldessarini RJ, Friedberg J. Discontinuing antidepressant treatment in major depression. *Harv Rev Psychiatry* 1998;5:293.

145 Haddad P. Newer antidepressants and the discontinuation syndrome. *J Clin Psychiatry* 1997; 58 (suppl 7): 17-22.

146 Dilsaver SC. Withdrawal phenomena associated with antidepressant and antipsychotic agents. *Drug Safety* 1994; 10: 103-104.

147 Haddad P. Newer antidepressants and the discontinuation syndrome. *J Clin Psychiatry* 1997; 58 (suppl 7): 17-22.

148 Rosenbaum JF, Fava M, et. al, Selective serotonin reuptake inhibitor discontinuation syndrome: A randomized clinical trial. *Biol Psychiatry* 1998; 44: 77-87.

149 National Depressive and Manic-Depressive Association. Most patients report troublesome side effects, modest inprovement using current anti-depression treatments: New survey also shows satisfaction with treatment and care among people with depression. Press Release. Nov 30, 1999. http://www.ndmda.org/deptreat.htm.

150 National Depressive and Manic-Depressive Assoc. 2000 Nov 29.

151 Byrne SE, Rothschild AJ. Loss of antidepressant efficacy during maintenance therapy: Possible mechanisms and treatments. *J Clin Psychiatry* 1998; 59: 279-288.

CHAPTER SEVEN

STRESS
and
ANXIETY

The patients came in rapid succession. First came June, a women in her 60s who looked much younger than her age. On June's list of concerns was her long term use of Xanax,® a prescription drug to combat anxiety, a mental disorder. Twelve years ago, her doctor had diagnosed her with a mental condition called *panic disorder*, and Xanax three times a day had been part of her life ever since.

Numerous times she had tried to break free of the drug. Each time the story was the same. Withdrawal symptoms, including severe *anxiety*, brought her right back to her daily medication routine. June finally concluded that she was hopelessly addicted.

Then came Ralph, a young man in his mid-30s. Ralph had a history of problems with psychiatric difficulties that included *anxiety*. One of the many medications he took was Ativan,® another anxiety-combating drug, closely related to Xanax. Ralph was struggling with whether he should be using Ativan or whether he should be taking something milder—perhaps even a non-drug remedy.

Last came Bob, an international businessman in his 50s. Bob's fast-paced life seemed to fuel his concerns with *stress*. He asked, "Doctor, what medication do you recommend for stress?"

These three patients that came through my office are not unusual. Scenarios like theirs are common fare in the office of primary care physicians across the U.S. Why is stress so disturbing? Why are individuals willing to spend money on medications, make trips to the doctor's office, and even risk prescription drug addiction to combat stress or anxiety?

Stress may be a simple, temporary phenomenon in response to an unexpected life event. For example, that driver who cut you off in traffic last week may have contributed to your stress level at the time. But you are not likely to continue stewing over the episode a week later. For some people, however, stress or anxiety may develop into problems that are not short-lived, but ongoing.

With the launch of an activity of the Federal Government called Anxiety Disorders Education Program in the fall of 1996, the National Institute of Mental Health reminded our nation that currently some 16 percent of American adults under age 54[1,2,3] (or more than 19 million Americans[4]) suffer from anxiety disorders. These disorders exist in several forms. Later in the chapter we will look at the various kinds of anxiety disorders and define their characteristics.

Before giving attention to *anxiety disorders*, let us first look at *stress*. They are two separate mental conditions, but we will see that they are related.

What is Stress?

Stress is our response to problems and concerns that we encounter in life. Problems such as meeting deadlines, financial problems, or difficult family relationships can trigger stress. These problems are called *stressors*, and our reaction to them is called *stress*. In simple terms, the stressor is the *action*, and stress is your *reaction*, as illustrated in **Figure 1**.

We all have stressors of one kind or another in our lives. Examples of common stressors are portrayed in **Figure 2**.

It may be enlightening for you to identify your own life stressors. It could be the first step toward resolving a stress that you may have tried unsuccessfully to resolve, consciously or subconsciously. In order to fight a battle successfully you need to know the enemy. The most powerful strategies for combating stress often involve targeting the specific stressors that are attacking you. Later, for unspecified stressors, I will explain a number of helpful techniques such as deep breathing, physical exercise, and meditation.

STRESSORS AND STRESS

The pressures from the outside

Stress is your response to stressors

Figure 1

EXAMPLES OF STRESSORS

Work overload

Death

Life changing situations/events

Finances - Debt

Figure 2

The Burden of Suffering from Stress

Most of my patients do not need me to state the obvious, that the burden of stress seems to be steadily increasing for many. Stress levels are on the rise in most subgroups of populations in the western hemisphere, affecting individuals across the age spectrum in most, if not all, of the world's developed nations.[5,6] Ironically, those who are supposed to be helping us with our stress-related problems have not themselves escaped the sticky web of stress. A recent study revealed that, compared to other professionals, healthcare workers appear to be experiencing greater levels of depression, stress, and anxiety both on and off the job.[7]

Most Westerners are acutely aware of their stress load, and a library of scientific references only affirm that stress is on the rise and that some of us are facing more than our share. Whether we like it or not, stress and anxiety are part of every day living for most of us. And whether we are dealing with short-term effects or long-term struggles with anxiety disorders, what is called the "stress response" determines how stress will ultimately affect us. Let us take some time to better understand how *stress can contribute to anxiety* as well as cause dramatic physical and mental changes.

The Three-Step Response to Stress

Our body's response to stress is a carefully orchestrated process that is designed to help us free ourselves from hazardous circumstances. A sudden reaction to stress can be described as a "fight-or-flight" response, calculated to help us survive in a situation of imminent danger. As chemicals in our body play a major role in depression, they also drive our response to stress. Let us look at an example of a real life stress situation and how the human frame responds to it.

Celeste had an unusually long day at the office. That night, when she finally punched the time clock, she was greeted by exceptionally heavy traffic. The drive was strenuous. She was tired and had to struggle to keep from falling asleep.

After a 30-minute drive, Celeste breathed a sigh of relief and pulled into her driveway. As she walked toward her house, she barely noticed the neighbors' cat, but when she heard a deep feline growl, she immediately recognized that she was not dealing with an ordinary pet. Her mind kicked into high gear. She remembered a recent warning that rabid bobcats had been venturing into the neighborhood. Her heart automatically began to race, and with a sudden infusion of energy her weary body sprang to life. She bounded up the steps and into her house in a matter of seconds.

The body's response to a stressful situation like this is designed to be intense but temporary. In an acute situation like this, the effects of stress hormones are generally beneficial, providing the resources needed to deal with an emergency.

Stress pioneer Dr. Hans Selye says that our immediate response to an incident like Celeste experienced is the first phase of our reaction to a stress-producing event. He explains that our response is not dependent on the nature of the stressor. There is a similar response that occurs as a reaction to all types of stressors.[8] An individual's reaction to a new stressor is predictable and progressive, moving through three stages as illustrated in **Figure 3**.[9]

The first phase is an alarm reaction. When Celeste heard the growling bobcat, her body issued a call-to-arms, which was her alarm reaction. In the second phase, stage of resistance, Celeste had to quickly decide how to protect herself. She had to decide to fight the bobcat or else run from him, a "fight-or-flight" response. She chose to flee.

When it comes to other causes of stress, such as job stress, marital strain, financial demands, or a hundred other stressors, such stress may not be a short-term experience. We typically are exposed to stressors that

REACTIONS TO STRESSORS

Phase 1
Alarm reaction

Phase 2

State of resistance

Phase 3
State of exhaustion

Figure 3

127

remain in our environment for days, weeks, months, or even longer. When this happens, it may ultimately evolve into phase 3—a stage of exhaustion.

Once in this phase, if the stressor persists, disease or even death may be inevitable. There are classic examples of people dying of heart attacks in the face of some grave stressor. For those with weak hearts, a rabid bobcat or other sudden stressor may well provide sufficient stress to cause instant demise. However, most are able to cope with stressors—at least to some degree.

Physical Changes Caused by a Stressor

A sudden stressor causes several physical changes in the body to occur. They are listed in **Figure 4**.[10]

The increased muscular strength was obviously important in enabling Celeste to quickly escape from the bobcat. What pro-duced this increase? Five sudden changes in her body functions were necessary to bring it about. They are listed in **Figure 5.**

These five factors add up to an increase in energy in the blood being delivered to the active muscles.

What body processes commanded these increases to occur? They are the result of several glands that increased their output of hormones, called stress hormones. These increases, in turn, are caused by signals from the nervous system's reaction to the presence of the stressor.

Summarizing these actions, we see that electrical signals from the nervous system cause certain glands to increase their secretions of hormones, which increases the energy in the blood stream, causing the extra muscular strength needed to flee from danger. All of this happens in a few seconds.

Another change in the blood is an increased tendency for blood platelets to clot. This would have helped minimize the loss of blood if Celeste suffered lacerations in a scuffle. This complex system in the human frame works wonderfully in preserving our lives in the event of such emergencies.

PHYSICAL EFFECTS OF A SUDDEN STRESSOR

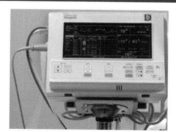

- Increased blood pressure
- Increased heart rate
- Increased heart contraction
- Dilated pupils
- Dilated bronchial tubes
- Increased muscular strength
- Release of glucose from liver
- Increased mental activity
- Increased metabolic rate
- Increased blood flow to active muscles
- Decreased blood flow to areas not needed for rapid activity, such as the kidneys and intestines

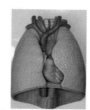

Figure 4

Ongoing Stressors vs. Sudden Stressors

Let us now consider an *ongoing stressor* in the life as opposed to an *instantaneous stressor*. The instant and short-lived changes now become lingering ones. The changes now cause these *benefits* to *become liabilities*, and could be very damaging to our health.

It is ironic, but the very nervous system and hormonal increases that can protect us when a stressor first appears are the same changes that can ultimately destroy us in the face of persistent stress. Our stress system is designed to help us deal with sudden, short-term conditions. It is not designed to be perpetually active in the face of persistent stressors. These facts support wise counsel found in Holy Writings, such as "do not let the sun go down on your wrath."[11] Whether it is anger or other stressors, we are best served to *confront and resolve them as soon as possible.*

Persistent stress can damage the body in many ways. Consider diabetes as an example. Americans are confronted by an epidemic of diabetes, with 800,000 new cases diagnosed each year. The toll in terms of amputations, kidney failure, heart attacks, stroke, and blindness is staggering.[12] For those with diabetes or risk factors for this disease, continued activation of stress hormones may be deleterious because of the increase in blood sugar.

Consider another example, disease of the heart arteries. The stimulation of an ongoing stress may not be accompanied by an increased blood supply because of narrowed flow passages in the arteries. This could result in a heart attack or a stroke. Also, an increase in blood pressure caused by an ongoing stressor could have a damaging and perhaps fatal effect. An increase in the tendency for the blood to clot is certainly unhealthful, and could be devastating in the face of diseased arteries. It is not a condition that we want to perpetuate beyond the temporary stressful situation.

Damage Caused by the Hormone "Cortisol"

As previously stated, the increase of several hormones in the blood stream are involved in protecting us from a sudden stressor. One of these hormones is *cortisol.* However, *ongoing high levels of cortisol caused by chronic and excessive stress* can wreak havoc upon the body, causing much physical and psychological damage. A list of damaging effects related to brain functions appears in **Figure 6**.[13,14,15,16,17,18,19]

Impaired memory, item 6, refers to one's verbal declarative memory (recalling names, telephone numbers, etc.). Similar memory impairment may arise in individuals who use cortisone-type medications for

medical conditions.[20] A case in point: children who take prednisone for asthma.[21]

Item 7, shrinkage of the brain, can be caused by prolonged increases in cortisol levels. This takes on great importance for elderly individuals, or even those of younger age who may sense that their mental acuity is slipping. More effective strategies to man-

CAUSE OF INCREASE IN MUSCULAR STRENGTH

- Stronger heartbeat
- More rapid heartbeat
- Increased blood pressure
- Increased blood sugar level
- Increased flow to active muscles

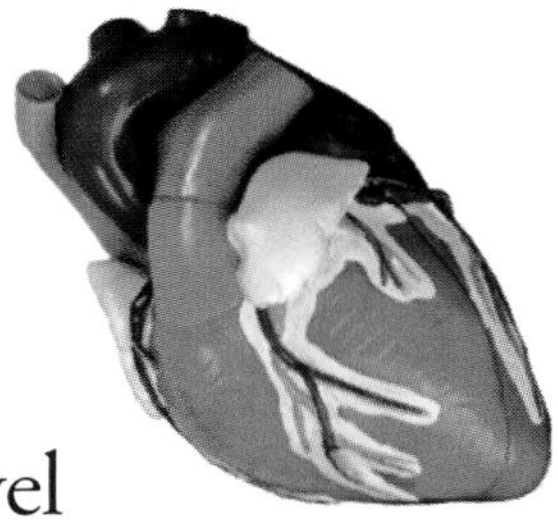

Figure 5

ELEVATED CORTISOL CAN DAMAGE BRAIN FUNCTIONS

1. Dementia (mental confusion)
2. Obsessive-compulsive disorder
3. Anorexia (aversion to food)

4. Depresssion
5. Panic anxiety
6. Impaired memory
7. Shrinkage of the brain

Figure 6

age stress without cortisol substances may slow the decline in memory performance.[22]

High cortisol levels damage the body in other ways. Some of them are listed in **Figure 7**.[23,24,25,26,27,28,29,30]

Item 7 in the figure is suppression of the immune system. Excess cortisol in the blood stream tends to weaken the immune system in two ways. First, it elevates blood sugar levels, which is a known detriment to the immune system.[31] Second, cortisol itself weakens the ability of certain white blood cells to kill bacteria.

A study related to the immune system revealed that higher than normal cortisol levels are linked to a decreased survival time in women with *advanced breast cancer.* These women had fewer and less powerful natural killer cells in their blood, and thus had impaired resources with which to attack the cancer.[32]

In a classic study of medical students, the stress of taking exams resulted in a decrease of certain white blood cells in the blood stream.[33] When a stressor is perpetuated for days or weeks, as in the case of

bereavement, the beleaguered immune system may be more susceptible to *infectious diseases or cancer.*

Another interesting study related to the immune system looked at two groups of workers who experienced a change in jobs. The first group voluntarily quit their job and found work elsewhere. Those in the second group were laid off and were forced to find another one, which was a stressful experience. The second group showed a greater risk of *lung cancer.*[34]

Research makes one thing clear—persistent stress has profound effects on our immune system. Cancer is typically present for months or years before diagnosis. Thus, a weakened immune system produced by persistent stress increases our risk of serious problems long before a cancer is diagnosed.

Stress Increases Risk of Heart Disease and Stroke

There are many studies indicating a strong connection between stress and artery blockage. Heart disease continues to be the leading cause of death in our nation. Growing insights into its connections with stress cannot be ignored. The relationships are remarkable both for individuals who have never had problems with their heart and for those suffering from known heart problems. The evidence indicates that stress may not only increase the risk of a *heart attack,* but failure to effectively deal with stress can also lead to *worse outcomes in the aftermath of a heart attack.*[35] Several studies that demonstrate the connection are recorded in **Figure 8**.[36]

Duke University researchers studied 132 patients with heart disease. Normal *everyday negative emotions* such as tension, sadness, and frustration were found to double or triple the risk of significant *decreases in blood supply to the heart muscle.*

Likewise, it was noted that *positive emotions,* such as feeling happy and in control, were associated with a *lower risk of reduced*

OTHER DAMAGES CAUSED BY HIGH CORTISOL

1. Peptic ulcers

2. Hypertension

3. Malnutrition

4. Chronic active alcoholism

5. Decreased libido

6. Resistance to alcohol and narcotic withdrawal

7. Suppressed immune system

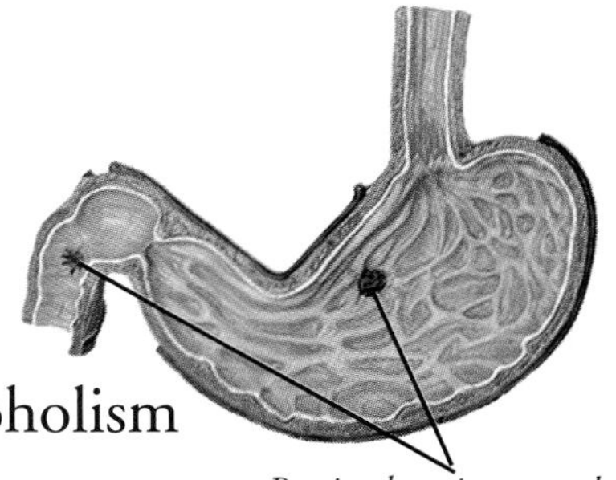

Peptic ulcers in stomach and duodenum

Figure 7

blood supply to the heart muscle. The Duke researcher demonstrated that even the low levels of ordinary stress that we experience may decrease blood supply to the heart.

As shown in **Figure 8**, programs that teach cardiac patients how to manage stress can reduce the occurrence of artery blockage. Dr. James A. Blumenthal of Duke University in Durham, North Carolina, and colleagues there and elsewhere studied a group of patients with coronary artery disease (CAD) and documented artery blockage during mental stress testing. Patients that were instructed in the methods of managing stress had far less cardiac events than those who did not take the program. Dr. Blumenthal concluded that instructions in ways to manage stress are a very important part of cardiac rehabilitation, extending the health and life of individuals involved.

The Dutch investigators in **Figure 8** analyzed 37 studies that examined results of cardiac rehabilitation programs that included instructions in stress reduction. They found positive effects on blood pressure, cholesterol, body weight, smoking behavior, physical exercise, and eating habits, along with a 34 percent reduction in cardiac mortality and a 29 percent reduction in recurrence of heart attack.

When it comes to stroke, the basic underlying disease process is very similar to heart attack. Both disease states are characterized by blockage in blood vessels supplying vital organs. As expected, *stress increases the risk of stroke*.[37] In a group of Finnish men age 42 to 60, those who had the greatest *stress-induced blood pressure increases showed the greatest amount of blockage in their carotid arteries*.[38] Studies linking stress to blockage in neck arteries have implications beyond that of stroke risk. Such blockage is viewed as an indicator of the *extent of blockages throughout the body*, including arteries feeding the heart and other vital locations.

Sudden stressors do not affect all people equally, according to research performed at Ohio State University. Researchers falsely accused participants of shoplifting, and then gave them five minutes to defend themselves.[39] The stressor was equal in intensity for each participant. All knew that their defense speech was being videotaped and judged. Those subjects with a *family history of heart disease* demonstrated *greater elevations of total and LDL cholesterol* (two cardiac risk factors) in response to this stressful experience.

Sudden mental stress not only increases cardiac risk factors like blood pressure and

STRESS AND ARTERY BLOCKAGE

Study	Findings
Duke University	Everyday negative emotions increase risk of reduced blood supply to the heart muscle. Positive emotions lower the risk.
Duke University	Teaching cardiac patients to manage stress reduced occurrences of artery blockage.
Dutch Investigators	Teaching cardiac patients to manage stress caused a 34% reduction in cardiac mortality and a 29% reduction in recurrence of heart attacks.
Dutch Investigators	Teaching cardiac patients to manage stress caused positive effects on blood pressure, cholesterol, body weight, smoking behavior, physical exercise, and eating habits.
Dr. Thom. W. Karmarck	Greatest stress-induced blood pressure increases showed the greatest amount of blockage in their carotid arteries.

Figure 8

cholesterol; it also increases the risk of dangerous—and even life-threatening—*heart rhythm problems*. Research performed at Yale University found that, among predisposed individuals, stressful emotions can provoke certain potentially fatal heart rhythm problems.[40]

When comparing the effects of sudden mental stress with that of chronic or ongoing stress, it is found that *chronic stress is also devastating to cardiac health*. As previously mentioned with respect to lung cancer, lack of control over one's work situation has been linked with chronic stress in many studies. This predictor of chronic stress load also impacts heart health. A study of British government workers found those who felt they had little or no control over their job had lower blood levels of heart-protective HDL cholesterol. Some researchers believe that hormones such as adrenaline and cortisol may be directly contributing to the adverse cholesterol patterns occurring as a result of stress.[41]

As with sudden stress, a decrease in HDL is not the only cholesterol abnormality associated with chronic stress. *Total cholesterol also tends to rise under the influence of perpetuated stresses*. Researchers have demonstrated that individuals with a family history of heart disease have a greater tendency for their cholesterol to rise in response to stress.

We have examined some of the evidence linking stress with immune impairment, cancer risk, and heart disease. However, there are many other conditions that may be triggered by stress and its effect on weakening the immune system as outlined in **Figure 9**.

Each of these maladies deserve a closer look. The first on the list is herpes.

Stress and Herpes

Once someone is exposed to the herpes virus, it sets up lifelong residence in the nervous system. *Prolonged exposure to stress* can increase the risk of an *outbreak of this painful genital state*. In one six-month study, researchers in San Francisco studied 58 women ages 20 to 44, all with a history of the recurrence of visible genital herpes.[42] High levels of anxiety and persistent stress predicted the recurrence of herpes. Interestingly, the researchers found *no connection with short-term stressful experiences*.

Stress and Asthma

The second malady listed is asthma. Stress and immune system interactions are involved here. *Stress can trigger asthma attacks*; this is not surprising in view of the known risk factors that have been linked to this disorder. Those who are victims of poverty are at high risk of getting asthma. Also, those who experience family dysfunction (including recent unemployment or bereavement), depression, alcoholism, and inability to cope with financial difficulties are also at high risk.[43]

Asthma is clearly more than an inherited disease. Identical twins provide a powerful example. When one twin has asthma,

OTHER DISEASES AND CONDITIONS AGGRAVATED BY STRESS

- Herpes
- Asthma
- HIV to AIDS
- Eczema
- Psoriasis
- Irritable bowel syndrome
- Reproductive health
- Hip fracture

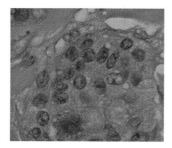

Herpes virus

Figure 9

only about 20 percent of their identical siblings also have the disorder. Parent-reported stressful events as well as parenting difficulties and lower marital satisfaction have all been linked to the development of early childhood asthma.[44]

A review of medical research found that some patients could trigger an asthmatic episode when they attempted to inhibit strong emotions such as aggression or fear. At the same time they found that some patients' asthma improves when disturbed social interactions are improved.[45] On the whole, these and other lines of evidence clearly suggest that *perpetuated stressors can play a role in the development of asthma as well as flare-ups of the condition.*

Stress Can Increase the Risk of HIV Progressing to AIDS

We have seen that heart disease, stroke, cancer, genital herpes, and asthma can be aggravated by stress through the weakening of the immune function. However, no discussion of diseases related to the immune system would be complete without mentioning infection with HIV (the human immunodeficiency virus). A recent study of HIV-infected patients involved some with stressors in their lives that were greater than the normal day-to-day-stressors that we all have. Those with the greatest stressors had a greater drop in certain critical white blood cells.[46] This study provides evidence suggesting that stress can increase the risk of early HIV progressing to AIDS. The good news is that researchers did not find any connection between normal stresses of everyday living and the development of AIDS.

Stress, Eczema, and Psoriasis

Researchers at Boston's Tufts School of Medicine found that increased levels of a hormone called CRH can be caused by stress. This hormone stimulates a certain group of white cells in the body.[47] These cells are involved in aggravating skin allergies such as eczema and psoriasis.

Stress and Digestion

British researchers recently reported a link between stress and a common intestinal condition called irritable bowel syndrome. In this condition, patients suffer from a variety of complaints that may include abdominal pain, bloating, diarrhea, or constipation. The remarkable findings showed that emotional distress seems to be a cause of the disorder. More than 70 percent of people with this condition had undergone recent stressful events such as bereavement or the severing of a relationship.[48]

Stress and Reproductive Health

Concerns regarding infertility seem more prevalent than ever. Stress appears to have a broad range of effects on reproductive health. A study showed that stress can cause an increase in a certain group of hormones which impair male fertility by reducing sperm counts.[49]

In another study of more than 200 pregnant women, some were under stress caused by a combination of high workplace demands and heavy responsibilities in the home. They had nearly five times the risk of pregnancy complications when compared with less-stressed women.[50] Further insights into this relationship has been provided by earlier research. In a previous study, it was demonstrated that working women who had even one child at home had higher levels of cortisol in the blood. The damaging effects of this stress hormone are mentioned earlier in this chapter.[51] In a separate study of more than 100 women employed outside the home, those who did not have children had lower cortisol levels throughout the entire day. Perhaps most surprising was the fact that having more than one child at home did not further elevate cortisol levels.

Regarding birth defects, current research indicates that stress—particularly around the time of conception and during the first three months of pregnancy—significantly increases the likelihood of such problems.[52] Even if conception occurs and a child does not suffer from a birth defect, stress can usher in other pregnancy complications. Certain types of stress, including high-stress working situations, have been linked to increased risk of premature delivery.[53] Pre-term babies are at higher risk of both short-term and long-term health problems. They may also be afflicted with learning disabilities.

Stress and Hip Fracture

When used as treatment for a medical condition such as asthma, cortisone-type medications can have deleterious effects on bone strength. It should come as no surprise that medical researchers have uncovered a linkage between stress and hip fractures. A study of some 18,000 Norwegian women who were at least 50 years old, found that indicators of mental distress such as loneliness and life dissatisfaction predicted an increased risk of hip fracture.[54]

The investigators thought that there was more to the story than higher cortisol levels. Part of the connection may be explained by a linkage between mental distress and a failure to maintain a healthy lifestyle on other fronts. For example, women suffering under the greatest loads of distress are more inclined to smoke and engage in poorer eating habits.

Some of the effects of stress listed in **Figure 9** may not be as dramatic as other life-threatening and health-robbing conditions that we have examined. Nonetheless, looking at these additional stress-health relationships helps to make an important point—*perpetuated stress is a powerful factor that can wreak havoc on the human frame in many ways.*

Let us now look at some of the social effects of stress.

Social Effects of Stress

With stress taxing one's physical, mental, and financial resources, it should come as no surprise that there are profound social effects of stress. In fact, the social effects of stress are so well accepted in our culture that stress is typically used as an excuse for impaired social interactions. Just reflect for a minute on typical excuses you have heard. "I'm sorry, I had a hard day at work," or "Forgive me. The baby kept me awake all last night."

Regarding these social effects of stress, chronic stress may present different dangers at different times in our life cycle. Such research has disturbing implications for the cycle of abuse that is often seen in families where those who are under stress from being abused ultimately become abusers themselves.

Stress and the Brain

Stress can affect essentially every level of self—physical, social, spiritual, and mental. It is the last of these four domains—that of mental health—where the effects of stress often produce the greatest cause for concern. *The state of our mental health determines who we are. Without good mental health, our quality of life severely suffers* in the physical, social, and spiritual domains.

Stress has also been linked to certain types of dissociative states, such as losing touch with your surroundings while day dreaming, or something as major as memory disorders in which you block out whole chapters of your life. In fact, a recent report suggests that out-of-body, near-death experiences may be manifestations of a dramatic dissociative state.[55]

Dissociative states commonly occur as a result of major life stresses. During dissociation, affected individuals perceive that their mind is detached from their emotional state or even their body.[56] Dissociative states can happen to anyone in the right circumstances. Such an occurrence does not necessarily indicate mental instability. The evidence indicates that out-of-body, near-death experiences are much more suggestive of altered mental states than they are of some type of spiritual experience. The brain can become astonishingly altered from extreme stress, trauma, or lack of oxygen.

A discussion of stress and the mental processes would not be complete without mentioning substance abuse. There is no question that drugs of abuse take a major toll on the mental faculties. Although substance abuse is often an adult problem, society's sympathies are most aroused when we expand the discussion to children. Indeed, drugs have become a great concern for parents. Though programs to prevent drug abuse abound, medical research suggests that one very valuable strategy is often overlooked. *Helping children to better cope with stressors may decrease their risk of future substance abuse.*[57]

Damaging Effects of Stress: Putting it All Together

We have seen the broad range of the effects of stress. I have only highlighted the tip of the iceberg regarding the enormous physical, mental, and social toll exacted by stress. Only a small part of the research on this subject has been mentioned in this chapter.

The healthcare community tends to allow stress-related health problems to be overshadowed by other diseases, but my analysis and experience indicate that stress plays a major role in aggravating disease and lowering the quality of life for millions of people.

From this perspective it is especially important to note recent research findings drawn from a database of over 45,000 employees.[58] Although smoking, obesity, high blood pressure, and diabetes all help to increase average annual healthcare expenses, Dr. Ron Z. Goetzel and colleagues published a startling discovery in 1998. In a study of healthcare costs, two areas outstripped all other health risk factors that were considered—depression and stress. Specifically, average medical costs per year were a dramatic *70.2 percent higher for workers who reported depression.* Regarding those who had *high stress levels,* their average annual healthcare bill was *46.3 percent higher* than their less-stressed peers.

Research such as this is beginning to be noticed by those who control the healthcare pocketbooks. Insurers, HMOs, employers, and others who write many of the healthcare checks are taking note. Truly, the broad-reaching effects of stress underscore an important point—every one of us should be highly motivated to embrace a two-fold strategy. First, do what we can to control the stressors we face. Second, when faced with stressors that we cannot control, learn to manage stress in the most constructive way possible.

Anxiety Disorders[59]

Thus far, we have learned that stress can cause serious changes in our level of physical, mental, emotional, and spiritual health. We now turn our attention to anxiety disorders, which are a group of mental disorders brought about by stress. *When stressors persist, they can cause anxiety.*

You will remember that one of the instantaneous reactions to a sudden stressor is an increase in mental activity (listed in **Figure** 4). Our brains are programmed with the capacity to make split-second life-or-death decisions when we are stressed. Long after the stressor is gone, however, it can persist in our minds. For example, a traumatic life experience such as rape, war, or a natural disaster, can remain a mental stressor for years after the event transpired. When stressors persist—on any level—they can cause anxiety. To put anxiety in perspective, some important facts are laid out in **Figure 10.**

FACTS ABOUT ANXIETY

- Persistent stressors can cause anxiety.
- Anxiety is the most common mental disorder.
- It affects over 19 million Americans.
- It is treatable.
- Self-diagnosis is misdiagnosis in most cases.

Figure 10

TYPES OF ANXIETY DISORDERS

Generalized Anxiety Disorder (GAD): exaggerated worry and tension over everyday events and decisions.

Panic Disorder: episodes of extreme fear and dread that strike unexpectedly and repeatedly for no apparent reason—accompanied by intense physical symptoms.

Post-Traumatic Stress Disorder (PSTD): reaction to a terrifying event that keeps returning in the form of frightening, intrusive memories—brings on heightened vigilance and deadening of normal emotions.

Phobias—two types: **Specific phobia:** fear of an object or situation. **Social phobia:** fear of extreme embarrassment.

Obsessive-Compulsive Disorder (OCD): intrusive, unwanted, repetitive thoughts and rituals performed out of a feeling of urgent need.

Figure 11

Regarding the first fact in **Figure 10**, it is important to note that not all stressors are sufficient to cause an anxiety disorder, even if they are perpetuated. But for those who have a genetic predisposition to such a condition, long-term unresolved stress may provide fertile soil in which an anxiety disorder can germinate. So important are anxiety disorders, and so great is the toll (with some 19 million Americans affected), that we need to look at these conditions in detail.

Anxiety disorders are truly illnesses. As **Figure 10** states, they are the most common of all mental disorders, and they vary widely in severity. On one hand, there may be frequent feelings of anxiety with relatively little apparent disruption in a person's life. At the other extreme, bouts of profound anxiety can occur that terrify and immobilize the sufferer.

I do not present here an exhaustive study on these disorders, but certain information deserves our attention. Note that these disorders are treatable. Anxiety disorders often go undiagnosed and untreated for years. This is tragic, because prescription drug-therapies and non-medication strategies can be extremely successful.

Note also that self-diagnosis of these kinds of disorders may not be effective. Many individuals may misdiagnose themselves as merely "dealing with stress poorly" when in reality they may have a much more serious problem. Anxiety disorders are bona fide psychiatric conditions. They are best addressed by working with a qualified health professional.

Fortunately, there are a number of new insights emerging regarding the treatment of anxiety. I will share a number of these insights to provide a better understanding of treatment options and underlying causes.

An unfortunate feature of anxiety disorders is the company that they keep. About half of those who have a generalized anxiety disorder also have either a second anxiety disorder or depression. An awareness of a possible second disorder may help one look for indications of its presence.

How Can I Recognize an Anxiety Disorder?

There are five main forms of anxiety disorders. The National Institute of Mental Health (NIMH), a component of the federal National Institutes of Health, provides a brief overview of these disorders in a year 2000 publication. This information is listed in **Figure 11**.

Despite these identifying characteristics, people with anxiety disorders typically do not appear to the untrained eye to have major psychiatric problems. For example, an individual with a generalized anxiety disorder (GAD) may appear to be simply a worrywart. Often the individual is totally oblivious to the fact that he has a diagnosable psychiatric condition that can be treated.

The afflicted person may say, "I always thought I was just a worrier. I'd feel keyed up and unable to relax. At times it would come and go, and other times it would be constant. It could go on for days. I'd worry about what I was going to fix for a dinner party, or what would be a great present for somebody. I just couldn't let something go . . . sometimes I'd feel a little lightheaded. My heart would race or pound. And that would make me worry more."

Let us look more closely at each of the five forms of anxiety disorders listed in **Figure 11**.

Generalized Anxiety Disorder

GAD, the first one on the list, usually does not cause significant impairment. Affected individuals typically function quite well in society. The good news about this condition is that most people tend to grow out of it. Typically, symptoms seem to become less severe with age. However, debilitating cases of GAD can occur. Medication therapy and non-drug therapy may each be of help. Buspirone (BuSpar), a pre-scription drug, may provide some help. However, five non-drug therapies have also proven effective. They are called cognitive-behavioral therapy, regular physical exercise, biofeedback, relaxation techniques, and spiritual focus therapy. The last four treatments are explained in *Chapter 8*.

Caution should be used in taking drug therapy. There are at least three reasons why it may be a mistake to take this seemingly easiest route. First, it can take up to several weeks before buspirone produces any benefit. Second, it can cause a number of disconcerting side effects including dizziness, drowsiness, and nausea. Third, there are concerns about worsening of GAD when the drug is stopped. Many patients are generally not interested in a lifetime of medication if other strategies can address their problems.

Other brain chemicals play a role in anxiety pathways. Two critical ones are *serotonin* and *gamma-aminobutyric acid* (GABA). Both of these compounds are called *inhibitory transmitters*. They have the ability to dampen brain pathways that are involved in stress and anxiety. Further reinforcing the accuracy of these connections are a number of medications that can boost serotonin levels. In many cases these drugs not only can alleviate depression, but can also help ease the effects of anxiety disorders. Fortunately, we are not dependent on medications only to boost our levels of this vital brain chemical. In *Chapters 4* and *5*, I give a number of ways in which you can improve serotonin levels in your brain. The important message is that even if you are not depressed, you may find that you can better combat the everyday stresses and anxieties of life if you pay attention to these serotonin-boosting strategies.

Drug treatment strategies are emerging that target other chemical messengers in the brain. Promising treatments are emerging that increase *gamma amino butyric acid* (GABA) levels in order to reduce anxiety and panic attacks. Another brain chemical called *substance-P* also appears to play a role in mood disorders. Preliminary work suggests that medications to block the effects of this compound may help reduce both anxiety and depression.

Panic Disorder

The second form of an anxiety disorder in **Figure 11** is panic disorder. What is panic disorder? It is a condition wherein individuals experience what is called a panic attack. They feel like they are losing control or going crazy and may have strong feelings of impending doom. Physical symptoms of panic disorder are listed in **Figure 12**.

In its least disturbing form, panic disorder causes particularly troubling symptoms.

Panic attacks are not limited to those who have panic disorder. Such attacks occasionally occur in people who are free of mental illness. They also commonly accompany other psychiatric conditions such as social phobia (fear of embarrassment), gen-

eralized anxiety disorder, and major depression. To be diagnosed with panic disorder, a person must have had at least two unexpected panic attacks and either be worried about future attacks or take precautions to avoid the same. In those with the disorder, the severe anxiety between attacks can actually result in a full-blown phobia. For example, if someone had a panic attack while riding the train, they may develop a fear of trains.

Research has revealed familial tendencies to anxiety disorders. Some investigators pin the blame for panic disorders on repeated life stresses in genetically susceptible individuals. It is not yet clear how big a role stress plays in the development of these disorders. Regardless of the mechanism, recent studies suggest that people with panic disorder have a lowered threshold for activating their mechanisms for combating stress.

Affected individuals tend to subconsciously perceive non-threatening situations as dangerous, and thus their stress systems become activated. Effective non-drug treatment regimens utilize cognitive-behavioral therapy (CBT), which is explained in **Figure 13**.

Panic disorders and phobias tend to run together in families. It is important to recognize that panic disorders can progress into phobias, which are fourth on the list of anxiety disorders of **Figure 11**. Thus, panic symptoms should be addressed early to prevent such a progression. Phobias are addressed in the next section.

The decision whether or not to seek treatment should not be taken lightly. Untreated panic disorder has been demonstrated to significantly *increase the risk of suicide*. SSRI medications such as Paxil® are often effective in treating it. I use benzodiazepines such as Xanax® short-term (for less than 30 days) to help severe life-threatening panic disorder until the SSRI medication and lifestyle therapies have a chance to work. It is very important for panic dis-

PHYSICAL SYMPTOMS
OF PANIC DISORDER

- Pounding heart
- Chest pains
- Sweating
- Lightheadedness or dizziness
- Trembling or quivering
- Nausea or other stomach problems
- Shortness of breath
- Numbness or tingling

Figure 12

order patients to recognize that they are not actually having a heart attack (although it often feels like one) and that their severe symptoms will soon pass without having to visit an emergency room. Such reassurance itself can be therapeutic.

Post-Traumatic Stress Disorder

The name of the third anxiety disorder listed in **Figure 11**, post-traumatic stress disorder (PTSD), indicates the primary characteristic of this malady. It typically occurs in individuals who have lived through a severe, emotionally traumatic experience. The typical marks of PTSD are found in **Figure 14**.

The condition can be debilitating and may interfere with close personal relationships. PTSD can result in a myriad of reactions as listed in **Figure 15**.

The victim also tends to avoid situations that trigger uncomfortable memories.

Recent research suggests that individuals who suffer from PTSD may be at higher risk of later engaging in criminal behavior resulting from an aggressive attitude and impaired self-control.[60] Still other research is uncovering links between PTSD and increased risk of chronic diseases like heart disease.[61]

PTSD was first brought to public attention in a very circumscribed context called "shell shock" in war veterans. This condition now afflicts more than five million Americans each year and results from any of a variety of traumatic events. These can include experiencing (or seeing others traumatized by) rape or sexual abuse, other criminal victimization, natural disasters such as hurricanes or earthquakes, and serious car wrecks or other transportation-related injuries.

PTSD is not an inevitable result of severe stressors. Even among those exposed to extreme trauma, only about 9 percent actually develop PTSD. However, even some 20 years after combat exposure, rates approach 15 percent in groups such as Vietnam veterans.

The fact that not all traumatized individuals develop PTSD underscores one of the most important aspects of stress theory. Genetic factors, personal coping styles, and

COMPARISON OF COGNITIVE AND TRADITIONAL BEHAVIOR THERAPY

Traditional Behavior Therapy: Attempts to help the patient blame his disorder on *something* or *someone* else. Supposed resolution of the behavior problem occurs when the individual somehow "deals" with the identified "cause."

Cognitive Behavior Therapy: Attempts to help the patient determine what *action* or *change in behavior* he should take to effect a cure for his disorder.

Figure 13

TYPICAL MARKS OF POST-TRAUMATIC STRESS DISORDER

- Victim has lived through severe emotional experience.

- Victim has frightening thoughts and memories.

- These thoughts are triggered by ordinary life events.

- Disease was first seen in shellshocked war veterans.

Figure 14

other social factors all seem to have an impact on whether or not PTSD develops. There is new evidence suggesting that a person who receives strong social support following a traumatic event is less likely to develop PTSD.[62]

Even when individuals develop PTSD, they often do not have all of the characteristics of the disorder, and the length and extent of their recovery is also variable. Approximately 50 percent of affected individuals recover fully within six months. On the other extreme, some patients are dogged by the condition for decades or even the rest of their lives.

The options for treatment depend on the nature of the problems associated with any given case of PTSD. If depression and sleeping difficulties are present, antidepressants and/or anxiety-reducing medications may be prescribed. PTSD is another anxiety disorder where cognitive-behavioral therapy typically forms an important part of the treatment. As pointed out earlier, strong social support such as building better ties to family, friends, and the community may also help to ease PTSD symptoms.[63]

Although the untreated condition can be ongoing, treatment can result in rapid improvement of the condition. One study of rape-induced PTSD found that 12 behavioral therapy (non-drug) sessions are sufficient to alleviate most PTSD symptoms in the majority of patients.[64]

It is important to point out the variability in PTSD and its related symptoms from one afflicted person to another. For example, recent research suggests that the passage of time may work better at healing certain aspects of this disorder than others. Researchers studied the lives of 78 Armenians who were among the thousands who experienced a major earthquake and extreme political violence in the late 1980s. They found that the symptoms of depression traced to traumatic events tended to resolve over time. However, other symptoms of post-traumatic stress did not improve over a three-year course.[65]

The Armenians' experience is instructive but not necessarily typical of others who have PTSD. The Armenians were constantly surrounded by reminders of prior traumatic events (buildings destroyed by the earthquake, media reports of ongoing political violence, etc.). In many cases of PTSD there may be numerous triggers of the distressing memories, but direct tangible reminders of the actual traumatic event are often not present.

One of the greatest tragedies with a treatable anxiety disorder like PTSD is the lengthy time delay before patients seek treatment. The average delay is eight years.[66]

REACTIONS OF POST-TRAUMATIC STRESS VICTIMS

- Nightmares
- Sleeping problems
- Daytime fears
- Depression
- Withdrawal
- Cannot trust others
- Emotional numbing
- Feelings of helplessness

Figure 15

Phobias

Phobias are characterized by extreme, irrational fear. One example is extreme fear of spiders. Specific phobias like this are common, striking more than 1 in 10 people.

Depending on how easy it is to avoid the source of the phobia, the disorder may or may not be particularly debilitating. However, if the object that is feared is frequently encountered, affected individuals may seriously alter their lives in an attempt to deal with their condition. Further complicating the natural history of phobias is the fact that only *about 20 percent of adult phobias are resolved without treatment.*

Unlike many of the anxiety disorders, specific phobias generally do not result from exposure to a single stressful event. More typically, the stressor is an attitude communicated by other family members or close friends. It is not hard to imagine that a mother with an inordinate fear of spiders or thunderstorms is likely to pass that same irrational fear to her children.

In contrast to specific phobias there are also social phobias. Social phobias are characterized by being inappropriately afraid or uncomfortable in specific social situations. These phobias can be markedly intensified by an experience of public embarrassment or some other stressful experience in public.

Fortunately, effective treatments exist for phobias, as we saw in the case of other anxiety disorders. Treatments are described in **Figure 16**.[67]

Once phobias are diagnosed, specific cognitive-behavior therapy (CBT) techniques may be helpful. One technique exposes the patient to the phobic situation in small incremental steps. Non-drug cognitive behavioral therapy either alone or with additional medications (such as antidepressants or the anti-anxiety drugs known as benzodiazepines) can completely prevent panic attacks in 70 to 90 percent of suffers.[68] CBT and related therapies typically bring significant improvement within eight weeks.

No medications have emerged for treating specific phobias. However, when it comes to social phobias, some medications have proven effective, including antidepressants called MAO inhibitors.[69] Also, a class of drugs called beta blockers has helped a specific form of social phobia called performance phobia. These drugs have become popular among performers such as entertainers, who may take the drugs before a concert.

Another application of CBT is the use of breathing exercises. Proper or diaphragmatic breathing focuses on slow, deep breaths that rely on the diaphragm, the large muscle that separates the chest and abdominal cavities. Such deep breaths can combat a common relative of anxiety—taking rapid shallow breaths. Rapid breathing is itself problematic since it can dramatically decrease carbon dioxide levels in the blood and result in dizziness or fainting, tingling of the mouth and fingers, and muscle spasms. About 75 percent of patients improve significantly with such CBT approaches.

Obsessive-Compulsive Disorder

Obsessive-compulsive disorder (OCD)

TREATMENTS FOR PHOBIAS

- Gradual exposure to what the victim fears
- Slow, deep breathing from the diaphragm
- MAO inhibitors (drugs) for social phobias
- Beta-blockers (drugs) for social phobias
- Cognitive-behavior therapy
- Anti-anxiety herbs or drugs

Figure 16

141

is a disorder with two obvious characteristics—obsessions and compulsions. A classic example would be an inordinate fear of germs, which is addressed by repeated meticulous hand washing that far exceeds any normal health concern. Fear of germs is the obsession and the repetitive hand washing is the compulsion. The disturbing obsession is perceived as a problem that must be fixed, and it results in a compulsive attempt to resolve it.

We are not talking about normal concerns for hygiene or safety (e.g., rechecking to see if your house is locked). If the activities associated with the disorder consume at least an hour a day and are very distressing to the point of interfering with daily life, it qualifies as a case of OCD.

The progression of OCD varies with the individual victim, as described in **Figure 17**.

PROGRESSION AND TREATMENT OF OBSESSIVE-COMPULSIVE DISORDER

- Symptoms may wax and wane in severity.

- Tends to run in families.

- Tends to be accentuated in the face of life stresses.

- Treatments include non-drug behavioral therapies and drug medications.

- Drugs that boost serotonin are effective.

Figure 17

The classic behavioral therapy for OCD is called exposure and response prevention. In this treatment, the OCD sufferer is exposed to a situation that is the focus of the obsession and then is assisted in avoiding the usual ritual.

Regarding pharmaceuticals, *drugs that increase brain serotonin levels have demonstrated effectiveness.* These include Anafranil® as well as the group of antidepressant drugs known as Selective Serotonin Reuptake Inhibitors (SSRIs). Among the SSRIs are popular drugs like Celexa®, Prozac®, Luvox®, Paxil®, and Zoloft®.

In a recent press release from the National Institute for Mental Health, some interesting observations on the treatments of obsessive-compulsive disorder (OCD) were made. *Drugs that boost brain serotonin levels help 75 to 80 percent of patients dramatically.* However, the researchers report that it is "most fascinating" that they see *at least the same amount of improvement with non-drug behavioral treatments.*

Summary of Insights on Anxiety Disorders

It is no surprise that a number of "standard" therapies for anxiety disorders involve medications. Nonetheless, I want to reemphasize one of my themes—that *lifestyle therapies can often have profound effects on brain chemistry.* The value of the non-drug cognitive-behavioral therapy (CBT) in many of the anxiety disorders testifies to the fact that there are options for treatment in the mental health arena besides drug regimens.

Unfortunately, among those doing treatment research, there is not as much interest in dietary approaches and lifestyle therapies as there is in medication strategies. Why is this so? It is a direct result of the huge amounts of money and resources that pharmaceutical companies pour into the hands of medical researchers. There are few, if any, powerful players that have a vested commercial interest in people doing more walking or other exercising, or eating more fruits and vegetables.

Even though the amount of research on drug treatments for anxiety disorders far exceeds the research on lifestyle treatments, these non-drug therapies have been shown to be practical and effective—without the inevitable risk of side effects caused by medications. Until more controlled research is done, I would recommend that those inclined to utilize lifestyle therapies for anxiety disorders should work with qualified health practitioners to carefully monitor their progress. By all means, if you are on medication for an anxiety disorder, *do not stop it abruptly*. Even if you no longer need a medication, drugs that affect brain chemistry should be gradually decreased in dosage. And that process should be conducted with expert professional advice.

The bottom line in our growing understanding of anxiety disorders is that they can be serious conditions, but are often very open to treatment. Therapies of documented benefit include both medication regimens and non-drug behavioral techniques. I am convinced that many of the lifestyle approaches *for depression* documented in this book may also offer significant promise *for anxiety disorders*. In dealing with either one of these conditions, I recommend *a competent medical practitioner who would include lifestyle therapies* as part of the treatment program.

Depression Links with Stress, Anxiety, and Suicide

Major depression in one family member typically exerts major stresses on other family members. As the Surgeon General's report on mental health aptly expressed, "disability and suffering [from major depression] are not limited to the patient. Spouses, children, parents, siblings, and friends experience frustration, guilt, anger, financial hardship, and, on occasion, physical abuse in their attempts to lessen or cope with the depressed person's suffering."[70]

Anxiety commonly accompanies major depression. Among individuals with a diagnosis of major depression, almost half of them also have full-blown anxiety. The fact that anxiety and depression so often go hand in hand has led many researchers to propose that these conditions have common causative factors. Levels of serotonin in the brain are of great interest. As we have seen, *many anxiety disorders are improved by medications that boost levels of the serotonin hormone*. The importance of serotonin is more fully presented in *Chapter 8*.

What about suicide? Does anxiety lead to suicide? We learned in *Chapter 2* that depression is a major factor leading to suicide.[71] Depression may result in loss of the will to live, and may or may not lead to suicide. However, some degree *of anxiety, frustration, or stress* may push a depressed person over the brink and result in an *attempted or completed suicide*.

Conclusion

In this chapter we have studied several mental disorders. We have learned that stress, a common disorder, can lead to anxiety, which has five separate but related disorders. We have seen that each of these disorders can inflict damage to many parts of the body, aggravate or even bring on a wide variety of diseases, and lower the quality of life for millions of people.

The importance of recognizing the disorders and the features by which they can be identified were presented, along with effective treatments. The treatments include non-medication therapies, various counseling techniques, and prescription drugs.

The message of this chapter can be summarized as follows:

1. Stress and anxiety are more prevelant in our society than in former times, and they continue to increase year by year.

2. They inflict serious and sometimes fatal physical damage on our bodies.

3. New types of treatments can be effective with a minimum use of prescription drugs in many instances.

The next chapter is a continuation of the subject matter of this one. Here we will look at additional treatments for stress and anxiety that are in the category of self-help.

Also, cautions in taking certain popular drugs used to treat stress and anxiety are pointed out. Lifestyle factors are presented that are amazingly effective in combating these mental disorders.

References—

[1] Goldberg DP, Lecrubier Y. (1995). Form and frequency of mental disorders across centres. In T. B. Ustun & N. Sartorius (Eds.), *Mental illness in general health care: An international study.* (pp. 323–334). New York: John Wiley & Sons.

[2] Magee WJ, Eaton WW, et al. (1996). Agoraphobia, simple phobia, and social phobia in the National Comorbidity Survey. *Archives of General Psychiatry*, 53, 159–168.

[3] Regier DA, Farmer M E. (1990). Comorbidity of mental disorders with alcohol and other drug abuse. Results from the Epidemiologic Catchment Area (ECA) Study. *Journal of the American Medical Association*, 264, 2511–2518.

[4] National Institute of Mental Health. Facts about anxiety disorders. 2000 Dec 7.

[5] Sax LJ. The 34th annual survey of over 360,000 US college freshmen. University of California, Los Angeles (UCLA). Reuters Limited 1999 Jan 24.

[6] Crystal DS. Psychological maladjustment and academic achievement: A cross-cultural study of Japanese, Chinese, and American high school students. *Child Dev* 1994 Jun; 65(3):738-53.

[7] Weinberg A, Creed F. Stress and psychiatric disorder in healthcare professionals and hospital staff. *Lancet* 2000 Feb 12;355(9203):533-537.

[8] Selye H. The evolution of the stress concept. *Am Sci* 1973 Nov-Dec;61(6):692-699.

[9] Selye H. The evolution of the stress concept. *Am Sci* 1973 Nov-Dec;61(6):692-699.

[10] Guyton AC. The autonomic nervous system: the adrenal medulla. In: *Textbook of Medical Physiology*–8th edition. Philadelphia, PA:WB Saunders, Co., 1991 p. 672-676.

[11] Ephesians 4:26. *The Holy Bible.* Authorized King James Version.

[12] National Institute of Diabetes and Digestive and Kidney Disease. National Diabetis Clearinghouse. NIH Publication No. 99-3892, March 1999.

[13] Maeda K, Tanimoto K, et al. *Neurobiol Aging* 1991;12:161-163.

[14] Inael TR, Kalla NH, et al. The dexamethasone suppression test in obsessive-compulsive disorder. *Psychiatr Res* 1982;6:152-160.

[15] Roy-Byrns PP, Uhda TW, et al. The CRH stimulation test in patients with panic disorder. *Am J Psychiatry* 1986;143:396-399.

[16] Gold PW, Gwirtsman H, et al. Abnormal hypothalamic-pituitary-adrenal function in anorexia nervosa: pathophysiologic mechanisms in underweight and weight-corrected patients. *N Engl J Med* 986;314:1335-1342.

[17] Seeman TE, McEwen BS, et al. Increase in urinary cortisol excretion and memory declines: MacArthur Studies of Successful Aging. *J Clin Endocrinol Metab* 1997;82:2458-2465.

[18] Lupien SJ. Stress-induced declarative memory impairment in healthy elderly subjects: relationship to cortisol reactivity. *J Clin Endocrinol Metab* 1997 Jul;82(7):2070-2075.

[19] Lupien SJ. Cortisol levels during human aging predict hippocampal atrophy and memory deficits. *Nat Neurosci* 1998 May 1(1):69-73.

[20] Lupien SJ. Stress-induced declarative memory impairment in healthy elderly subjects: Relationship to cortisol reactivity. *J Clin Endocrinol Metab* 1997 Jul;82(7):2070-2075.

[21] Bender BG, Lerner JA, Poland JE. Association between corticosteroids and psychologic change in hospitalized asthmatic children. *Ann Allergy* 1991;66:414-419.

[22] Lupien SJ. Cortisol levels during human aging predict hippocampal atrophy and memory deficit. *Nat Neurosci* 1998 May 1(1): 69-73.

[23] Chrousos GP, Gold PW. The concepts of stress and stress system disorders, overview of physical and behavioral homeostasis. *JAMA* 1992 Mar;267(9):1244-1252.

[24] Chrousos GP. A healthy body in a healthy mind—and *vice versa*—the damaging power of "uncontrollable" stress. *J Clin Endocrinol Metab* 1998 Jun;83(6):1842-1845.

[25] Malazowaki S, Muzzo S, et al. The hypothalamic-pituitary-adrenal axis in infantile malnutrition. *Clin Endocrinol* 1990;32:461-465.

[26] Risher-Flowers D, Adinoff B, et al. Circadian rhythms of cortisol during alcohol withdrawal. *Adv Alcohol Subst Abuse* 1988;7(3-4):37-41.

[27] Von Bardeleben U, Heuser I, et al. CRH stimulation response during acute withdrawal and after medium-term abstention from alcohol abuse. *Psychoneuroendocrinology* 1989;14(6):441-449.

[28] Wand GS, Dobs AS. Alterations in the hypothalamic-pituitary-adrenal axis in actively drinking alcoholics. *J Clin Endocrinol Metab* 1991 Jun;72(6):1290-1295.

[29] Chrousos GP, Gold PW. The concepts of stress and stress system disorders, overview of physical and behavioral homeostasis. *JAMA* 1992 Mar;267(9):1244-1252.

[30] Sephton SE. Diurnal cortisol rhythm as a predictor of breast cancer survival. *J Natl Cancer Inst* 2000 Jun 21;92(12):994-1000.

[31] Nedley N, *Proof Positive: How to Reliably Combat Disease and Achieve Optimal Health through Nutrition and Lifestyle.* Ardmore, OK: Nedley Publishing, 1999 pp. 171,183,184.

[32] Sephton SE. Diurnal cortisol rhythm as a predictor of breast cancer survival. *J Natl Cancer Inst* 2000 Jun 21;92(12):994-1000.

[33] Kiecolt-Glaser JK, Glaser R, Strain EC, et al. Modulation of cellular immunity in medical students. *J Behav Med* 1986;9(1):5-21.

[34] Jahn I, Becker U, Jockel KH, Pohlabeln H. Occupational life course and lung cancer risk in men. Findings from a socio-epidemiological analysis of job-changing histories in a case-control study. *Soc Sci Med* 1995 Apr;40(7):961-75.

[35] Blumenthal JA, et al. Stress management and exercise training in cardiac patients with myocardial ischemia. Effects on prognosis and evaluation of mechanisms. *Arch Intern Med* 1997 Oct 27;157(19):2213-2223.

[36] Gullette EC, et al. Effects of mental stress on myocardial ischemia

during daily life. *JAMA* 1997 May 21;277(19):1521-1526.

[37] Matthews KA, et al. Stress-induced pulse pressure change predicts women's carotid atherosclerosis. *Stroke* 1998 Aug;29(8): 1525-1530.

[38] Kamack TW, et al. Exaggerated blood pressure responses during mental stress are associated with enhanced carotid atherosclerosis in middle-aged Finnish men: Findings from the Kuopio Ischemic Heart Disease Study. *Circulation* 1997 Dec 2; 96(11):3842-3848.

[39] Stoney CM, Hughes JW. Lipid reactivity among men with a parental history of myocardial infarction. *Psychophysiology* 1999 Jul;36(4):484-490.

[40] Lampert R, et al. Destabilizing effects of mental stress on ventricular arrhythmias in patients with implantable cardioverter-defibrillators. *Circulation* 2000 Jan 18;101(2):158-164.

[41] Everson SA, Lynch JW. Interaction of workplace demands and cardiovascular reactivity in progression of carotid atherosclerosis: Population based study. *BMJ* 1997 February 22;314:553.

[42] Cohen F, Kemeny ME, Kearney KA, Zegans LS, Neuhaus JM, Conant MA. Persistent stress as a predictor of genital herpes recurrence. *Arch Intern Med* 1999;159(20):2430-2436.

[43] Gordon GH, Bernstein MJ. Psychiatric mimics of allergic airway disease. *Immun and Aller Cl of North Am* 1996 February;16(1):199-214.

[44] Klinnert MD, Mrazek PJ, Mrazek DA. Early asthma onset: The interaction between family stressors and adaptive parenting. *Psychiatry* 1994 Feb;57(1):51-61.

[45] Geoffrey GH, Bernstein MJ. Psychiatric mimics of allergic airway disease. *Immun and Aller Cl of North Am* 1996February;16(1):199-214.

[46] Evans DL, Leserman J. Severe life stress as a predictor of early disease progression in HIV infection *Am J Psychiatry* 1997;154(5):630-634.

[47] Theoharides TC, Singh LK, et al. Corticotropin-releasing hormone induces skin mast cell degranulation and increased vascular permeability, a possible explanation for its proinflammatory effects. *Endocrinology* 1998 Jan;139(1):403-413.

[48] Chassany O, Marquis P. Validation of a specific quality of life questionnaire for functional digestive disorders. *Gut*1999 Apr;44(4):527-533.

[49] Ge RS, Hardy DO. Developmental changes in glucocorticoid receptor and 11beta-hydroxysteroid dehydrogenase oxidative and reductive activities in rat Leydig cells. *Endocrinology* 1997 Dec;138(12):5089-5095.

[50] Luke B, Avni M. Work and pregnancy: The role of fatigue and the "second shift" on antenatal morbidity. *Am J Obstet Gynecol* 1999 Nov;181(5 Pt 1):1172-1179.

[51] Light KC. Stress in employed women: A woman's work is never done if she's a working mom. *Psychosom Med* 1997 Jul-Aug;59(4):360-361.

[52] Carmichael SL, Shaw GM. Maternal life event stress and congenital anomalies. *Epidemiology* 2000 Jan;11(1):30-35.

[53] Brett KM, et al. Employment, job strain, and preterm delivery among women in North Carolina. *Am J Public Health* 1997 Feb;87(2):199-204.

[54] Forsen L, et al. Mental distress and risk of hip fracture. Do broken hearts lead to broken bones? *J Epidemiol Community Health* 1999 Jun;53(6):343-347.

[55] Greyson B. Dissociation in people who have near-death experiences: Out of their bodies or out of their minds? The Lancet 2000;355:460-463.

[56] Surgeon General's Report materials: Chapter 4 Adults and Mental Health.

[57] Taylor J, et al. Individual differences in electrodermal responsivity to predictable aversive stimuli and substance dependence. *Psychophysiology* 1999 Mar;36(2):193-198.

[58] Goetzel RZ, et al. The relationship between modifiable health risks and health care expenditures. An analysis of the multi-employer HERO health risk and cost database. The Health Enhancement Research Organization (HERO) Research Committee. *J Occup Environ Med* 1998 Oct;40(10):843-854.

[59] The material in this section is based on several references that are not shown as specific endnotes. These references are:

a. Mental Health: A Report of the Surgeon General, chapter 4.

b. National Institute of Mental Health. Anxiety Disorders. NIH Publication No. 97-3879 Printed 1994, Reprinted 1995, 1997 Accessed on line at http://www.nimh.nih.gov/anxiety/anxiety.cfm

c. National Institute of Mental Health. Anxiety Disorders Research Fact Sheet. NIH Publication No. 00-4504. Printed May 2000.

No specific endnote notations are shown when the material was obtained from one of these sources. However, information used from other sources is cited where appropriate.

[60] Cauffman E, et al. Posttraumatic stress disorder among female juvenile offenders. *J Am Acad Child Adolesc Psychiatry* 1998 Nov;37(11):1209-1216.

[61] Boscarino JA, Chang J. Electrocardiogram abnormalities among men with stress-related psychiatric disorders: Implications for coronary heart disease and clinical research. *Ann Behav Med* 1999 Summer;21(3):227-234.

[62] Summerfield D. War and mental health: A brief overview. *BMJ* 2000 Jul 22;321(7255):232-235.

[63] Summerfield D. War and mental health: A brief overview. *BMJ* 2000 Jul 22;321(7255):232-235.

[64] National Institute of Mental Health. Press Release. "Launch of the NIMH Anxiety Disorders Education Program" www.nimh.nih.gov/publicat/anxiety.htm; accessed on August 3, 2000.

[65] Goenjian AK, et al. Prospective study of posttraumatic stress, anxiety, and depressive reactions after earthquake and political violence *Am J Psychiatry* 2000 Jun;157:911-916. National Institute of Mental Health. Press Release. "Launch of the NIMH Anxiety Disorders Education Program" www.nimh.nih.gov/publicat/anxiety.htm; accessed on August 3, 2000.

[66] National Institute of Mental Health. Anxiety Disorders. NIH Publication No. 97-3879 Printed 1994, Reprinted 1995, 1997 Accessed on line at http://www.nimh.nih.gov/anxiety/anxiety.cfm.

[67] National Institute of Mental Health. Panic disorder treatment and referral: Information for health care professionals. NIH Publication No. 94-3642 Printed 1994.

[68] National Institute of Mental Health. Anxiety Disorders. NIH Publication No. 97-3879 Printed 1994, Reprinted 1995, 1997 Accessed on line at http://www.nimh.nih.gov/anxiety/anxiety.cfm.

[69] National Institute of Mental Health. Press Release. "Launch of the NIMH Anxiety Disorders Education Program" www.nimh.nih.gov/publicat/anxiety.htm; accessed on August 3, 2000.

[70] Mental Health: A Report of the Surgeon General. Department of Health and Human Services, National Institutes of Health, National Institutes of Mental Health, 1999 p. 244.

[71] Angst J, Angst F, Stassen HH. Suicide risk in patients with major depressive disorder. *J Clin Psychiatry* 1999; 60 Suppl 2:57-62; discussion 75-6, 113-116. Cited in: Mental Health: A Report of the Surgeon General, chapter 4.

DEPRESSION

CHAPTER EIGHT

STRESS *without* DISTRESS

This chapter will look at additional treatments for stress and anxiety that are in the category of self-help. Also, cautions in taking certain drugs that are commonly used to treat stress and anxiety are pointed out. Lifestyle factors are presented that have been proven to be amazingly effective in combating these mental disorders.

We will see in this chapter that there are many approaches for dealing with stress that can be helpful. Many of those that are most valuable are underutilized. I introduced some of them in my book *Proof Positive* in the chapter on stress. Nonetheless, many wanted me to go beyond the points I made there. This chapter significantly expands on my previous work. For those who have not read *Proof Positive*, I will reiterate some of the important points here.

I spelled out the important distinction between stress and stressors in the previous chapter. This understanding lays the ground work for a self-examination for each of us in determining the stressors that are present in our own personal lives.

Identify Your Own Stressors

To identify your own life stressors, it is best done in solitude with no distractions. With the TV, radio, and CD player off, with the phone unplugged, and no one else around, take some time to reflect on your life. Specifically, what things are currently bothering you? What do you consider to be stressors in your life?

A constructive way to uncover the different types of stressors is to ask the same questions journalists ask when writing a story for the news media. They want answers to the Five Ws—Who, What, When, Where, and Why? Examine each of these areas as they relate to your life. For example, who in your life is a stressor, or in what situations does he or she increase your stress level? A woman may feel that she has a wonderful husband, but it still stresses her when he turns the temperature down five degrees at bedtime. Perhaps a stressful "When and Where" is the morning commute through hectic traffic.

After you have identified your major stressors, what is the next step? You basically have the option of two strategies for dealing with each of them. The first option is to avoid or remove a stressor. Since this is not always possible or desirable, the second option is what I call "Healthy Adaptation."

Two Choices for Combating a Stressor

I will illustrate these two options with a hypothetical scenario. Let's say a new neighbor moves into the apartment next to yours. You go out of your way to make him feel welcome. You knock on his door with a cheery greeting, some fresh baked goods, and an offer to help with the move. Instead of accepting your kindness, he refuses your cooking and offer of assistance. He sullenly responds, "So, you live next door, eh? Let's keep out of each other's way and we'll get along just fine." With that, he closes the door.

You are pretty out of sorts when you go to bed that night at your usual midnight hour. Your mood is not helped by the pounding rock 'n' roll music that jars you out of sleep at 4 a.m. It is the new neighbor. Despite your aggravation, you decide to keep your cool and follow his advice to "keep out of each other's way." After four mornings in a row with rock music blasting at 4 a.m., you realize you have a major stressor in your life. How can you constructively deal with it?

Healthy Adaptation

Remember, there are two basic strategies. First, you can avoid or remove the stressor, or second, you can make a "healthy adaptation." Taking the first strategy, you could call the landlord and try to get your neighbor to change his ways. Or, you could take the direct approach and confront the neighbor. If you fear retaliation, another way to avoid or remove the stressor would be for you to move from your apartment. Each of these options may or may not work— although each would carry with it some consequences that might bring new stresses.

Taking the healthy adaptation route, you respond in a way to get the stressor to work *for you*. Let's say you've been thinking that your midnight retirement hour is too late anyway (good thinking!). Since your evening schedule is flexible, you plan to crawl into bed at 9 p.m. You decide to use the 4 a.m. rock music as your alarm clock, though it is not your favorite choice when

it comes to musical styles. After you arise, you go to a quiet part of the apartment and take time for some spiritual reading, prayer, and reflection. Then you get some much-needed exercise, and follow with a shower and a good breakfast. You still have plenty of time to arrive at work on time.

Whether waking up at 4 a.m. sounds like a viable strategy in your life or not, it illustrates the point. To the extent that you can take a stressor and use it in some way to work for you, you demonstrate a healthy adaptation. Healthy adaptation is very different from merely ignoring a stressor. If the rock music keeps you awake, you really cannot ignore it. Even if you sleep intermittently with the resonating accompaniment, you are likely to become extremely frustrated because of impaired sleep.

Take note that ignoring a stressor is rarely a healthy response. However, when a seemingly overwhelming stressor confronts you (particularly on either the social, mental, or spiritual level), sometimes the best option may be to ignore it. If you are so stressed that constructive options are not apparent, ignoring the presence of the stressor may allow you to progress from the stage of alarm to that of resistance. With this approach, you can then look at more constructive ways to adapt. When it comes to physical stressors like noise, unwanted music, or the pain of illness, there is sometimes no way to ignore them.

Avoid the Stressor by Fleeing

There are other unhealthy ways to deal with stressors. Another is escapism. This technique may find you making a 4 a.m. call to your 24-hour travel agency. You impulsively reserve a seat on the next plane to Tahiti. While you are soaking up the sun on the exotic beach, it may seem that escape has worked to your advantage. You are free of the raucous neighbor and are really enjoying yourself.

However, when you return home, the 4

a.m. concerts continue unabated and reality sets in. You are fired from your job for an unapproved absence, and the credit card bill from the trip arrives. In no time, your stress level is higher than it ever was. Indeed, escapism is not an optimal way to respond to a stressor. It can take a higher toll on your health than the original stressor did. It is easy to see escapism as the only strategy to buy some time in the face of an overwhelming situation, but the end results can be devastating.

Many see escapism as an extension of ignoring a stressor. When you mentally ignore a stressor, you remain in the environment where the stressor is confronting you without addressing it. The stressor continues to work on your physiology no matter how much you think you are ignoring it. When you physically escape from a stressor's sphere of influence, your body can get some respite. The trip to Tahiti illustrated this. Yet, if the escape was impulsive, it often includes a hefty price tag.

Most of the time escapism occurs only on a mental level—and is an extension of ignoring the stressor. The person remains in the presence of the stressor, but turns to a mind-altering escape to help forget about its presence. Such escape can be as diverse as watching television or taking a mixed drink. This type of escapism is worse than a futile attempt to ignore the stressor. Since you are still in the stressor's domain, the effects of stress on your body are perpetuated and the escape routes themselves are bad for your body and mind, sapping your reserves further.

To be more specific, alcohol impairs the brain's frontal lobe where decision-making and constructive solutions are based. Viewing television, even in its highest form, takes time away from activities such as exercise that could help enhance your coping reserves or defuse stress. More on exercise later.

Sometimes avoiding or removing a stressor is relatively easy; other times it is difficult or impossible. Consider the case of a nicotine addict. After three unsuccessful attempts at quitting cigarettes, Bill recognized that every relapse occurred when he went to a bar for a few drinks after work. Clearly, he recognized that drinking alcohol in a bar is a significant stressor for him. After all, it has continued to undermine his best resolutions to put smoking behind him. If his jaunts to the bar are a rare occurrence, it may be relatively easy for Bill to decide to completely avoid that questionable environment.

Consider Sue. She is having problems with a fellow manager. Even though she and Renee are in equal positions in the business, their mutual disrespect is obvious. They are rarely in the same meeting without a subtle undercurrent of demeaning insinuations. Clearly, Sue's stressful predicament is harder to deal with than Bill's smoking problem, since she can't avoid or remove a workplace stressor. She could try covert practices to get Renee fired, but it is typically a costly process both in terms of time and effort—not to mention the emotional resources expended. Often the only prompt way to remove workplace stressors is to quit the job (although changing shifts, transfers, and other options are sometimes available).

When confronted with the choice of walking away from the job or putting up with a stressor, many people opt for the latter. The results can take a devastating physical and emotional toll.

These cases show a clear need for option two—healthy adaptation. Let's examine how we can increase the likelihood of identifying and implementing constructive options.

Plan Properly

Proper planning and organization are key parts to healthy adaptation, since impulsive solutions typically fail and are neither healthy nor adaptive. Proper planning involves first determining what it will take to implement a strategy before you begin. If the option appears both reasonable and viable, then you can move to the next step in the planning process—specifically determining the optimal strategy to put into place.

Proper planning and organization are also important ways to avoid stressors. You likely can identify times in your life where you were confronted with major stressors only because you failed to plan properly. For example, you are stressed when you are late to work because of forgetting your lunch and having to go back.

Long-Range Systematic Stress Management

As we have discussed, the optimal ways of dealing with stressors include avoiding them, removing them, or getting them to work for you through healthy adaptation. If none of these approaches work in your specific circumstances, are there construc-

tive steps that you can take to maintain low stress levels in the future on an ongoing basis?

Fortunately, there are additional steps that can be taken that will have an ongoing effect in combating stress. The most powerful include lifestyle habits that help decrease the effects of stress, enabling us to live successfully in the presence of stressors.

A Four-Point Lifestyle Attack on Reducing Stress

Let's look at a description of a lifestyle that will reduce stress on an ongoing basis. A number of established stress-relieving practices could be integrated into our daily routine that will help us in all aspects of our being. Stress affects us in all of these aspects, as listed in **Figure 1**.

Strategies to deal with stress need to address each of the four aspects in the figure. In this section of the chapter, we will look at each of them. The first one is the *physical aspect*.

A Physically Healthy Lifestyle Reduces Stress

A physically healthy lifestyle is of great value in dealing with stress. The more efficiently your body functions, the better you will be able to have the coping resources that you need. A healthy body helps give you the upper hand in coping with life's stresses. Even if exposed to stressors that you have not yet removed or adapted to, better physical health will help to shield you from the health-robbing effects of these stressors.

Practices that will improve and maintain physical health are listed in **Figure 2**.

One critical element of a healthy lifestyle is *proper nutrition*. In the book **Proof Positive**, I go to great lengths to describe optimal diet and nutrition strategies. In a nutshell, this involved nine key areas. These are illustrated in **Figure 3**.

If some of these points seem hard to

THE FOUR ASPECTS OF OUR BEING

Physical

Mental

Spiritual

Social

Figure 1

accept, please note the thousands of medical references in my book **Proof Positive** that support these points. If you are not following a healthy lifestyle and are not willing to try it, you owe it to yourself to see the positive proof of the merits of the above dietary recommendations. The overwhelming evidence is there.

Research demonstrates that such a nutritional program boosts energy levels and improves mental clarity. Improved mental function and physical stamina are key ingredients in enhancing your ability to deal with life's stressors. A bonus provided by this program is that it also helps prevent chronic diseases like heart disease, diabetes, high blood pressure, and cancer.

Regular Physical Exercise

Regular physical exercise is another vital component of a healthy lifestyle that will be a deterrent to stress. Long known to help stave off heart disease, stroke, and some types of cancer, regular exercise can also help protect against the physical effects of daily stress. Medical literature demonstrates that *regular physical exercise is an important aid to mental health and stress control.*[1,2] Regular moderate exercise also appears to help the immune system, thus conceivably helping to offset stress-related immune suppression.[3,4,5]

Interestingly, *mind-engaging exercise* may have additional benefits. For example, getting involved with some vigorous yard work, gardening, or chopping wood, may prove even more beneficial than a walk. After all, you may unwittingly ponder your stress level while walking. Doing a practical physical task often requires more mental attention than walking or bicycling, making it less likely that you will engage in thoughts of your stress during your stress-relieving exercise.

In a study of 135 college students, those who exercised on a regular basis were more likely to take life's daily stresses in stride

PRACTICES THAT OPTIMIZE PHYSICAL HEALTH

- Proper nutrition

- Regular physical exercise

- Avoidance of "legal drugs" such as nicotine, caffeine, and alcohol

- Minimizing unnecessary prescriptions and over-the-counter medications

Figure 2

KEY PRACTICES FOR OPTIMAL NUTRITION

- Adopt a plant-based vegetarian diet.

- Avoid "refined foods" by choosing as many foods as possible in their natural state (e.g., whole grain bread *vs.* white bread).

- Eat only enough calories to maintain your ideal weight.

- Avoid stimulants such as caffeine and related compounds (e.g., theobromine in chocolate).

- Eat a good breakfast.

- Eat two or at the most three meals per day.

- Avoid snacking.

- Keep supper light; skip the evening meal altogether.

- Drink an abundance of water between meals (up to 8 glasses per day).

Figure 3

compared with their less physically-active counterparts.

Study participants filled out a questionnaire assessing the daily hassles they encountered during the past week—such as car trouble, running late for appointments, or arguments with coworkers. A second questionnaire listing their major life events, mood, physical activity, and overall health was also submitted. Highly stressed students who engaged in less exercise reported *21 percent more anxiety* than students who exercised more frequently. Exercise helped them get their mind away from their stressors—providing a time-out period.[6]

Exercise can also be a short-term strategy for enhancing your body's stress-coping capacities. When my patients encounter excessive stress, I instruct them to engage in some type of aerobic exercise at the very time that they feel the pressure. A 30-minute brisk walk in the fresh air, a run, or a bicycle ride can give you "a new lease on life." Regular physical exercise is also beneficial in anxiety states. People who physically exercise on a regular basis experience less depression and anxiety.[7] People who are already depressed or anxious will improve with regular physical exercise—the improvement is similar to the improvement experienced with medications—but without the side effects.[8]

Regarding physical symptoms, those who reported exercising less frequently during periods of high stress had *37 percent more physical symptoms of stress* than their counterparts who exercised more often. Many other studies have shown the converse; that is, *mental stress* takes a toll on *physical health*. Examples of health problems related to stress are documented in the previous chapter.

A study with laboratory rats looked at how *physical activity affects the brain*. Rats ran for exercise for eight weeks before 90 minutes of stress exposure and then were compared with rats that had not exercised before being exposed to stress. The results are shown in **Figure 4**.[9]

The implication from **Figure 4** is that if you were a diligent exerciser and exposed to stress, your brain would be much better equipped to handle the situation than would the brain of a sedentary person. If you were a diligent exerciser and you cut your finger, you would heal faster than a non-exerciser. If you broke your leg, the bone would heal faster. If you contracted a virus, your immune system would work more efficiently to return you to health. Notice that none of these strategies for combating stress involves the use of drug medications.

EXERCISE REDUCES STRESS IN LABORATORY

Rats that exercised regularly:

- Had lower levels of damaging protein in stress-related parts of their brains

- Released less norepinephrine, a stress hormone

- Appeared to help them recover more quickly from infections.

Figure 4

Massage

There is clear evidence that *massage helps humans to deal with stress*. The mechanisms by which massage exerts its effects are not completely understood. What is not clear is whether those stress-relieving effects are due to the physical benefits of massage, physical contact with another supportive individual, or a combination of the two. Without knowing whether it works mostly on a physical or social level, I have arbitrarily placed it in the physical category.

In one illuminating study, family members massaged children who were suffering from juvenile rheumatoid arthritis. Children with mild to moderate juvenile rheumatoid arthritis were massaged by their parents 15 minutes a day for 30 days (while a control group engaged in relaxation therapy). *The children's anxiety and stress hormone (cortisol) levels were immediately decreased by the massage.* Over the 30-day period their pain decreased according to self-reports, parent reports, and their physician's assessment of pain (both the incidence and severity). Pain-limiting activities were also increased.[10]

Massage also appears to benefit individuals who have primary psychiatric disorders. A 30-minute back massage was given daily for a five-day period to 52 hospitalized children and adolescents with personality problems who were also depressed. Compared with a control group who viewed relaxing videotapes, *the massaged subjects were less depressed, less anxious, and had lower saliva cortisol levels after the massage.* In addition, nurses rated the subjects as being less anxious and more cooperative on the last day of the study, and nighttime sleep increased over this period.[11]

Caffeine—It Raises Stress Hormones

I continue to marvel that many patients who struggle with stress and anxiety have not yet made a break with caffeine. Due to society's acceptance of this drug, the issue is worth belaboring. The message needs to be heard—*caffeine directly raises stress hormones.* The American Psychiatric Association says caffeine-induced disorders [of coffee drinkers] may be characterized by panic attack symptoms that resemble primary mental disorders.[12] Perhaps the greatest irony is that individuals may actually use caffeine to treat the results of stress-related problems.

A wake-up cup of coffee may seem vital to a person struggling with stress-induced insomnia, yet the caffeine may be part of what is keeping the person up that night. I challenge every one of you who drinks caffeine to enjoy two weeks of caffeine-free living. Many who have tried it are amazed at the increased quality of their lives and become convinced that *caffeine was doing much more to accentuate their stress problems than to help.*

The American Psychiatric Association also warns coffee drinkers of a malady called "Caffeine Intoxication." This occurs shortly after drinking 2 to 3 cups of coffee within a few minutes of each other. Five or more of the signs listed in **Figure 5** will likely develop during or shortly after caffeine use.

A caffeine addict should expect to experience withdrawal symptoms such as headache, sleepiness, laziness, and decreased alertness. They are usually most severe for only a day or two. In the following five days, they generally taper off and disappear.[13]

Alcohol, Stress, and Anxiety

Perhaps one of the most common self-

CAFFEINE INTOXIFICATION SYMPTOMS

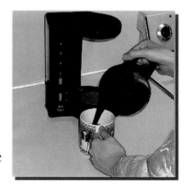

- Restlessness
- Nervousness
- Excitement
- Flushed face
- Diuresis (frequent urination)
- Gastrointestinal disturbance
- Muscle twitching
- Rambling flow of thoughts, speech
- Cardiac arrhythmia
- Periods of hyperactive behavior
- Psychomotor agitation

Figure 5

153

treatment approaches for stress is an after-work drink. I wonder if this practice has taken on a new legitimacy as the result of what appears to be a strong publicity effort orchestrated by the alcohol industry to establish drinking as a healthful practice. However, according to recent research, nothing could be further from the truth when it comes to combating stress. Alcohol weakens our capability to cope with stress and anxiety by lowering the level of three hormones in the brain that are needed to cope with stress in several ways. The hormones are listed in **Figure 6**.

The first two hormones in the figure are beneficial in warding off anxiety. Animal studies reveal that heavy drinking can lower brain levels of important hormones like serotonin and GABA that help control anxiety.[14] These same chemicals together with another brain messenger, dopamine, when in abundance, help provide a sense of reward or pleasure. Consequently, alcohol *may not only interfere with attempts to address anxiety*; it may further *undermine mood by increasing the risk of depressive symptoms.*

Animal researchers discovered that a high intake of alcohol weakens the hypothalamus' ability to release the key stress-activating hormone called corticotropin releasing hormone (CRH).[15] Research in human subjects has linked low levels of CRH with depressive problems. This has been studied in the relatively common condition called postpartum depression, where women sink into a depressive mood following delivery of a child. Greater reductions in CRH following childbirth caused an increased risk for depression in the new mothers.[16]

Many may drink alcohol to seek relief from short-term stress. The reality is that the effects of alcohol are detrimental whether the stress is short-term or long-term. It can contribute to long-term anxiety and depression, and in the short-term it actually undermines the capability of the body to respond to stress.

Minimize Drug Medicine Usage

What about drug medications? Are they of any help? Yes, there is a place for drug therapies. I do not advocate long-term reliance on drug therapies, and in my years of medical experience I have found that drugs are generally not a panacea for most conditions.

I have great respect for the physiologists and pharmacologists who are helping us to better understand brain circuitry. Such studies are largely aimed at the development of new prescription drugs for treating mental illnesses and many other diseases. However, I feel it is important to discover what options exist in the form of *non-toxic lifestyle therapies*. Serotonin and melatonin provide perfect examples. We are not dependent on medications to boost levels of these vital brain chemicals. Sunlight exposure increases levels of serotonin in the brain.[17] I devote an entire chapter in my book ***Proof Positive*** on how to increase melatonin levels naturally.[18]

Drug Therapy:
Benzodiazepines

Benzodiazepines are one of the most common drug families used to treat stress and anxiety. Many popular anti-anxiety

ALCOHOL AND STRESS

Stress-relief Hormones Reduced by Alcohol

- Serotonin

- GABA

- CRH

Figure 6

drugs are in this family. The list includes Xanax,® Klonopin,® Valium,® Ativan,® Paxipam,® and Librium.® Although these drugs may have a place in certain severe anxiety disorders, I mention them primarily to discourage their widespread use because of side effects. Benzodiazepines are associated with a host of risks. These are illustrated in **Figure** 7.

Other Drugs with Side Effects

This long list of side effects for benzodiazepines does not mean they are worse than any other medication options. Benzodiazepines have been around for a long time, providing ample time to see their side effects first hand. Newer drugs that have a shorter list of side effects may have no better track records after we have another 15 or 20 years to learn about all their side effects. *The bottom line is that every drug medication has side effects.*

I have not highlighted these problems with benzodiazepines because they were the easiest target among the medications used for stress and anxiety. Benzodiazepines actually look mild when compared to Monamine Oxidase Inhibitors (MAOIs). Included in this class are drugs like Nardil® and Parnate® that are prescribed for depression, panic disorder, and obsessive-compulsive disorder. Because of their high potential for serious side effects, they are usually used only when other medications are not effective.

Individuals taking MAOI drugs along with Prozac, a serotonin-blocking drug, *have had fatal reactions.* Serious interactions with a variety of common over-the-counter cough medications and decongestants can also occur. A list of other side effects of these drugs is provided in *Chapter 6*.

There has been a rise in popularity of the newer class of antidepressants known as selective serotonin-reuptake inhibitors (SSRIs). It is no doubt due in part to their frequent effectiveness in dealing with anxi-

ety, yet with potentially fewer serious side-effects than other medications used for anxiety and stress. Drugs in this class include Prozac,® Zoloft,® Paxil,® Celexa,® and Luvox.® They are not without their problems. They can take up to four weeks before their full effect is demonstrated. During that delay, users may actually experience an increase in anxiety. In addition, SSRIs have a list of side effects of their own. They can be seen in *Chapter 6*.

Although quite helpful for some types of anxiety disorders, SSRIs are either not helpful or only marginally helpful for others. For example, when it comes to social phobias, SSRIs may help, but relapse is typical unless cognitive-behavioral treatments are also employed.

Long before the SSRIs came on the scene, the tricyclic antidepressants (TCAs) were the mainstay of depression therapy. In addition to still being used in a variety of depressive disorders, TCAs are also used for certain stress-related symptoms (e.g., insomnia) as well as certain anxiety disorders.

SIDE EFFECTS OF BENZODIAZEPINES

- Drowsiness
- Fatigue
- Dependence/addiction
- Risk of "rebound symptoms"
- Stomach and intestinal distress
- Impairment of performance
- Appetite stimulation
- Drug interactions
- Intolerance to alcohol
- Increased risk of injuries
- Birth defects
- Respiratory problems

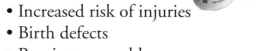

Figure 7

The TCAs also carry with them an unenviable list of side effects that are listed in *Chapter 6.*

I have not listed every drug that is used in the context of anxiety and other dysfunctional stress-related behaviors, but I have tried to provide you with enough information to underscore the adage that every drug has side effects. This has motivated me to avoid medication therapies whenever possible. Indeed, in the context of this chapter, I can say that *lifestyle measures should be the primary means used to control stress.*

This concludes the presentation of our attack against stress that involves our *physical health*. You will recall that this is the first of a four-point attack that is listed in **Figure 1**. We will now look at the second point of attack listed in the figure, which involves our *social health*.

Good "Social Health" Combats Stress

There is overwhelming evidence that the level of our "social health" is an important factor in the attack against stress. By social health, I mean the quality of our social relationships with our parents, siblings, other family members, and friends. Let us consider the human relationships in our infancy and early life.

Importance of Good Relations in Early Life

There is no question that human relationships in early life affect how we handle stress as adults. In an interesting animal study, baby rats that were removed from their mothers for a short time early in life showed an increased stress response months later.[19] Researchers at Montreal's McGill University have found that the converse is also true. Rats who get more physical attention in early life (maternal licking and grooming) tend to be more resilient in the face of stressors.[20]

Does this animal research apply to humans? In this case we are not without some insights. One of the human experiments in recent years occurred in Romania. There, under the Ceaucescu regime, enlarging the population became a political priority. One of the sad results of stern political policies was a huge increase of orphaned children, many of whom received little intimacy in early life. Observations of these children shows startling similarities to the rats that were denied optimal maternal physical attentions. The touch-deprived Romanian orphans tended to develop into children who show elevated cortisol levels and a greater response to stress.[21]

Intimacy between mother and child also brings benefits to the mother. At least this appears to be true in the case of breast-feeding. Preliminary data from a study of 59 women indicates that those who exclusively breast-fed their babies had the lowest amount of stress.

Even if parents make mistakes very early in their child's development, all is not lost. There is evidence that positive parenting skills can help school-age children deal more effectively with stressful life experiences. Researchers in Rochester, New York, studied a group of more than 100 children raised in a high stress, inner city environment who were seven to nine years old.[22] Half were from families with an annual income of less than $15,000. Stressors included neighborhood violence, family turmoil, and family separation.

The main factor that predicted how well a child would handle stress was *good parenting skills of their caregivers*. The good parents tended to have more nurturing involvement with their children during both their preschool and school-age years. They showed more consistent disciplinary practices, had good mental health themselves, and projected more positive expectations for their children's future.

One of the most interesting findings of the Rochester group was that the good parents were not invariably the result of good childhood homes. The very positive message is that *even if individuals experience abuse or neglect in their childhood, they can overcome that background and become excellent parents themselves.*

The Value of Personal Associations

Researchers say that those who prefer to deal with problems alone, rather than reach to others for comfort, may face higher stress levels and increased health risks. "We need real support from other people, and those who don't acknowledge it are going to feel besieged," Dr. Jonathan Schedler, a Harvard research psychologist, remarked in an article on facing stress.

The real key to personality-based stress may be a simple distrust of others, a distrust that sometimes leads to isolation. A series of occurrences that leads to increased stress is shown in **Figure 8.**

As the figure shows, distrust of others can finally lead to a weakened immune system. Researchers have discovered that *the immune system is greatly weakened for those who report feelings of loneliness.* Schedler says that the emotional attitudes we carry with us can help dictate stress and illness levels. "It has to do with whether you see the people in your life as benevolent[kindhearted] or malevolent [malicious]— whether they offer nourishment or frustration," he explained.[23]

Commitment to Causes That Help Others

One wonderfully constructive way to control stress is commitment to an honorable cause that helps others. A window on this topic is provided by medical research documenting the benefits of volunteerism. In a study of retirees, *those who volunteered more than 10 hours a week demonstrated a greater sense of purpose* as documented by significantly higher scores on a specific "Purpose in Life" test.[24]

Helping others provides a sense of meaning or purpose in life that is critical in dealing with certain stressors. A study performed on physicians provides an interesting and related insight. Namely, those doctors who had *the greatest sense of purpose in life had the least amount of anxiety regarding death*—the fear of which can be a great stressor.[25]

Participating in the lives of others on a social basis has been found to have significant physiological benefits. For example, in one study of patients who had recently undergone heart surgery, *higher levels of social participation* were associated with *better health six months after surgery.*[26] This cumulative evidence in the research literature clearly indicates the stress-relieving benefits of engaging in causes that are respectful to both God and man. It is well established that those who go through life fulfilling their own personal desires, but not being mindful of the needs of others, actually deprive themselves of the health-giving benefits of altruism and loving kindness. We each need to become personally involved in causes that meet God's approval and help humanity.

FACING PROBLEMS BY YOURSELF

—Steps leading to stress—

1. Distrust of others

2. Isolation

3. Feelings of loneliness

4. Weakened immune system

—Result—
Increased stress and higher risk of disease

Figure 8

IMPROVING THE IMMUNE SYSTEM

"If thou draw out thy soul to the hungry, and satisfy the afflicted soul; then shall thy light rise in obscurity, and thy darkness be as the noonday: and the Lord shall guide thee continually, and satisfy thy soul in drought, and **make fat thy bones**: *and thou shalt be like a watered garden, and like a spring of water, whose waters fail not."* Isaiah 58:10,11

Figure 9

The Holy Word provides further insights relating personal health to performing deeds of kindness. Notice the passage quoted in **Figure 9**.

As we "draw out thy [our] soul to the hungry, and satisfy the afflicted soul," we are promised that our darkness will be as the noonday. We will experience God's special guidance and blessing. When we go through our own personal times of crisis, it may look as if we are in a spiritual time of drought—cut off from all spiritual and emotional sustenance. Even in those situations, God promises to satisfy our souls if we are helping others. We see in this promise a profound description of a person under stress that ultimately finds relief by helping others. Part of the fulfillment of that promise comes as a God-ordained consequence of assisting others in *their* affliction.

God's promise to "make fat thy bones" could also be translated as "strengthen thy bones." The Hebrew word rendered "make fat" or "strengthen" is often used in the Bible with strong military connotations. For example, in Numbers 31:5 the Bible speaks of "twelve thousand [men] armed for war." The word translated "armed" is the very same Hebrew word that is translated "made fat" in Isaiah 58. This word then has the connotation of equipping to fight.

In other words, God's promise to "make fat thy bones" suggests that our bones are outfitted for battle, just as a soldier is armed for war. This battle imagery is very appropriate when we think of the role of our immune system. White blood cells are critical immune system cells that form in the internal recesses of our bones known as the marrow. Thus, if an individual's immune system has gone awry, it is not uncommon to extract a sample of the bone marrow to study the problem. Our key immune system cells depend on a healthy bone marrow.

Also forming in the bone marrow are the red blood cells, which carry vital oxygen to all parts of the body. The platelets, which protect us from bleeding to death when we are injured, are produced there. Our bones clearly play a vital role in protecting our health. It is no idle promise for the Scriptures to pledge to strengthen our bones. In these words is a sublime assurance of God's extra help in fortifying us against stress and illness if we become involved in causes that honor Him as well as our fellow humans.

This concludes the section on social health and its relation to stress and anxiety. The third aspect of our strategy to combat stress involves our *mental health*.

Good Mental Health Combats Stress

Research suggests that mental health is a necessary part of our assault against stress. Listening to good music has the potential to enhance our mental health. There is much evidence that music has unique stress-relieving properties.

Good Music Benefits the Mind

One of the questions that arises about music is whether it has natural stress relieving benefits or provides learned cues to relax. One way of addressing this issue is to look at the effect of music on newborns. Although it could be argued that fetuses are exposed to sounds in the womb, they have probably not learned techniques of relaxation in connection with their exposure to music.

Let us examine a study of premature and low birth-weight babies in a newborn intensive care unit regarding their exposure to music. There were 52 babies in stable condition that were restricted to their incubators. Half of them were exposed to lullabies and children's music three times a day (no rock). The other half had no music. Stress behaviors were observed in both groups of babies, along with weight, caloric and formula intake, and length of stay in the hospital. The babies exposed to music had greater weight gain, increased appetite, and a reduced length of their hospital stay.[27]

Studies at Presbyterian University Hospital at the University of Pittsburgh and another study reported in *The Journal of the National Cancer Institute* revealed that sedative music has many benefits, as shown in **Figure 10**.

Deep Breathing, Classical Music, and Sounds of Nature for Relieving Stress

Although deep breathing is often connected with Eastern meditative styles, the advantages of breathing exercises may well be obtained without incorporating such meditative practices.

A study was made in which the participating subjects were given a task that caused mental stress, which raised their blood pressure. Upon finishing the task, researchers measured the average time it took for the blood pressure to return to normal, which was 3.7 minutes. The subjects then repeated the task, followed by *deep breathing exercises*. This time, in 2.7 minutes their blood pressure was normal. In the third test the subjects listened to *classical music* after the task. The time to normal blood pressure was

2.9 minutes. The fourth test involved listening to *sounds of nature* (ocean waves, rain, etc.). The time was 3.0 minutes.

Deep breathing, classical music, and natural sounds all helped recovery from a sudden stressor.

Health of the Frontal Lobe of the Brain

The health of the frontal lobe of the brain is very important in combating stress and depression. This is covered in *Chapter 9*. Here we will look at just one aspect of frontal lobe health. It has to do with the role of the frontal lobe in controlling impulsive actions. If you find that some of the stressors in your life are a result of handling stressful situations in an aggressive manner, you should seriously consider my recommendations for strengthening your frontal lobe. *Violence and aggression are the result of failing to cope with stressors.* Research indicates that optimizing frontal lobe function may be vital to decreasing the tendency to violent or aggressive responses to stressors.

BENEFITS OF SEDATIVE MUSIC

- Reduces anxiety

- Has profound effect on brain's rhythm and function

- Increases relaxation

- Reduces need for pain relievers in cancer patients and childbirth

- Boosts socialization

- Decreases symptoms in "disturbed and inaccessible" psychiatric patients

Figure 10

Perhaps one of the clearest illustrations of the importance of frontal lobe function comes from studies of Vietnam veterans with head injuries. Nearly 300 Vietnam veterans were studied who had penetrating wounds at various locations on the head.

The results indicated that *veterans with injury to the frontal lobe consistently demonstrated greater aggression and violence tendencies* than those with injuries in other brain areas.[28] Thus, a healthy frontal lobe is important if we want to possess good self-con-

trol. In addition, many other benefits will be realized if we have a healthy frontal lobe. How can we attain it? *Chapter 9* has answers to this question.

Scriptural Advice: Do Not Be Anxious About the Future

Another key approach to controlling stress is to refrain from being anxious about the future. Without proper planning, it is natural to become anxious about the future. A student who is preparing for an upcoming test, for example, is benefited by a certain amount of stress. This type of stress should provide motivation to study and prepare for the examination. However, it would be self-defeating to be worried and anxious about the test if you are prepared for it.

Actually, worry tends to incapacitate, whereas a healthy attitude toward the stressor—seeing it as a challenge—tends to motivate. Fearful of his lack of knowledge, the student may be tempted to say, "Why even try? I can never master this subject in time for the test." A more constructive attitude would involve organization and planning without worry. The student may say, "I still have three hours this evening; let me see what I can learn." Again, the Scriptures are of help on this point, as quoted in **Figure 11**.

Jesus is not speaking here against planning. This would contradict another statement from Jesus in Luke 14:28 that lends implicit support to *the importance of planning.* This Bible statement is quoted in **Figure 12**.

Jesus is saying, "Once you properly plan and carry out that plan, do not worry about tomorrow." In other words, tomorrow will bring what it will.

However, in our illustration of taking a test, it would be foolish for a student who was not studying to say, "I am at peace. I will not worry about the test next week. God will help me when the day comes." On the other hand, the student who is diligently

DO NOT BE ANXIOUS ABOUT TOMORROW

"Take therefore no thought for the morrow: for the morrow shall take thought for the things of itself."

—Matthew 6:34

Figure 11

PROPER PLANNING AND ORGANIZATION

"For which of you, intending to build a tower, sitteth not down first, and counteth the cost, whether he have sufficient to finish it?"

—Luke 14:28

Figure 12

studying should not worry that the teacher will make the test too difficult, or that studying will not help or that a failing grade will be the result.

Worry and anxiety about things that we cannot change are self-defeating. No one today can address what tomorrow will bring. However, if the problem exists today and needs to be addressed today, then we should address it today. It takes planning, organization, and motivation. Before we have the time or opportunity to address the issue, we should not worry about it. Jesus is calling us to do whatever work or planning that is necessary for today. At the same time He is advising us to stop agonizing over the future. Such worrying will always be a source of significant stress, and is counterproductive.

Freedom from worry may not only help us combat stress; it may also have profound benefits regarding our body functions. As I point out in *Chapter 9* on the frontal lobe, spontaneous regression of cancer (SRC) may be linked to a mental attitude that is free of worry. In SRC, a person with a fatal cancer survives independent of any treatment.

Adequate Rest and Sleep Promote Mental Health

Anxiety can short circuit one of the most important stress-relieving lifestyle choices—adequate rest. We all need adequate rest if we want to have good mental health. Four dimensions of rest are presented in **Proof Positive**.[29] Two of those are applicable here. First, sleep is a needful restoring process for maintaining our defense against stress and anxiety. Second, stress and anxiety can prevent us from getting our required sleep. They are key causes of insomnia.

Dr. James Perl in his book, **Sleep Right in Five Nights**, observes that anger—one of the most common human responses to stressors—is a cause of insomnia for many

people.[30] These two points lay the foundation for a vicious cycle, as described in **Figure 13**.

Strong Spiritual Health Combats Stress and Anxiety

One way to break the vicious cycle of rest *vs.* stress is to bring your concerns to God through an active process of meditation and prayer. Realizing that you can trust God with the future may be the missing ingredient in addressing this dilemma.

VICIOUS CYCLE WITH STRESS AND SLEEP

- Stress interferes with sleep.
- Insufficient sleep leads to more stress.
- More stress increases sleep-lessness.
- More sleeplessness leads to still more stress.

Figure 13

THINK ON THESE THINGS

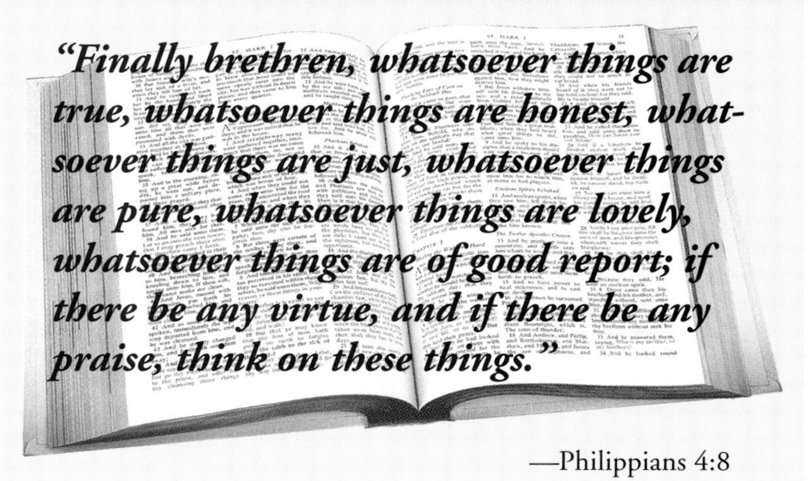

"Finally brethren, whatsoever things are true, whatsoever things are honest, whatsoever things are just, whatsoever things are pure, whatsoever things are lovely, whatsoever things are of good report; if there be any virtue, and if there be any praise, think on these things."

—Philippians 4:8

Figure 14

Think on Elevated Themes

Thinking on elevating themes is a tremendous benefit. The Holy Scriptures again provide meaningful guidance, as quoted in **Figure 14**.

The Scriptures admonish us to direct our minds to elevating attributes such as truth, honesty, purity, and goodness. If we want to master stress and have it work for us rather than against us, we need to focus on uplifting themes. Unfortunately, most of us have a tendency to dwell on the negative. It is easy to forget the many good things that we have enjoyed in the past and are presently experiencing. We tend to concentrate on our troubles.

We must strive to focus on what we do have—rather than on what we lack. Let us not allow the bad to overshadow the good, but in the words of the old hymn, let us "Count our many blessings—name them one by one." Such an attitude will help strengthen our immune systems and our abilities to cope with difficulties. Advice that should be a help to all who want to optimally manage stress is quoted in **Figure 15**.[31]

Some families formally express gratitude and praise to God at mealtime. This is a good start, but a spirit of gratitude and praise goes beyond a few short prayers each day. It implies a continuous attitude of thankfulness for all the good gifts God has given to us. Such a realization of God's blessings will go far in warding off distress.

A "spirit of gratitude and praise" should be awakened in all of us, especially in this country, because of the many blessings the Lord has provided. There is a sharp contrast between the many comforts that the average American has in life with the lack of such comforts in many other parts of the world. The severity of stressors in the life of the average American is small by comparison.

THE TOP PRIORITY IN HEALTHFUL LIVING

Nothing tends more to promote health of body and of soul than does a spirit of gratitude and praise.

Figure 15

GROUND RULES TO AVOID CRITICIZING

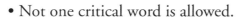

A two-week exercise

- Not one critical word is allowed.
- If your children do something good, praise them for it.
- If they do something bad, do not criticize.
- In all their activities the stipulations are the same.
- Speak only positively to others.
- If you slip, start the program over.

Figure 16

Beware of a Critical Spirit

In my stress control seminars I give an assignment to the participants that, ironically at first, they usually find to be stressful. The assignment is to *refrain from saying anything critical about anyone or anything for a minimum of two weeks*. The ground rules are stated in **Figure 16**.

Fortunately, the seminar spans eight weeks because virtually everyone finds it necessary to begin again the second day. Some may require a third or even a fourth beginning. The first few days are very stressful. However, when the two weeks are successfully finished, no one as yet has expressed regret regarding the assignment. In general, participants feel that it was a rewarding experience that helped to change their outlook on life and encouraged them to focus on the good.

This does not mean that criticism should never be offered. The class exercise is simply calculated to help people become more aware of their habits of faultfinding. It is designed to demonstrate to the participants that, with effort, they can control their acts of criticism and thereby realize *benefits to themselves and others*.

Certainly, criticism can be beneficial if it is appropriate, constructive, and tactfully given. However, much of our criticism has its roots in a negative attitude. Worse still, we often are critical of things over which we have absolutely no control or influence. Such criticism damages ourselves and others. Furthermore, it tends to foster negative attitudes in those around us.

Nearly 100 years ago, author Ellen White captured the essence of such concerns in the powerful counsel to fellow Christians stated in **Figure 17**.[32]

I cannot help wondering how much better this world would be if we all followed the counsel in **Figure 17**.

Christian Meditation

Another measure for controlling stress is Christian meditation. I believe we have a critical need for meditation and prayer on a daily basis. It is a form of rest and rejuvenation that few appreciate to its fullest extent. This topic is explained more fully in *Chapter 9* on the frontal lobe, as well as in the final chapter of this book. However, the importance of the subject warrants a description here as well.

Meditation and prayer have their greatest benefits when they provide a *respite from stressful thoughts and feelings*, and an opportunity to find solutions for dealing with life's most pressing stressors. In order for such processes to occur, the *reasoning powers of the brain must be active during the meditative process*. Our highest intellectual powers, including spiritual reasoning, reside in part of the brain called the frontal lobe.

As described in the chapter on the frontal lobe, when this brain region is intimately involved in our thinking, a type of brain wave called the beta wave predominates. If you were to measure the instantaneous electrical voltages in the brain by an electroencephalogram (EEG) and it showed a beta wave, it would indicate that thinking and reasoning is occurring, characterized by dynamic frontal lobe activity.

Studies show that Christian meditation stimulates beta activity in the frontal lobe. This is what one would expect. After all, prayer from the biblical perspective is an extremely active process. Whether we are reflecting on God's goodness, thanking Him for helping us in specific ways, seeking to know His will in a perplexing situation, or praying for individuals who have specific needs, Christian meditation and prayer create an active frontal lobe.

For clarity, the characteristics of Chris-

CHRISTIAN RECOMMENDATIONS FOR DEALING WITH CRITICISM

"When we are tempted to murmur or complain at something someone has done, praise something in that person. Say, 'Satan, I have defeated your temptations this time.' Cultivate the habit of thankfulness. Praise God over and over again for His wonderful love in giving Christ to die for us. It never pays to think of old grievances. God calls upon us to cultivate His mercy and His matchless love, that we may be inspired with praise."

Figure 17

tian meditation are summarized in **Figure 18**.

Even though it can involve a high level of mental activity, Christian meditation and prayer are also very relaxing. A biofeedback monitor can be used to detect the relaxation of the body inherent in such meditation. For those unfamiliar with the process, biofeedback is simply a means of making any internal process of the human body externally visible by the use of monitoring devices attached to the skin.[33]

One method of assessing tension is by measuring the skin's electrical resistance.[34] When a person is emotionally tense, there tends to be a drop in this resistance. The skin more readily conducts an electric current that can be measured by an electric meter.[35] The familiar lie detector test works on this principle.

As part of a medical school class, I carried a portable biofeedback monitor that took such a measurement as I went through my daily routine. I was impressed that it demonstrated *the most relaxed state when I was actively praying to God*. Biofeedback for general use is explained at the end of this chapter.

Not All Meditation Styles are Effective

Not every form of meditation, however, is characterized by beta activity and frontal lobe involvement. In sharp contrast to Christian meditation stand the meditative practices popularized in the eastern hemisphere, called Eastern meditation. It appears that its effectiveness results from a form of escapism. Many research studies have demonstrated an accentuation of what is called an *alpha brain rhythm instead of the beta rhythm* when an experienced subject engages in such Eastern-based practices as yoga or transcendental meditation.[36]

Alpha waves are brain waves of a lower frequency (8 to 13 cycles per second)[37] than beta waves. Such waves indicate that a person has entered into *a trance-like state where frontal lobe activity is weak*. When the brain has an alpha rhythm, it cannot critically analyze incoming information. From the standpoint of both this alpha brain rhythm and the means to induce the meditative state, *Eastern meditation is strikingly similar to hypnotism.*

Eastern Meditation and Hypnosis

Hypnosis, by design, bypasses the frontal lobe as it helps the subject enter a trance-like state. Eastern religions use the principle of a solitary focus to induce a meditative state, similar to the technique employed by the hypnotist. As one author explains, mental focus for transcendental meditation can be achieved by focusing on a single word (called a mantra), a single shape, or a body part. He mentions that another ancient practice is to focus on the navel, the forehead, or some other body part.[38] Just as the hypnotist requires this single-minded focus and an environment free from all outside diversions, so does the meditator.

The characteristics of Eastern meditation are summarized in **Figure 19**.

CHRISTIAN MEDITATION CHARACTERISTICS

- Christian meditation and prayer provide a respite from stressful thoughts and feelings.

- Reasoning powers of the brain *must be active* during the meditative process.

- The beta brain wave in the frontal lobe predominates, which fosters *active reasoning*.

- Our highest intellectual powers, including spiritual reasoning, reside in the frontal lobe.

Figure 18

Dr. Herbert Benson, a Harvard researcher and physician, has presented what some have called a secular version of Eastern meditation. However, Benson uses the same elements as the Eastern meditator and the hypnotist—a quiet environment and a single-minded focus (in his case, a word or phrase of Hindu worship).[39] Benson also mentions another essential element in this process—a passive attitude. In fact, he states that this is "perhaps the most important of the elements."[40] Rice observes that all of these Eastern-style meditative relaxation techniques emphasize a passive attitude.[41]

It is this *passive* attitude with a prominent alpha brain wave that illustrates one of the greatest problems with this meditative style. Although it may temporarily provide relief and relaxation by removing the mind's focus on certain stressors, the practice does not appear able to help in subsequently dealing with stressors in a constructive way.

This stands in sharp contrast to the reflective meditation of the Christian. With biblical meditation and prayer, the emphasis is on an *active* reflection that helps focus the frontal lobe. Rather than striving for a passive state that *represses thoughts*, Christian meditation emphasizes communion with God, *thinking His thoughts*, *sensing His presence*, and knowing His will. In addition to providing release from stress, this type of meditation provides an opportunity to get meaningful answers and solutions to problems.

There is further concern that the passive mental state cultivated by these meditative techniques may do more harm than good. It has long been known that Eastern meditation and secular relaxation training may have deleterious effects on the nervous system. A classic study found that, when compared with an American control group, yoga produced higher levels of sympathetic activity with increased adrenaline output. Thus, yoga produced *the same physical reactions as a sudden stressor*, which was ex-plained in the previous chapter. This was true for most measurements made on Eastern yoga practitioners.[42]

In another study, subjects who received training in transcendental meditation displayed *a higher cardiovascular stress response* after learning this meditative practice.[43]

We see that problems arise when *escapist meditative practices* are employed in place of *constructive strategies* to deal with stressors. Such a hypothesis is consistent with work cited by Dr. Larry Dossey. Research that studied stress hormones before, immediately following, and two days after surgeries yielded a surprising result. Immune-weakening stress hormones significantly increased only in those that had formal relaxation training. Those who apparently addressed their anxieties and fears without using escapism relaxation techniques did not show the rise in stress hormones.[44]

Mind Control

A third difficulty with Eastern methods relates to their potential danger when employed in a group setting. Remember that in Eastern-style meditation, alpha

EASTERN MEDITATION AND HYPNOSIS

- Eastern meditation is in sharp contrast to Christian meditation.

- An alpha brain rhythm is present instead of beta rhythm.

- This signifies a trance-like state in which information bypasses the frontal lobe.

- *Like hypnotism, thoughts are repressed and reasoning is absent.*

- *The meditator is open to mind control.*

Figure 19

waves predominate and the reasoning powers of the frontal lobe are suppressed. In such a hypnotic-like state, an individual may record information and suggestions without interpretation and without frontal lobe evaluation. Some have thus wondered whether Eastern religious cults take advantage of adherents who enter a meditative state in a group setting. Such critics point out that the brain would be in a state where it would not critically analyze any information it received. The meditator would then be extremely susceptible to mind control. These concerns appear to be well-founded. Such meditation in a group setting, or anywhere, should especially be avoided.

Spiritual Focus Therapy

One area of counseling that is often neglected by psychologists and physicians is what I call "spiritual focus" therapy. This may hold the most promising non-drug therapy for stress and anxiety disorders. Since I am a Christian, I will expound on the ancient words of Christ and Scripture to give perhaps new meaning to the role of true spirituality in a person's life.[45] No matter what your religious affiliation, I think you will be able to grasp the broad principles of spirituality by studying this section. Spiritual focus therapy is outlined in **Figure 20.**

"Come unto Me, all ye that labor and are heavy-laden, and I will give you rest."[46] These words of comfort were spoken to the multitude that followed Jesus. The Savior had said that only through Himself could men receive a knowledge of God. He had spoken of His disciples as the ones to whom a knowledge of heavenly things had been given. But He left none to feel themselves shut out from His care and love. All who labor and are heavy-laden may come unto Him.

Scribes and rabbis, with their punctilious attention to religious forms, had a sense of want that rites of penance could never satisfy. Publicans and sinners might pretend to be content with the sensual and earthly, but in their hearts were distrust and fear. Jesus looked upon the distressed and heart burdened, those whose hopes were blighted, and who with earthly joys were seeking to quiet the longing of the soul, and He invited all to find rest in Him.

Tenderly He bade the toiling people, "Take My yoke upon you, and learn of Me; for I am meek and lowly in heart: and ye shall find rest unto your souls."[47]

In these words Christ is speaking to every human being. Whether they know it or not, all are weary and heavy-laden. All are weighed down with burdens that only Christ can remove. He has borne the burden of our guilt. He will take the load from our weary shoulders. He will give us rest. The burden of care and sorrow He will also bear. He invites us to cast all our care upon Him; for He carries us upon His heart.[48]

The Elder Brother of our race is by the eternal throne. He looks upon every soul who is turning his face toward Him as the Savior. He knows by experience what are the weaknesses of humanity, what are our wants, and where lies the strength of our temptations; for He was in all points

SPIRITUAL FOCUS THERAPY

Christ extends an invitation to all who are weary and heavy-laden. The invitation is, "learn of Me"... "cast your cares upon Me"... and "take My yoke upon you."

He promises that the result will be:
You will find **rest** . . .
You will be kept in **perfect peace**
You will **delight to do His will**
You will be used to **bless others**

Figure 20

tempted like as we are, yet without sin. He is watching over you, trembling child of God. Are you tempted? He will deliver. Are you weak? He will strengthen. Are you ignorant? He will enlighten. Are you wounded? He will heal. David, the psalmist stated in the same psalm that the Lord "telleth the number of the stars;"[49] and yet "He healeth the broken in heart, and bindeth up their wounds."[50]

"Come unto Me," is His invitation. Whatever your anxieties and trials, spread out your case before the Lord.[51] Your spirit will be braced for endurance. The way will be opened for you to disentangle yourself from embarrassment and difficulty. The weaker and more helpless you know yourself to be, the stronger you will become in His strength. The heavier your burdens, the more blessed the rest in casting them upon the Burden Bearer. The rest that Christ offers depends upon conditions, but these conditions are plainly specified. They are those with which all can comply. He tells us just how His rest is to be found.

"Take My yoke upon you," Jesus says. The yoke is an instrument of service. Cattle are yoked for labor, and the yoke is essential that they may labor effectually. By this illustration Christ teaches us that we are called to service as long as life shall last. We are to take upon us His yoke, that we may be co-workers with Him.

The yoke that binds to service is the law of God. The great law of love revealed in Eden, proclaimed upon Sinai, and in the new covenant written in the heart, is that which binds the human worker to the will of God. If we were left to follow our own inclinations, to go just where our will would lead us, we should fall into Satan's ranks and become possessors of his attributes. Therefore God confines us to His will, which is high, and noble, and elevating. He desires that we shall patiently and wisely take up the duties of service. The yoke of service Christ Himself has borne in humanity. He said, "I delight to do Thy will, O

My God: yea, Thy law is within My heart."[52] "I came down from heaven, not to do Mine own will, but the will of Him that sent Me."[53] Love for God, zeal for His glory, and love for fallen humanity brought Jesus to earth to suffer and to die. This was the controlling power of His life. This principle He bids us adopt.

There are many whose hearts are aching under a load of care because they seek to reach the world's standard. They have chosen its service, accepted its perplexities, adopted its customs. Thus their character is marred, and their life made a weariness. In order to gratify ambition and worldly desires, they wound the conscience, and bring upon themselves an additional burden of remorse. The continual worry is wearing out the life forces. Our Lord desires them to lay aside this yoke of bondage. He invites them to accept His yoke; He says, "My yoke is easy, and My burden is light." He bids them seek first the kingdom of God and His righteousness, and His promise is that all things needful to them for this life shall be added.[54] *Worry is blind*, and cannot discern the future; but *God sees the end from the beginning.*[55] In every difficulty He has His way prepared to bring relief. Our heavenly Father has a thousand ways to provide for us, of which we know nothing. Those who accept the one principle of making the service and honor of God supreme will find perplexities vanish, and a plain path before their feet.

"Learn of Me," says Jesus; "for I am meek and lowly in heart: and ye shall find rest." We are to enter the school of Christ, to learn from Him meekness and lowliness. Redemption is that process by which the soul is trained for heaven. This training means a knowledge of Christ. It means emancipation from ideas, habits, and practices that have been gained in the school of the prince of darkness. The soul must be delivered from all that is opposed to loyalty to God.

In the heart of Christ, where reigned perfect harmony with God, there was perfect peace. He was never elated by applause, nor dejected by censure or disappointment. Amid the greatest opposition and the most cruel treatment, He was still of good courage. But many who profess to be His followers have an anxious, troubled heart, because they are afraid to trust themselves with God. They do not make a complete surrender to Him; for they shrink from the consequences that such a surrender may involve. Unless they do make this surrender, they cannot find true peace.

It is the love of self that brings unrest. When we are born from above, the same mind will be in us that was in Jesus, the mind that led Him to humble Himself that we might be saved. Then we shall not be seeking the highest place. We shall desire to sit at the feet of Jesus and learn of Him. We shall understand that the value of our work does not consist in making a show and noise in the world, and in being active and zealous in our own strength. The value of our work is in proportion to the impartation of the Holy Spirit. Trust in God brings holier qualities of mind, so that in patience we may possess our souls.

The yoke is placed upon the oxen to aid them in drawing the load, to lighten the burden. So with the yoke of Christ. When our will is swallowed up in the will of God, and we use His gifts to bless others, we shall find life's burden light. He who walks in the way of God's commandments is walking in company with Christ, and in His love the heart is at rest. When Moses prayed, "Show me now Thy way, that I may know Thee," the Lord answered him, "My presence shall go with thee, and I will give thee rest." And through the prophets the message was given, "Thus saith the Lord, Stand ye in the ways, and see, and ask for the old paths, where is the good way, and walk therein, and ye shall find rest for your souls."[56,57] And He says, "O that thou hadst hearkened to My commandments! then had thy peace been as a river, and thy righteousness as the waves of the sea."[58]

Those who take God at His word, and surrender their souls to His keeping, their lives to His ordering, will find peace and quietude. Nothing of the world can make them sad when Jesus makes them glad by His presence. In perfect acquiescence there is perfect rest. The Lord says, "Thou wilt keep him in perfect peace, whose mind is stayed on Thee: because he trusteth in Thee."[59] Our lives may seem a tangle; but as we commit ourselves to the wise Master Worker, He will bring out the pattern of life and character that will be to His own glory. And that character which expresses the glory—character—of Christ will be received into the Paradise of God. A renovated people shall walk with Him, for they are worthy.

As through Jesus we enter into rest, heaven begins here. We respond to His invitation, "Come, learn of Me," and in thus coming we begin life eternal.

SHORT-TERM STRESS REDUCERS

1. Herbal therapies

2. Fasting

3. Biofeedback

4. Relaxation

5. Calcium relieves Pre-Menstrual Syndrome

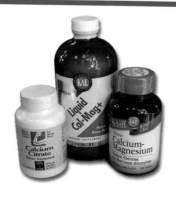

Figure 21

Short-Term Strategies for Reducing Stress

In addition to adopting long-range lifestyle strategies for combating stress, there are a number of short-term strategies that are helpful. These strategies can be employed in one of two ways. First, they can be employed to help you during an acutely stressful time in your life (e.g., short-term use of the herb, Kava-kava). They can also be used to help in optimizing your coping skills in general (e.g., in the case of biofeedback). **Figure 21** lists selected short-term strategies for reducing stress. You will note that some lifestyle therapies can also be used as short-term strategies.

Herbs and Stress

Research on most herbs has been limited, but some herbs appear to be helpful in alleviating stress. The following are considered to be effective.

Kava-kava is helpful for nervousness, stress, and anxiety.[60] Lavender is suggested for loss of appetite, nervousness, and insomnia.[61] Lemon Balm is recommended for nervousness and insomnia.[62] Valerian can help nervousness, insomnia, stress, and anxiety.[63] For more complete information including side effects and dosages on these herbs see *Chapter 6*.

Herbs to Avoid

Just as some herbs may have a role in combating anxiety, other herbs can actually perpetuate problems. Guarana provides one such example. Guarana is a product from the seeds of the Amazonian liana Paullinia cupana, and has recently gained enough popularity to become a cultivated product. It is rich in caffeine and is widely used in Brazil for the production of stimulants, soft drinks, and sweets. It has recently been introduced in certain American products and herbals. Guarana is a fairly potent central nervous system stimulant, most likely due to its caffeine, theophylline, and theobromine content.

In the May 2000 issue of *Herb & Dietary Supplement Report*, registered pharmacist Daniel T. Wagner makes an important connection with depression and the use of guarana. There he warns that certain antidepressants, specifically Wellbutrin, could theoretical be dangerous if used in conjuction with guarana.[64]

Fasting and Stress Management

I discussed the role of certain nutrients in dealing with stress. Although there is definite merit in certain dietary modifications in dealing with stress over the long haul, there is evidence that caloric restriction or even *short-term fasting* may have a beneficial effect in *short-term stress processes.*

Perhaps one of the most interesting examples of the benefits of fasting is provided by a group of compounds called heat shock proteins (HSP). As you may gather from their name, these compounds made by your body actually can help you deal with the stress of severe heat as well as other physical trauma. Interestingly, fasting augments production of an important heat shock protein. Whether this has implications for helping us deal with other aspects of stress is unclear. However, it does raise interesting questions about the practice of fasting that has been historically linked with seeking spiritual resources—often in the context of stressful situations.

Rats that had their calorie intake restricted by 60 percent had an extended mean and maximum life span and a decrease in the onset of age-related diseases such as heart disease, arteriosclerosis, and cancer. Caloric restriction lowers the body temperature set point and allows the body to utilize nutrients by metabolizing body fats instead of carbohydrates. Also, calorie restriction is thought to retard the activity of aging related to free radical reactions.[65]

Relaxation Training and the Immune Response

Training a patient how to relax has been demonstrated to prevent stress-related declines in immune function. Thirty-four medical student volunteers had their blood tested for cellular immunity one month before school exams and again on the second day of exams. Half of the group took relaxation therapy between the two blood sample times. On the second blood test, their blood showed significantly higher immunity than the group that did not participate in relaxation training.[66]

Biofeedback

Biofeedback is a tool that monitors body functions such as heart rate, skin electrical resistance, etc. as the patient is exposed to various life situations. The measurements are correlated with such reactions as the degree of relaxation the patient feels. Relaxation tech-

niques help the patient learn how to relax.

Sensors are attached to the skin at various locations on the body that measure muscle tone, skin resistance, heart rate, blood pressure, etc., which vary according to the amount of stress. The individual hooked to the machine can then identify how different strategies affect the measured stress indicators. The intent is to help the patient improve awareness of stress-inducing cues, become more aware of the symptoms of stress, and gain more effective skills to manage stress.

Biofeedback has been shown to help address a number of conditions that may have connections with stress.[67] These include headaches,[68] high blood pressure, attention deficit disorder (ADHD),[69] urinary incontinence[70] and Raynaud's disease[71] (a painful cold-induced hand condition). An excellent review published in *The Integrative Medicine Consult* highlighted these benefits. That source also observed that in a series of some 18 studies of biofeedback for high blood pressure, there was an average drop of 7.8 points systolic and 5.6 points diastolic.

Research on Raynaud's disease and biofeedback is particularly interesting as it relates to stress hormone mechanisms. Specifically, biofeedback is able to impact on the same adrenaline-related hormonal systems that fuel our stress responses.[72]

Exciting relationships are also emerging when it comes to biofeedback and addictions. Of perhaps greatest interest in the context of this chapter is the evidence that the nervous system circuitry involved in anxiety and depression may be related. Specifically, biofeedback strategies that are designed to foster more beneficial brain function in alcoholics appear to not only decrease anxiety, but also depression and the tendency to relapse.[73,74]

CALCIUM IN COMMON FOODS

Food Item	Amount	Calc (mg)
Oatmeal	1c.	19
Lentils	1c.	38
Quinoa grain	1c.	102
Rutabagas	1c.	115
Dandelion greens	1c.	147
Mustard greens	1c.	152
Baked beans	1c.	154
Sesame seeds (dried)	2Tbs.	176
Blackstrap cane molasses	1Tbs.	176
Kale	1c.	179
Turnip greens	1c.	249
Filberts/Hazelnuts (dried)	1c.	254
Soybeans (green)	1c.	261
Figs (dried)	10	269
Whole milk	1c.	290
Amaranth grain	1c.	298
Nonfat skim milk	1c.	301
Collard greens	1c.	357
Carob flour	1c.	358
Lambsquarters	1c.	464

Figure 22

Calcium Relieves Pre-Menstrual Syndrome Stress

Many women have an increase in anxiety and irritability in connection with their monthly cycle. The evidence shows that it is not all in their heads. In fact, recent research suggests that a calcium deficiency may be wholly or partly to blame in some women.

A three-trial study demonstrated that supplements of elemental calcium are effective for relieving PMS-related mood and behavioral disturbances. Tests indicate that during the menstrual cycle, ovarian steroid concentrations rise, causing a depletion of calcium. Calcium supplementation in a dosage of 1,000 to 1,200 mg/day (a dosage commonly recommended to promote strong bones) may relieve PMS symptoms, including irritability, depression, anxiety, mood swings, bloating, social withdrawal, headache, and cramps. The calcium content of foods is listed in **Figure 22.**

Insuring adequate calcium intake or taking calcium supplements may help decrease symptoms of a female condition that often has stress-connections. Interestingly, stress may increase PMS symptoms while PMS symptoms can become severe stressors which increases stress—another vicious cycle.

Conclusion

This chapter is a continuation of the previous one. Both deal with stress and anxiety, two mental disorders that are separate but related. The previous chapter defines stress and the various forms of anxiety and explains how to identify them. We saw that these disorders can inflict damage to many parts of the body and aggravate or lead to a variety of diseases not seemingly related to mental disorders. A number of treatment strategies are given.

This chapter presents additional treatments for stress and anxiety, many of which involve self-help. They include the adoption of lifestyle improvements that are very effective in combating these mental disorders. The use of drug medicines, where necessary, is spelled out. Herbs that are beneficial are listed.

The messages of this chapter can be summarized as follows:

1.   Stress and anxiety can be relieved and even conquered without drugs by adopting improvements in lifestyle habits.

2.   Improvements in physical health, social health, mental health, and spiritual health can be made that will provide relief and even victory over stress and anxiety.

3.   Methods by which we can accomplish these improvements are spelled out and are in the self-help category.

4.   Drug medicines may be necessary for a time, but caution is needed because of side effects.

5.   Certain herbs have a place in combating these disorders.

References—

[1] Tanji JL The benefits of exercise for women. *Clinical Sports Med* 2000 Apr; 19(2):175-85, vii.

[2] Glenister D. Exercise and mental health: A review. *J R Soc Health* 1996 Feb;116(1):7-13.

[3] Hoffman-Goetz L, Pedersen BK. Exercise and the immune system: A model of the stress response? *Immunol Today* 1994 Aug;15(8):382-387.

[4] Nieman DC, Henson DA, et al. Physical activity and immune function in elderly women. *Med Sci Sports Exerc* 1993 Jul;25(7):823-831.

[5] Nieman DC. Exercise, infection, and immunity. *Int J Sports Med* 1994 Oct;15 Suppl 3():S131-141.

[6] Carmack CL, et al. Aerobic fitness and leisure physical activity as moderators of the stress-illness relation. *Ann Behav Med* 1999 Summer;21(3):251-257.

[7] Martinsen EW. Physical fitness, anxiety and depression. *Br J Hosp Med* 1990 Mar;43(3):194,196,199.

[8] Hales RE, Stolt J. Exercise as a treatment option for anxiety and depressive disorders. *Mil Med* 1987 Jun;152(6):299-302.

[9] Moraska A, Fleshner M. Voluntary physical activity prevents stress-induced behavioral depression and anti-KLH antibody suppression. *Am J Physiol Regul Integr Comp Physiol* 2001 Aug;281(2):R484-9.

[10] Field T. *J Pediatr Psychol* 1997 Oct; 22(5):607-617.

[11] Field T. *J Am Acad Child Adolesc Psychiatry* 1992 Jan; 31(1):125-131.

[12] American Psychiatric Association. *Diagnostic and Statistical Manual of Mental Disorders* (DSM-IV). 1996. P 212-214.

[13] Nedley N. *Proof Positive: How to Reliably Combat Disease and Achieve Optimal Health through Nutrition and Lifestyle.* Ardmore, OK: Nedley Publishing, 1999 p. 411.

[14] Heinz A, Mann K, et al. Serotonergic dysfunction, negative mood states, and response to alcohol. *Alcohol Clin Exp* Res 2001 Apr;25(4):487-495.

[15] Lee S, et al. Prolonged exposure to intermittent alcohol vapors blunts hypothalamic responsiveness to immune and non-immune signals. *Alcohol Clin Exp Res* 2000 Jan;24(1):110-122.

[16] Chrousos G, et al. *Annals of Internal Medicine* August 1,1998; 129:229-240.

[17] Rao ML, Muller-Oerlinghausen B, et al. The influence of phototherapy on serotonin and melatonin in non-seasonal depression. *Pharmacopsychiatry* 1990 May;23(3):155-158.

[18] Nedley, N. Proof Positive: *How to Reliably Combat Disease and Achieve Optimal Health through Nutrition and Lifestyle.* Ardmore, OK: Nedley Publishing, 1999 p. 193-236.

[19] National Institute of Mental Health. Anxiety Disorders Research Fact Sheet. *NIH Publication No. 00-4504.* Printed May 2000.

[20] Liu D, et al. Maternal care, hippocampal glucocorticoid receptors, and hypothalamic-pituitary-adrenal responses to stress. *Science* 1997 Sep 12;277(5332):1659-1662.

[21] Eisenberg L. Experience, brain, and behavior: The importance of a head start. *Pediatrics* 1999 May;103(5 Pt 1):1031-1035.

[22] Wyman PA, et al. Caregiving and developmental factors differentiating young at-risk urban children showing resilient versus stress-affected outcomes: A replication and extension. *Child Dev* 1999 May-Jun;70(3):645-659.

[23] Schedler J, *Health* 1997 April; 74-78.

[24] Weinstein L, Xie X, Cleanthous CC. Purpose in life, boredom, and volunteerism in a group of retirees. *Psychol Rep* 1995 Apr;76(2):482.

[25] Viswanathan R. Death anxiety, locus of control, and purpose in life of physicians. Their relationship to patient death notification. *Psychosomatics* 1996 Jul-Aug;37(4):339-345.

[26] Jenkins CD, Stanton BA, Jono RT. Quantifying and predicting recovery after heart surgery. *Psychosom Med* 1994 May-Jun;56(3):203-212.

[27] Caine J. The effects of music on the selected stress behaviors, weight, caloric and formula intake, and length of hospital stay of premature and low birth weight neonates in a newborn intensive care unit. *J Music Ther* 1991 Winter;28(4):180-192.

[28] Grafman J, Schwab K, et al. Frontal lobe injuries, violence, and aggression: A report of the Vietnam Head Injury Study *Neurology* 1996 May;46(5):1231-1238.

[29] Nedley, N. Proof Positive: *How to Reliably Combat Disease and Achieve Optimal Health through Nutrition and Lifestyle.* Ardmore, OK: Nedley Publishing, 1999 p. 211-236.

[30] Perl J. Sleep right in five nights: A clear and effective guide for conquering insomnia. New York, NY: William Morrow and Company Inc., 1993 p. 167.

[31] White EG. Mind Cure. In: *The Ministry of Healing.* Nampa, ID: Pacific Press Publishing Association, 1905. p. 251.

[32] White EG. True Worship. In: *Bible Training School.* 1902-1917 (a periodical) October p. 1. Found In: Ellen G. White Estate. The Published Writings of Ellen G. White. Version 2.0 (CD-ROM), 1995.

[33] Rice PL. The Concentration Techniques: Meditation and Biofeedback. In: *Stress and Health: Principles and Practice for Coping and Wellness.* Pacific Grove, CA: Brooks/Cole Publishing Company, 1987 p. 309.

[34] Rice PL. The concentration techniques: Meditation and biofeedback. In: *Stress and Health: Principles and Practice for Coping and Wellness.* Pacific Grove, CA: Brooks/Cole Publishing Company, 1987 p. 313.

[35] Rice PL. The concentration techniques: Meditation and biofeedback. In: *Stress and Health: Principles and Practice for Coping and Wellness.* Pacific Grove, CA: Brooks/Cole Publishing Company, 1987 p. 313.

[36] Rice PL. The concentration techniques: Meditation and biofeedback. In: *Stress and Health: Principles and Practice for Coping and Wellness.* Pacific Grove, CA: Brooks/Cole Publishing Company, 1987 p. 305-312.

[37] Guyton AC. *Textbook of Medical Physiology* 8th edition. Philadelphia, PA: W.B. Saunders Co., 1991 p. 662-663.

[38] Rice PL. The concentration techniques: Meditation and biofeedback. In: *Stress and Health: Principles and Practice for Coping and Wellness.* Pacific Grove, CA: Brooks/Cole Publishing Company, 1987 p. 308.

[39] Benson H. *The Relaxation Response.* New York, NY: William Morrow and Company Inc., 1975 p. 19.

[40] Benson H. *The Relaxation Response.* New York, NY: William Morrow and Company Inc., 1975 p. 19.

[41] Rice PL. The concentration techniques: Meditation and biofeedback. In: *Stress and Health: Principles and Practice for Coping and Wellness.* Pacific Grove, CA: Brooks/Cole Publishing Company, 1987 p. 308.

[42] Wenger MA, Bagchi BK. Studies of autonomic function in practitioners of Yoga in India. *Behavioral Science* 1961;6:312-323.

[43] Puente AE, Beiman I. The effects of behavior therapy, self-relaxation, and transcendental meditation on cardiovascular stress response.

J Clin Psychol 1980 Jan;36(1):291-295.

[44] Dossey L. *Healing Words: The Power of Prayer and the Practice of Medicine.* New York, NY. HarperCollins Publishers, 1993:62-63.

[45] White EG. *Desire of Ages.* Public domain book. 1898;Pp. 328-333.

[46] Matthew 11:28. *The Holy Bible.* KJV.

[47] Matthew 11:29. *The Holy Bible.* KJV.

[48] 1 Peter 5:7. *The Holy Bible.* KJV.

[49] Psalm 147:4. *The Holy Bible.* KJV.

[50] Psalm 147:3. *The Holy Bible.* KJV.

[51] As did Hezekiah in Isaiah 37:14. *The Holy Bible.* KJV.

[52] Psalm 40:8. *The Holy Bible.* KJV.

[53] John 6:38. *The Holy Bible.* KJV.

[54] Matthew 6:26-34. *The Holy Bible.* KJV.

[55] Revelation 21:6. *The Holy Bible.* KJV.

[56] Ex. 33:13, 14. *The Holy Bible.* KJV.

[57] Jer. 6:16. *The Holy Bible.* KJV.

[58] Isa. 48:18. *The Holy Bible.* KJV.

[59] Isa. 26:3. *The Holy Bible.* KJV.

[60] *Physicians' Desk Reference for Herbal Medicines*, First Edition;1998:1043-1045.

[61] *Physicians' Desk Reference for Herbal Medicines*, First Edition;1998:929-930.

[62] *Physicians' Desk Reference for Herbal Medicines,* First Edition;1998:967-969.

[63] *Physicians' Desk Reference for Herbal Medicines*, First Edition;1998:1204-1207.

[64] Schafer AT, Microscopic examination of Guarana powder—Paullinia cupana Kunth Arch Kriminol 1999 Jul-Aug;204(1-2):23-27.

[65] Ehrenfried JA , Evers M, et al. Caloric restriction increases the expression of heat shock protein in the gut. *Annals of surgery* 1996 May(5):593.

[66] Kiecolt-Glaser JK, et al. Modulation of cellular immunity in medical students. *J Behav Med* 1986 Feb;9(1):5-21.

[67] "Biofeedback: A tool in learning to regulate the body" Oct 20, 1999 issue of *The Integrative Medicine Consult.*

[68] Holroyd KA, Penzien DB. Pharmacological versus non-pharmacological prophylaxis of recurrent migraine headache: A meta analytic review of clinical trials. *Pain.* 1990;42:1-13.

[69] Lubar JF, et al. Evaluation of the effectiveness of EEG neurofeedback training for ADHD in a clinical setting as measured by changes in T.O.V.A. scores, behavioral ratings, and WISC-R performance. *Biofeedback and Self Regul.* 1995 Mar;20(1):83-99.

[70] Mathewson-Chapman M. Pelvic muscle exercise/biofeedback for urinary incontinence after prostatectomy: An education program. *J Cancer Educ.* 1997;12(4):218-223.

[71] Freedman RR. Physiological mechanisms of temperature biofeedback. *Biofeedback Self Regul* 1991;Jun;16(2):95-115.

[72] Freedman RR Physiological mechanisms of temperature biofeedback. *Biofeedback Self Regul* 1991; Jun;16(2):95-115.

[73] Saxby E; Peniston EG. Alpha-theta brainwave neurofeedback training: An effective treatment for male and female alcoholics with depressive symptoms. *J Clin Psychol.* 1995 Sep;51(5):685-693.

[74] Peniston E, Kulkosky P. Alpha-theta brainwave training and beta-endorphin levels in alcoholics. *Alcohol Clin Exp Res* 1989 Apr;13(2):271-279.

CHAPTER NINE

THE FRONTAL LOBE *of the* BRAIN

Many reasoned that it would be the next major break through in depression treat- ment. Their logic was com- pelling—many cases of depression seem to be caused or perpetuated by religious, spiri- tual, or moral concerns. They said if the source of these deleterious spiritual thoughts and depression were removed, the malady may be minimized or even cured.

Such a treatment strategy appeared to help Joan's obviously depressed state. She feared that she had committed the "unpar- donable sin." Surgeons performed *a fron- tal lobotomy* on her—the new promising depression treatment. The front part of her brain was surgically removed.

The results were remarkable. Immedi- ately following the surgery, Joan's depres- sive ideas about an unforgivable sin had lifted. However, there was something dis- turbing about the results. The surgery had affected more than her depressive thoughts. It soon became apparent that her wisdom, judgment, and insight were all compro- mised. Joan's spirituality had been pro- foundly impacted. When asked about the Holy Spirit, Joan said, "What Holy Spirit? There is no Holy Spirit."

In my book ***Proof Positive*** I describe other cases of those who had their frontal lobes removed. Like Joan, depressive

thoughts actually seemed to be resolved with frontal lobotomy. However, the changes in personality, character, and re- sponsibility have been so disconcerting that frontal lobotomy has fallen into virtual dis- use in psychiatric surgery. To better appre- ciate the importance of the frontal lobe, consider the classic case of Phineas Gage.

Gage lost the function of his frontal lobe as the result of a serious brain injury. Following a remarkable recovery from that profound trauma, he looked the same, talked the same, and walked the same. But fundamentally he was a different person. Before the accident, Phineas was a well- loved and responsible husband. He was hard working and intelligent. He was known for his high morals and exemplary record as a railroad foreman.

After the accident, Gage's moral decline was immediately evident. He became overly emotional and was prone to outbursts of anger. Phineas lost interest in spiritual things, became irreverent, and used con- stant profanity. He forsook respect for so- cial customs and became totally irrespon- sible. He went from a prized employee to the unemployment rolls. Dr. John Harlow, his physician, stated that the accident de- stroyed Gage's "equilibrium or balance, so to speak, between his intellectual faculty and his animal propensities." Phineas

Gage's traumatic frontal lobotomy cost him his personality, his moral standards, and his commitment to family, church, and loved ones.[1]

Depression's Most Important Lobe

Why am I bringing up an antiquated surgery in a book devoted to cutting-edge insights on depression? There is one simple answer. A proper understanding of the frontal lobe is vital to developing a total line of attack for treating and preventing depression. Removing parts of the frontal lobe apparently helps certain types of depression in the short term. However, the procedure actually appears to put some individuals at very high risk for depression.

Research suggests that if the dominant hemisphere of the frontal lobe is removed or compromised, depression is more likely to result.[2,3,4] The dominant hemisphere is typically the left hemisphere in right-handed individuals, and vice versa. However, other research suggests that removal or damage to *either the left or right frontal lobe* can produce depression.[5]

Ironically, two people with the same frontal lobe damage can result in very different behavioral consequences. In one case it may result in depressive symptoms with slowing of body movements, apathy, indifference, and lack of drive. In the other case the result may be like Phineas Gage, with loss of sexual inhibitions, indifference to rules, lack of concern for others, inappropriate joking, and loss of sensitivity to the consequences of one's actions.[6]

One interpretation of these divergent responses is that the sensitive nerves of the frontal lobe, if damaged, lose their ability to check certain emotional tendencies that are present below the surface of the personality. Some have a predisposition to depression that will surface if these higher control centers are damaged. Others do not tend toward depression but rather toward a socially unacceptable sensuous behavior and lack of restraint. These different responses to frontal lobe damage merit an examination of their relationship to depression.

An individual who displays inappropriate, uninhibited behavior may seem happy-go-lucky, untroubled, and even euphoric, but in reality may be displaying telltale signs of frontal lobe impairment. If so, when his surrounding circumstances change, that impairment can lead to outright depression.

Increased Knowledge of Frontal Lobe and Depression Relationship

The pivotal role of the frontal lobe in depression has only recently been recognized, as stated in **Figure 1**. Historically, neuroscientists interested in depression focused on the *emotional* areas of the brain, namely the limbic system, amygdala, and other lower brain structures (see *Chapter 1* and *Appendix II* for details on brain structure). They identified the frontal lobe as the analytical control center of the brain without any significant role in the emotions. In the 1990s and 2000s, understanding began to change as researchers recognized that the brain's frontal lobe is far more than a control center. It is intimately involved in *emotional well-being*.

Much of this exciting new information regarding the frontal lobe's role in depression occurred as a result of very sophisticated brain scans, including PET scans

FRONTAL LOBE'S INVOLVEMENT IN DEPRESSION

Before 1990, the frontal lobe's role in depression was not well recognized. Its intimate involvement in our emotional well-being is now affirmed.

Figure 1

(positron emission tomography), SPECT scans (single photon emission computed tomography) and regional blood flow scans.[7] These brain-imaging techniques represent a technology far different than conventional CT (Computerized Axial Tomography) scans and MRIs (Magnetic Resonance Imaging).

CT scans and MRIs can show very detailed pictures of brain *structures*. However, PET, SPECT, and regional blood flow scans are able to assess brain *function*. These high-tech scanning devices are very expensive and consequently quite scarce. They are typically found in university research centers but not in your average neighborhood health care facility. Despite the scarcity of these high-end tools, university-based researchers use them with dramatic results. They have gained new insights into the frontal lobe.

Depressed Victims Have Low Blood Flow to Frontal Lobe

It is now well established that one of the main characteristics of virtually all depressed individuals—no matter what the underlying cause—is a *significant decrease in the frontal lobe's blood flow and activity*.[8,9] The decreased activity is in the foremost portion of the frontal lobe. It is called the "prefrontal cortex." This is the area of the brain that is indeed the control center of the brain — but it is much more. It is now recognized as the site of behavior planning,[10,11] decision-making,[12] emotional control, self-awareness,[13] and self-independence.[14] The many functions of the prefrontal cortex portion of the frontal lobes are displayed in **Figure 2.**

Frontal Lobe Portions Have Distinct Functions

The prefrontal cortex is made up of several portions, and each has a different job to do. One part appears to be involved in knowledge, reasoning, and perception processes.[15] It is closest to the side of the brain and farther from the forehead, and is called the "dorsolateral prefrontal cortex." Another region of the prefrontal cortex appears to be related to social and emotional functions.[16] This region is closer to the forehead and in the middle behind the eyes. It is called the "orbitomedial prefrontal cortex."

Additional involvement of the dorsolateral prefrontal cortex is reported by Sarazin and colleagues.[17] These French researchers demonstrated that "executive functions" were also housed primarily in the dorsolateral prefrontal cortex. Such executive functions included conceptual elaboration, working memory, selective attention, verbal fluency, and recall.

A number of behavioral abnormalities were linked to the orbitomedial prefrontal cortex. Behavioral disorders linked to this prefrontal area included apathy, restlessness, impulsiveness, indifference to rules, decrease in attention, personality changes, and impairment of intellectual and emotional control. It is also important to note that the orbitofrontal area of the prefrontal cor-

FUNCTIONS OF THE PREFRONTAL CORTEX

1. Control center of the brain
2. Behavior planning
3. Decision-making
4. Emotional control
5. Self-awareness
6. Self-independence

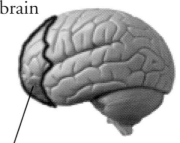

Prefrontal cortex

Figure 2

tex was linked to impaired ability to make realistic, appropriate plans and to carry them out.

Brain connections as identified by Sarazin and colleagues are illustrated in *Appendix I*.

Cases of Depression with Frontal Lobe Damage

A person who has a stroke has brain damage resulting from a lack of blood supply to the brain. A Korean study by Kim and colleagues found that strokes caused by damage to the frontal lobe are closely related to depression.[18] The location of brain damage in 148 stroke patients revealed that 75 percent of those with a stroke in the medial (central) part of the frontal lobe suffered from depression. In contrast, those with strokes in other brain areas had no depression. Of further interest, 100 percent of those with medial frontal lobe strokes also demonstrated "emotional incontinence" (inappropriate laughter or crying, or both). A summary of these findings is listed in **Figure 3**.

As we have seen, brain damage can result from surgical removal, injury, or stroke. It can also result from Alzheimer's disease. Regardless of what process damages the frontal lobe, the results tend to be the same. Hirono and colleagues found that Alzheimer's patients with more damage to their frontal lobes tend to exhibit significantly more depression.[19] This study also yielded another finding of interest in light of our earlier exploration of connections between the frontal lobe and behavior. Those with greater depression were significantly more likely to have other behavioral problems, such as, anxiety, delusions, and lack of personal discipline.

So far we have looked at *adult populations* regarding the connections between frontal lobe damage and depression. A study of depressed adults and *adolescents* who never experienced structural brain injuries has been made. Surprisingly, the same brain areas were linked to depression.[20] Another study of a group of depressed adolescents by Harvard medical researchers led by R.J. Steingard showed altered brain metabolism in the critical orbitofrontal regions of the frontal lobe.[21]

Other evidence has been amassed for the connection between frontal lobe structures close to the middle of the brain (referred to as "medial") and their relationship to emotions in general, and depression specifically. The University of Arizona's R.D. Lane and colleagues used PET scanning to identify brain areas associated with three basic emotions—happiness, sadness, and disgust. They discovered that each of these emotions resulted in enhanced activity in the medial prefrontal cortex.[22]

Several Parts of the Frontal Lobe are Involved

Thus far we have seen the role of the medial orbitofrontal portion of the frontal lobe in relation to depression and emotions. I must point out that other regions in the

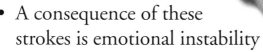

RESULTS OF STROKES IN MEDIAL PREFRONTAL LOBE

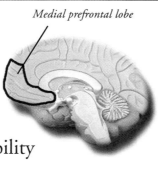

Medial prefrontal lobe

- Depression can be caused by strokes in the medial part of the frontal lobe.

- A consequence of these strokes is emotional instability

- Depression is not generally caused by strokes in other parts of the brain.

Figure 3

frontal lobe also are involved with emotions and depressive illness. Nothing is simple when it comes to human brain function. British researchers Bench and colleagues have repeatedly demonstrated that in addition to the structures close to the middle of the brain (like the medial orbitofrontal territory), there are other brain regions that play a key role in emotions—and that are affected by depression.

Foremost among these other areas is the region toward the back and sides of the front portion of the frontal lobe (the dorsolateral prefrontal cortex). In the experience of Bench's group, decreased blood flow (and resultant decreased activity) of the left dorsolateral prefrontal cortex actually causes greater mood disturbances and slowing of body movement (*psychomotor retardation*) that accompany depression, than changes in other brain areas.[23,24]

Although different groups may argue about which area of the frontal lobe is the most important in depression, there is no question that *reductions in frontal lobe function lie at the heart of depression*. Its function is related to the blood flow and nerve chemistry. However, associations between frontal lobe impairment and depression raise the chicken-or-egg question. What really came first? Does depression cause changes in the frontal lobe or do frontal lobe problems set the stage for depression?

Cause and Effect – Impaired Frontal Lobe and Depression

Drevets presents compelling evidence that *frontal lobe problems are the cause, and the effects are depressive symptoms*.[25] Even after depressive symptoms are resolved, abnormalities persist in the orbital and medial prefrontal cortex areas. The evidence suggests that these frontal lobe areas affect emotional behavior and stress, suggesting from Drevets' perspective "that dysfunction involving these regions may be involved in the cause of depressive symptoms."

Complementing this research is growing evidence that *enhancing frontal lobe function early in life may provide a safeguard against depression*. In another report by Steingard and colleagues, the Harvard researchers attempted to probe the roots of depression by studying the brains of depressed children with MRIs.[26] They compared 65 children and adolescents with depression to a control group of psychiatric patients who were not depressed. *The depressed children had significantly smaller frontal lobes.*

Summary statements regarding the connection between depression and the frontal lobe appear in **Figure 4**, along with two views of a typical PET scan.

Other Portions of the Brain are Involved

I would be negligent to leave the impression that the frontal lobe is the only brain area that is involved in depression. It clearly is not. A host of brain structures can either affect or be affected by depression. Other well-studied examples include deep internal brain structures such as the hippocampus, the amygdala, and oth-

DEPRESSION FROM MALFUNCTION OF FRONTAL LOBE

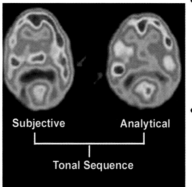

Typical PET scan

- Virtually all depressed individuals have significantly decreased frontal lobe blood flow and activity.

- Studies suggest that a decrease in frontal lobe function is the cause of depression, and not the effect.

Figure 4

ers.[27,28,29,30] However, my purpose in singling out the frontal lobe is not only because of its strong connection with depression, but also for three other critical reasons.

First, the frontal lobe holds the position as the preeminent control center for all conscious brain functions, including the ability to identify and implement strategies to help alleviate depression. Indeed, Drevets suggests that dysfunction of the prefrontal cortex is related to depression through its inability to modulate deeper internal brain structures like the amygdala.[31] Second, this brain region has been linked to other symptoms that can complicate depression, such as violence. And third, a growing body of evidence suggests that relatively simple lifestyle choices can improve frontal lobe performance, as we shall discover later in the chapter. **Figure 5** puts the frontal lobe into perspective.

THE FRONTAL LOBE IN PERSPECTIVE

- The frontal lobe is the preeminent control center for all conscious brain functions, including the ability to identify and implement strategies to help alleviate depression.
- It has been linked to other symptoms, such as violence, that can complicate depression.
- Evidence indicates that *relatively simple lifestyle choices can improve frontal lobe performance*.

Figure 5

THE FRONTAL LOBE THE CROWN OF THE BRAIN

Scientific studies show the frontal lobe is the seat of
- *spirituality*
- *morality*
- *the will*

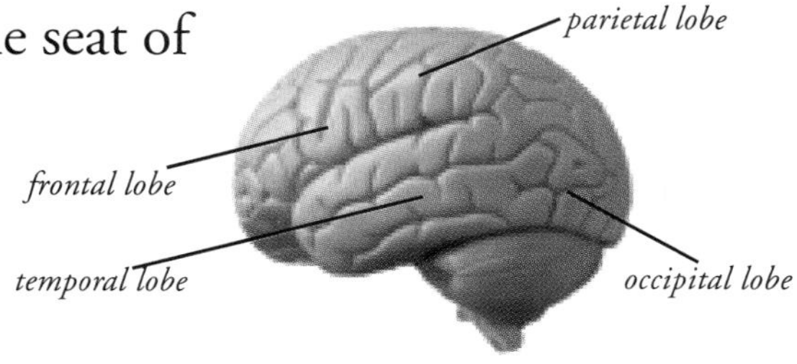

parietal lobe

frontal lobe

temporal lobe

occipital lobe

Figure 6

Sections of the Brain

To better appreciate the frontal lobe and its critical role in depression, we need to first review some brain anatomy. Then we will proceed to look in greater detail at some of the vital functions performed by this preeminent brain area.

Functions of the Frontal Lobe

The brain is divided into several sections, or lobes. Each lobe has specific functions. Behind the forehead are the frontal lobes. For convenience, we often refer to both the right and the left frontal lobes collectively as "the frontal lobe." It is the seat of judgment, reasoning, intellect, and the will.[32,33,34] *It is the control center of our entire being.* Some scientists refer to the frontal lobe as the "crown" of the brain. Studies show that this so-called crown performs a variety of vital functions. Some of these are listed in **Figure 6**.

Notice that there are four main lobes of the brain shown in the figure. The characteristics of spirituality, will, and morality determine our unique individuality, and they all reside in the frontal lobe. As we have observed, a person who incurs damage to the frontal lobe may not change in appearance, but if you interact with him, it is usually apparent that he is not the same person you once knew.

The Book of Books alludes to the significance of the frontal lobe in knowing God. The last book of the Bible makes a provocative statement, shown in **Figure 7**.

This text suggests that God's character ("His name") is reproduced in our character (exemplified by the frontal lobe, which is just behind the forehead).

Relative Size of the Frontal Lobe

It is fascinating to observe how the relative size of the frontal lobe differs among men and various beasts. *It is the frontal lobe that largely sets humans apart from the rest of the animal kingdom*, as shown in **Figure 8**.

Animals with the smallest frontal lobes are limited to instinct-driven performance. Those with larger frontal lobes are able to execute more complex functions. Cats, with only 3.5 percent of the brain in the frontal lobe, are limited in judgment and reasoning power. They have a very limited capability to analyze information and make judgments based on new information, so they basically rely on instinct. Dogs are more trainable with 7 percent of their brain being frontal lobe. Among the animals, chimpanzees have the largest frontal lobe—up to 17 percent of their brain. Humans, on the other hand, have 33 to 38 percent of their brain in the frontal lobe.

Some animals have other portions of the brain that are more developed than human beings. For instance, compared to humans, chimpanzees have much larger cerebellums—the brain area that controls coordination. This stands to reason, because chimps need well-honed balance and agility to swing from tree to tree. Birds also have very well developed cerebellums for flying, landing, and hunting. All of these activities require a high level of coordination. Other animals may have a much more generous occipital lobe—the brain center where vision is housed. Hence, their eyesight is generally much better than that of humans. Still other animals have more developed parietal lobes. What sets humans apart is clearly a significantly larger frontal lobe that provides the capacity for elevated

spiritual reasoning and superior learning ability. *It is the largest lobe of the brain.*[35]

Common Effects of Compromised Frontal Lobes

Through studies of accidental damage to the frontal lobes combined with the results of frontal lobotomies and studies of drugs that affect the front brain, scientists

THE FRONTAL LOBE AND KNOWING GOD

"And they shall see His face; and His name shall be in their foreheads."

Revelation 22:4

Figure 7

FRONTAL LOBE SIZE OF HUMANS vs. ANIMALS

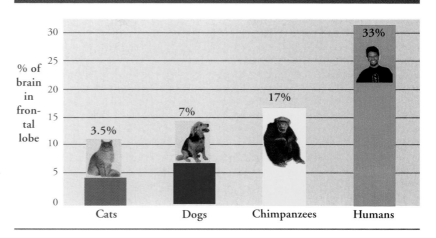

Figure 8

have identified many of the effects of compromised frontal lobes. These effects are listed in **Figure 9**.[36,37,38,39,40]

The first two effects of a compromised frontal lobe listed in the figure are "impairment of moral principle" and "social impairment." As an illustration of these effects, consider the following true story. One woman prior to going into frontal lobotomy surgery was asked, "What would you do if you lost a watch that you had borrowed?" She answered, "I would need to pay for the watch or buy one and return it." Following her recovery from surgery,

she was asked the same question. This time she answered, "I would have to borrow another watch!"

Regarding foresight, consider the very limited foresight a small child has. As he matures, the effect of frontal lobe development is apparent. At first, he can only conceptualize one day at a time. You can tell him that something is going to happen tomorrow, but he will remember it only if you remind him. As that child matures he will begin to gain more foresight. By the time he reaches second grade, he realizes that next year he will be in the third grade. As he continues to mature he will eventually be planning a career. The frontal lobe continues to develop for 30 years.[41] With proper training, as the child matures into an adult, he will ultimately realize that his actions today have a bearing on his eternity ahead. This is the highest development of the frontal lobe.

Abstract ideas (listed fourth and fifth in **Figure 9**) such as interpreting proverbs involve special brain processes. If you ask someone who does not have full frontal lobe capacities to interpret a proverb like "People in glass houses shouldn't throw stones," the reply may be, "Obviously, they will damage their houses." This example illustrates concrete reasoning—a mental process that tends to miss abstract concepts.

Regarding mathematical understanding, calculation actually occurs in the back part of the parietal lobe. Thus, even without frontal lobe function, you can have great mathematical skills in adding, subtracting, and multiplication. However, when it comes to higher mathematics that requires reasoning, such as algebra, geometry, and especially calculus, frontal lobe functions are required for flawless results.

An unimpaired frontal lobe is also a must if you want to empathize most effectively with someone who is beset with a problem. This is especially true if the person is going through something that you have never personally experienced.

EFFECTS OF COMPROMISED FRONTAL LOBES

- Impairment of moral principle
- Social impairment
  (loss of love for family)
- Lack of foresight
- Incapable of abstract reasoning
- Cannot interpret proverbs
- Diminished ability for mathematical understanding
- Loss of empathy
- Lack of restraint (boasting, hostility, aggressiveness)

Figure 9

FRONTAL LOBE DISEASES

- Mania
- Obsessive-compulsive disorder
- Appetite increase
- Depression
- Attention deficit hyperactivity disorder

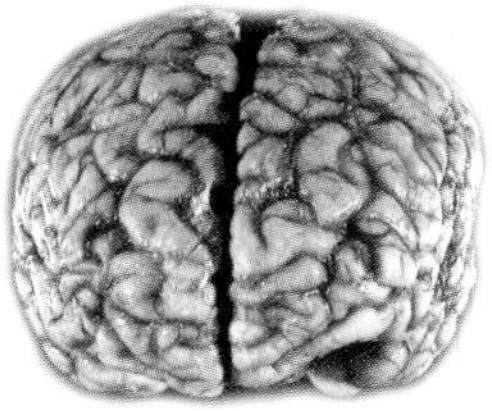

Figure 10

Psychological Diseases Are Rooted in an Impaired Frontal Lobe

We have looked at some evidence of an association between depression and frontal lobe dysfunction. Other psychiatric conditions can stem from frontal lobe deficiencies. It is not surprising that some psychological diseases have their roots in frontal lobe problems. Five of these disorders are listed in **Figure 10**.

The first one, "mania," is an emotional disorder characterized by remarkable activity, excitement, rapid flow of ideas, insomnia, and unstable attention span. It can have its root in compromised frontal lobe function. Second, "obsessive-compulsive disorder" (OCD) as characterized by uncontrollable intruding thoughts and resulting ritualized actions, can also arise from frontal lobe impairment. "Attention deficit hyperactivity disorder" (ADHD) is another result of frontal lobe problems.[42] Between 1990 and 1995, the number of people diagnosed with ADHD in the U.S. rose from 900,000 to more than two million, although this "official" statistic is probably inflated.[43]

Frontal Lobe Health Determines Our Character and Quality of Life

As we have seen, medical research has conclusively demonstrated the frontal lobe's vital role in determining our character. An impaired frontal lobe results in an impaired character. Self-control, trustworthiness, reliability, serious reading, abstract reasoning, and interpersonal relationships are all complex activities that depend upon a well-functioning frontal lobe. Accidental or surgically-planned damage to the frontal lobe is one thing, but what about damage that may result from an unhealthy lifestyle?

The most common causes of frontal lobe impairment today are not surgeries, occupational injuries, or other trauma. We will see that *the main cause of compromised frontal lobe function is harmful lifestyle habits*, as recited in **Figure 11**.

This is the most important message of this chapter. Secondary to this is the message is to protect yourself from damage to the frontal lobe from injuries caused by accidents and sports participation.

Depression Is Rooted in Our Frontal Lobe

I believe it is vital to recognize that *depression has its roots in the frontal lobe*. The frontal lobe can be compromised in ways that are not limited to surgeries or injuries. Many of our most cherished habits may give us short-term gratification but silently rob us of that which is of inestimable value—peak functioning of our frontal lobe. And when this highest part of our brain is impaired, it typically affects not only our emotional stability, but also *who we really are*.

The effects of lifestyle and nutrition on our frontal lobe are, in my opinion, ultimately more important than their effects on heart disease, cancer, osteoporosis, kidney failure, and all the other degenerative diseases combined. We need to make it top priority to protect our brain, *because our*

THE MAIN CAUSES OF COMPROMISED FRONTAL LOBE FUNCTION

Figure 11

quality of life originates here.

As we shall see, lifestyle choices protect the health of the frontal lobe, and a healthy frontal lobe puts us in the best position to take charge of our lives and to make the right choices. This means that as I make healthier choices, my frontal lobe performance improves, making future lifestyle changes even easier. Perhaps no frontal lobe function is as vital to making lifestyle changes easier than the *power of the will.* Willpower may not seem all that important in our daily lives, but it is absolutely essential. *Many of my patients have died because of deficient willpower.* I am not talking about individuals who lose the will to live. I am referring to the cases of thousands who died because they felt they did not have the willpower to change their lifestyles before it was too late.

Weak Willpower—the Road to Early Suffering and Premature Death

Today tens of thousands are languishing on their deathbeds because of willpower deficiencies. The consequences of a weak willpower are stated in **Figure 12**.

The cases listed in the figure and many other cases testify to the great dearth of willpower in our land. In fact, one of my greatest concerns while writing this book is that many of the important—and life changing—insights that I present will never gain a foothold in the lives of many readers. The reason? *A lack of willpower.*

Impaired Frontal Lobe Causes an Impaired Will

From this perspective, I underscore the fact that one of the frontal lobe's most vital functions is the will. Scientists have demonstrated that what we call "willpower" resides in the frontal lobe.[44] Dr. Bernell Baldwin, Ph.D., neurophysiologist at Georgia's Wildwood Lifestyle Center and Hospital, summarized some of the important literature on the will in an article written to leaders of faith communities. Baldwin pointed out that research on World War I veterans with shrapnel wounds to the brain uncovered weaknesses in willpower among those who injured the front of their brains. Those who sustained injuries to the back of their heads, however, experienced no *impairment of their will.*[45]

Perhaps this is why depression is often such a vicious cycle. Disease processes impair the very part of the brain that needs to be active in implementing mind-healing choices—the frontal lobe.

Closely related to willpower is our ability to discern the vital issues in overcoming a challenge. If we do not see the issues clearly, it is likely that we may not recognize our need to exert willpower to overcome a challenge. To illustrate this point, Dr. Baldwin cited the research of Russian scientist, A.R. Luria. Luria found that individuals with normal frontal lobes had the ability to draw rapid conclusions about the meaning of carefully designed pictures. Individuals with frontal lobe impairment could accurately describe components of the

CONSEQUENCES OF A WEAK WILL POWER

- Diabetics dying with end-stage heart and kidney disease due to lack of willpower: Not exercising, not controlling blood sugar.
- Smokers dying with cancer or heart disease due to lack of willpower to kick the habit.
- Those with high blood pressure having a stroke due to lack of willpower to control their blood pressure.

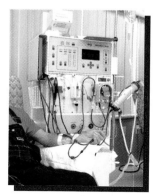

Dialysis

Figure 12

picture—but they tended not to see "the big picture"—the broader meaning behind the details.

This is very relevant to lifestyle change. Deficiencies in insight leave us destined to overlook how key lifestyle concepts apply to our own lives. Willpower shortfalls, on the other hand, predispose us to failure even in the areas where we clearly recognize that we have a problem. In short, the twin frontal lobe functions of *insight and will are both indispensable* to a successful application of all the lifestyle material that I present in this book. Unfortunately, for those who are depressed or have other impairments of the frontal lobe, it is possible that they will underestimate the importance of the solutions that I share within these pages. Furthermore, even if they recognize the need for lifestyle changes, their struggling frontal lobes may tell them that they are powerless to make such changes.

Impaired Frontal Lobe Weakens the Ability to Plan

The above relationships were underscored by the previously cited work of Sarazin and colleagues.[46] They found that impairment of the critical orbitomedial region of the prefrontal cortex was associated with serious deficiencies in the ability to make plans and carry them out. Deficits were apparent in three categories—*activating a plan, executing a plan, and controlling a plan.*

Activating a plan relates to one's ability to express, maintain, and initiate appropriate plans for the future. *Executing* a plan deals with sequentially implementing and maintaining a plan until the goal has been reached. It is the ability to choose a means to achieve a goal that empowers the individual to adjust to changes in the environment by implementing changes in the plan. Lastly, *controlling* a plan enables one to be aware of the consequences of his or her actions, respect social rules, and resist envi-

ronmental interference.

These three associations make a profound point. The areas of the frontal lobe responsible for emotional health are the very same areas that help us to successfully set goals and achieve them. This helps explain the vicious cycle of depression, as described in **Figure 13**.

The very brain areas that are affected by the disorder are the ones that we need most to enlist if we are going to find a solution. How then do we break the cycle? By identifying our personal habits that we need to prioritize, and enlisting the help of others to keep us focused on those behaviors that enhance the function of the frontal lobe.

It is a disturbing fact that *many mental health practitioners are not aware that current lifestyle habits of their patients may be contributing to psychological illness.* Standardized treatments such as psychological counseling and behavioral therapy are currently popular, and are sometimes beneficial in addressing depression at various stages. However, if those who feel the need for counseling would also adopt a truly healthy lifestyle as presented in this book,

THE VICIOUS CYCLE OF DEPRESSION

- To combat depression, the victim needs to be able to activate and follow a therapy plan (with proper guidance).

- The ability to plan and execute requires a functioning frontal lobe.

- But the victim in depression has decreased frontal lobe function.

- Thus, he has diminished ability to combat his disease.

Figure 13

they would see greater improvement in their mental health, and it would occur in a shorter time.

Injured Frontal Lobe Causes Violent Behavior

Problems with frontal lobe function are also linked to mental health issues that can produce behavior problems in someone who suffers from depression. This is a step beyond the connections already noted between frontal lobe impairment and other behavioral problems such as obsessive-compulsive disorder. A case in point is *violence*.

In a study of Vietnam veterans with head injuries, violent behavior was clearly linked to frontal lobe injuries.[47] The results indicated that patients with damage to the ventromedial frontal lobe (the middle portion of the lobe closest to the forehead) demonstrated greater aggression and violence tendencies than patients with damage to other brain areas and non-injured participants. The authors concluded that their findings "support the hypothesis that ventromedial frontal lobe lesions increase the risk of aggressive and violent behavior."

Since frontal lobe injuries are associated with both depression and violence, we would expect that *depression in combination with violence* would be seen in individuals with frontal lobes impaired for reasons other than injury. Indeed, this is the case. Depression and violence are clearly linked in several psychiatric studies.[48]

One study of 600 men by Teplin and colleagues looked at relationships between those who were jailed for violent behavior and those who were depressed. He found a strong correlation between violence and depression. Another study which involved female detainees showed similar correlation. Jordan and colleagues demonstrated similar increased rates of depressive problems, this time in incarcerated women—as opposed to jail detainees.[49]

These relationships are important from the standpoint of public health, but the linkage between violence and depression also poses unique risks for depressed patients as well. Recent research indicates that ventral frontal lobe dysfunction not only predisposes to violence toward others, but violence toward self in the form of *suicide*.[50]

The bottom line: the frontal lobe wields extensive control over mental health.

Strategies to enhance the frontal lobe are not limited to the prevention or relief of depression. They may also help avert some of the most socially damaging consequences of depression such as violent and criminal behaviors.

How Can I Improve Frontal Lobe Health?

So far, we have seen that a healthy frontal lobe is vital in the prevention of mental disorders as well as in the pursuit of a satisfactory quality of life. This begs the question, "How can I protect and enhance the health of my frontal lobe?" The remainder of the chapter is devoted to the answer to this question. We will examine two approaches. The first one considers therapies that require the services of a treating practitioner. Second, we will examine therapies that can be performed by the patient himself. These "therapies" include *actions to take* and *actions to avoid*.

Therapies Initiated by Practitioners to Optimize Frontal Lobe Function

Medical doctors and other healthcare practitioners have for centuries treated depression. The growing awareness of the frontal lobe's role in depression has been used to explain or justify the success of existing therapies, which mostly have centered around drug medicines. *I deal at length with current antidepressant medications* in *Chapter 6*; a lengthy repeat is not needed here. However, I will reiterate some of the most important details. Our understanding of the frontal lobe has helped to explain why many of the newer antidepressants are effective.

Serotonin Therapy—Boost the Levels

Drugs that boost brain serotonin levels appear to be treating an underlying problem in the vital prefrontal cortex. Autopsy studies of more than 200 individuals were conducted by researchers at the New York State Psychiatric Institute and Columbia University. They discovered that patients with a history of major depression had a reduced ability for the brain to utilize serotonin compared to individuals who never experienced a major depression.[51] Among the depressed individuals, those *who committed suicide had an even more reduced ability to utilize serotonin.* The reduced utilization of serotonin is the result of serotonin binding changes in the brain.

This finding is in harmony with earlier work of this same research group. Previously they had published data on serotonin binding changes in the ventral prefrontal cortex in correlation with suicide.[52] These reports have provided further evidence for a connection between this localized portion of the frontal lobe and both impulsive aggression and suicide.[53] Many practitioners have used evidence like this to encourage further use of drugs or other interventions that *boost serotonin levels.*

Serotonin levels can be increased with drugs and with diet. Chapter 6 has information on the drug approach and *Chapter 4* deals with the dietary approach. *Chapter 5* shows how sunlight and exercise can also increase serotonin levels. Later in this chapter we will discuss diet and serotonin.

Shock Treatments

Another therapy that has been bolstered and refined from our understanding of the key role of the frontal lobe is *shock therapy,* more commonly referred to as "shock treatments." For years, severely depressed people have been given shock therapy as the treatment of last resort after antidepressant drugs and psychological counseling had failed.

In shock therapy, electrodes are placed on the scalp. Electrical pulses strong enough to trigger a grand mal-type seizure are sent through the electrodes.[54] To prevent pain and physical injury from convulsions during the therapy, the patient is given general anesthesia. The treatments are usually given two to three times a week for several weeks. About 90 percent of the time the treatment works well—better, in fact, than drugs that only help in 60 to 70 percent of cases.[55] Evidence indicates that shock treatments work because it *changes brain function in the critical prefrontal cortex region.*[56]

Because of its effectiveness, estimates suggest that some 65,000 U.S. patients per year receive shock treatments. With an average of eight treatments per course yielding at least 500,000 treatments per year, the annual cost is approximately $200 million.[57] Besides its hefty price tag, it has other serious downsides including confusion and memory problems.

The memory problems include difficulty storing new memories and loss of previous memories.[58] The latter is usually the most problematic in the long term. It tends to affect memories of happenings that occurred close to the time of the shock sessions. However, the amnesia can extend back several months or even years.[59,60]

Although improvement can occur, recovery is typically incomplete, with irreversible amnesia persisting for some events.[61,62] Many patients may find little consolation in research documenting that *personal memory* (memory about themselves) tends to be less affected than the so-called *impersonal memory* (knowledge about the world and other events that they didn't experience personally).[63] Although quite rare, death can result from shock treatments, usually

187

due to heart stoppage.[64] Furthermore, the beneficial effects of elevating the mood of the patient may last as little as three to six months.

Memory problems from shock treatments should not be shrugged off. The association is even more troubling because *depression itself*—even without shock treatments—*can undermine memory.*

A summary of the status of shock treatments is shown in **Figure 14**.

Magnet Therapy

There are other emerging therapies for depression that have developed as a result of the growing understanding of the frontal lobe's importance. One of the most promising of these therapies is *magnet therapy.* Through this technique, brain researchers may have discovered another way to "jolt" the brain out of depression—without the harmful effects of shock treatments. Although magnet therapy is not as potent,

it does appear to have far fewer side effects. It is not an electric current, but a magnetic field that passes through the skull into the brain.

Magnet therapy relies on an age-old physics principle of the electromagnet. If an electric current is passed through a coil of wires, a magnetic field is generated perpendicular to the flow of electricity through the coil. Furthermore, if that generated magnetic field acts on a conductive medium (something that can, in turn, conduct electricity) an electric current will be generated in the medium (in a parallel but opposite direction as the current in the coil). The generator on your car uses this principle.

Magnet therapy is performed by placing a coil of wire over a selected portion of the scalp, such as the frontal lobe. Current is then intermittently pulsed through the coil, creating a strong on-and-off magnetic field. This magnetic field in turn creates a current in the brain. This current is strong enough to actually stimulate nerve cells causing them to "fire" (or, in technical terms, "depolarize").[65] Interestingly, nerve cell depolarization is based on the very same principles as shock therapy.

Magnet Therapy in the Left and Right Front Lobe

Although this therapy is relatively new, results are encouraging for relieving depression. The target for relieving depression with magnet therapy is the frontal lobe. Depression is characterized not only by generalized frontal lobe impairment, but also by deficiencies in particular areas of the frontal lobes. Emerging research takes these concepts one step further and suggests that there is also a functional imbalance between the right and left frontal lobes.[66] Major depression—and the negative symptoms associated with it—is caused and/or perpetuated by decreased left frontal lobe function (and blood flow) with respect to the right.[67,68,69] Because magnet therapy can be

SUMMARY OF THE STATUS OF SHOCK TREATMENTS

Shock treatment:

- has been in common use for decades
- is a treatment of last resort
- often used after drug and counseling therapy have failed
- is used only on severely depressed patients
- requires general anesthesia
- passes a heavy electrical current through the brain
- current triggers a grand mal type of seizure
- is expensive
- can seriously impair memory
- benefits may last only three to six months

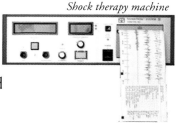
Shock therapy machine

Figure 14

used to stimulate or depress very specific areas of the brain, this treatment has added further support to these theories.

How can magnet therapy in one case stimulate, and in another situation depress the brain? It appears that *fast frequency repetitive magnet therapy* excites the brain area being treated, while *slow frequency repetition* inhibits—or "tones down"—brain activity.[70] By applying this knowledge, researchers have demonstrated that they can help treat depression by using either the treatments that stimulate the left frontal lobe,[71,72,73] or treatments that decrease activity in the right frontal lobe.[74,75]

The effectiveness of these two divergent therapies lends a significant measure of support to the theory that part of the problem in depression is due to greater impairment of left frontal lobe function compared to the right. Dr. Mark George recently provided further confirmation of these relationships in a 1999 review of magnet therapy that he co-authored. Dr. George revealed that in earlier unpublished work, his group had found that when depressed patients received the fast frequency version—expected to stimulate the right frontal lobe—their depression worsened.[76]

In this regard, magnet therapy, which can target a specific region, may actually be more beneficial than drug therapy, which has a generalized effect on the entire brain, or even shock therapy, which also cannot be precisely targeted.[77] Some preliminary research suggests that magnet therapy may be as good or better than any of the conventional therapies delivered by practitioners.[78,79,80,81] However, it is really too soon to bestow the garland of "champion of depression therapies" on magnet therapy.

The status of magnet therapy is summarized in **Figure 15**. There is more to be learned about this kind of therapy.

Shock Therapy vs. Magnet Therapy—Which is Better?

Shock therapy still appears to obtain superior effects in those with *severe psychotic depression*, a state in which the patient loses touch with reality.[82] In spite of questions about its success, magnet therapy still appears to fill a unique role. Because it can stimulate specific brain regions, it offers promise as an addition to drug medication. Another plus for magnet therapy: it has been demonstrated to enhance the effectiveness of serotonin-boosting medications.[83]

From the standpoint of side effects, magnet therapy has demonstrated that nerve cell firing can be induced without the extreme measures employed by shock treatments. Magnet therapy does not require anesthesia. Shock treatments cause painful stimulation of scalp pain receptors.[84,85] Magnet therapy is not particularly painful, although it can cause an occasional mild headache or discomfort at the site of the

STATUS OF MAGNETIC THERAPY FOR FRONTAL LOBE ENHANCEMENT

- This therapy is relatively new in treating the frontal lobe
- Induces a magnetic field through the frontal lobe
- Results are encouraging for relieving depression
- Can target specific areas of the frontal lobe
- Can stimulate or depress various portions of the frontal lobe
- Appears to have few side effects
- No anesthesia needed
- Cost is relatively low

Figure 15

coil. So far, magnet therapy's record looks relatively good when it comes to seizures, though it is of concern that a few have occurred.[86]

There is evidence that magnet therapy generally does not cause confusion or memory problems. Other studies have raised some concern about memory impairment.[87,88] A preliminary report from a study designed to look at mental side effects from magnet therapy treatments for depression found no evidence of memory problems.[89] Nonetheless, it may have other subtle emotional or hormonal effects.

There is conflicting preliminary evidence that stimulatory treatments over the left prefrontal cortex may increase short-term feelings of sadness (and decrease self-rated happiness) in normal volunteers.[90,91] Other research has documented elevations in levels of thyroid-stimulating hormones following magnet therapy treatments.[92]

Electromagnetic Radiation and Cancer

Lastly, there is little to ease public concerns about links between electromagnetic radiation and cancer. Conflicting data continues to be published. Recent pooled data showing a doubling of leukemia risk in children with greater exposure to magnetic fields has fueled greater concern in some circles.[93] Unfortunately, we do not have sufficient experience with the extremely strong magnetic fields that are repetitively used in the course of magnet therapy for treating depression. Thus, the jury is still out. The cancer concern remains another unknown risk with respect to this otherwise encouraging therapy.

Like any newer, promising treatment, magnet therapy must prove its safety and efficacy over time. At present, I think magnet therapy should be seriously considered when discussions gravitate to the alternative of shock therapy. However, I would not be anxious to put a moderately depressed loved one in line for the next available treatment. We really do not know enough about the long-term effects of such brain stimulation.

Magnet therapy has further increased my desire to find ways to target lifestyle therapies for depression. Are there ways that we can help the frontal lobe in general or aid in restoring balance between the right and left frontal lobes without the use of medications, shock treatments, or magnet therapy? Fortunately, the answer is a resounding "yes." And a host of thrilling lifestyle approaches provides that affirmative answer.

We will now leave the realm of therapies that require the services of a treating practitioner. Let us turn our attention to lifestyle therapies that can be performed by the patient himself. We will look at these lifestyle therapies by focusing on two categories.

First, we will consider *injurious* lifestyle factors that should be avoided, because they *suppress optimal front brain performance*. Next, we will discover *desirable* lifestyle factors that should be adopted because they *enhance the functioning of this key brain region*.

There are a number of lifestyle factors that suppress frontal lobe function. The use of several drugs will damage the frontal lobe. They are listed in **Figure 16**.

Let us look at the effect that each of these drugs has on the frontal lobe. We will begin with street drugs.

DRUGS THAT DAMAGE OUR FRONTAL LOBES

- Illicit drugs
- Certain prescription drugs
- Other legal drugs:
  - alcohol
  - caffeine
  - nicotine

Figure 16

Street Drugs Impair the Frontal Lobe

Many Americans are highly concerned about our nation's heavy and increasing use of drugs. There has been a sharp upturn recently in both the acceptance of illicit drugs and the use of those drugs among American youth, according to widely publicized surveys.[94] Parents are fearful that their children will use illicit drugs, become addicted, and suffer all the physical, mental, and social effects of addiction.

They also fear that their children might engage in high-risk behaviors that could ultimately cut short their young lives. This last concern is especially important. *A person who has ingested a drug can have blunted frontal lobe function, though his appearance may not show it.* Such impairment leads to risk-taking behavior that can result in an automobile accident, contracting HIV infection, or some other life-changing, life-ending event.

Drugs other than illicit drugs can also impair frontal lobe function. Many feel cheated if they pay to see a doctor and do not walk away with at least one prescription for a medicinal drug. Television, radio, and magazine ads bombard us with our need for over-the-counter and prescription remedies. *Caffeine and alcohol are culturally accepted drugs. Nicotine* use is socially stigmatized, but is still treated legally as a lifestyle choice and not the *powerfully addictive, mind-altering drug* that it really is. Nonetheless, these agents take a toll on frontal brain function.

Illicit Drugs and Mental Impairment

The dangers of illicit drugs on mental performance are well documented. There seems to be little need to belabor how such *mind-altering drugs transform the mind— including the frontal lobe.* This problem is worse than previously thought. There is growing evidence that drugs of abuse affect the brain *long after their short-term effects have worn off.* Recent research funded by the National Institute on Drug Abuse found that college students who were regular marijuana users had defects in their attention, memory, and learning as long as 24 hours after their last use of the drug.[95] Long after the high was over, the brain was still struggling along in low gear.

Marijuana, like its cousins alcohol and nicotine, has now been shown to harm the brain of the developing fetus. A mother who uses marijuana gives her child a life-long legacy of brain impairment.[96] For optimal frontal lobe function, *leave illicit drugs out of the picture.*

Alcohol Injures the Frontal Lobe

Alcohol directly effects the frontal lobe in addition to worsening the risk of medication side effects. In fact, it is one of America's most popular frontal lobe assailants. Let's examine some of the illuminating research, the conclusions of which are listed in **Figure 17**.

Several years ago alcoholics and non-alcoholics were studied by MRI and PET scans. *Among the alcoholics,* the MRI re-

ALCOHOL DAMAGES THE BRAIN

- Alcohol reduces frontal lobe activity.
- It weakens abstract thinking ability even in social drinkers.
- Loss of abstract thinking is worse among heavier drinkers.
- All of these effects are present even 24 hours after the last drink.
- Drinking less than the legal limit weakens judgment.
- Driving under these conditions causes nine times as many fatal accidents.
- Ingesting alcohol causes a loss of brain cells.

Figure 17

vealed a striking amount of *loss of frontal lobe gray matter*, where the brain's nerve cells are concentrated. This is in contrast to the deeper lying *white matter*, where the nerve fibers leaving those cells predominate. This loss of gray matter indicates an actual *loss of brain cells that are involved in critical frontal lobe functions*. PET scanning showed corresponding changes in brain function. *The alcoholics showed a lower glucose metabolism—indicative of less frontal lobe activity.*[97]

These frontal lobe-impairing effects are *not confined to heavy alcohol users*. Researchers found a *measurable decrease in abstract thinking ability* among 1,300 men and women who were social drinkers. These individuals drank as little as *one alcoholic beverage per week*. The men in the study had about *two drinking occasions per week* and consumed *two or three alcoholic drinks on those occasions*.

The women drank even less. On the average, they only drank *every fifth day* and consumed *two alcoholic drinks*. Even with these low levels of use, assessments of *mental functioning showed impairment*. In fact, as alcohol intake increased, their ability to think abstractly (a measure of frontal lobe performance) *decreased even more*.[98] Acute alcohol effects or intoxication could not explain these changes, since all assessments of mental function were done at least 24 hours after the last consumption of alcohol.

Many people believe that automobile accidents are more frequent among drinkers primarily because of the profound effects on coordination, judgment, and alertness seen in "drunks" and others who are manifestly intoxicated. However, in many cases the problem may actually relate to more *subtle deficiencies in judgment* that occur in seemingly unimpaired social drinkers.

Such alcohol-using drivers may have no impairment in coordination. Their speech may appear normal. However, a few moments later they may find themselves skidding off the highway or involved in a collision. The reason? *Impaired judgment* failed to provide adequate warning about necessary speed reductions to successfully negotiate a curve or stop in time to prevent an impending roadway emergency. Individuals with a blood alcohol concentration (BAC) of 0.05–0.09 percent, *less than the legal limit in many states, have at least nine times the risk of a fatal traffic accident* than if their BAC were zero.[99] This is largely due to the fact that alcohol impairs the frontal lobe long before it impairs other parts of the brain such as the coordination center.

Caffeine "Unbalances the Mind"

Caffeine has far-reaching effects on the brain. At least one of those effects comes as no surprise. After all, it is America's *preferred stimulant*. However, a heavy price is paid for that stimulation. Let us see how caffeine works and then explore some of its associated side effects.

Caffeine impinges on the brain's communication system in a number of ways. In exploring these relationships, we need to recall that brain cells talk to one another through chemical interchanges. Nerve cells release chemicals called "chemical messengers" (neurotransmitters) that are picked up by neighboring cells. These messengers then cause changes to occur in the cell that receives them. Some messengers cause stimulation of the recipient nerve cell, and others cause depression.

Caffeine's widespread influence focuses primarily on its ability to affect the levels of two chemical messengers: acetylcholine and adenosine. Caffeine disrupts the brain chemistry by increasing the level of acetylcholine and interfering with the transmission of adenosine. Thus, *caffeine upsets the delicate balance of nerve transmission in the brain*, which may have devastating consequences. Adenosine tones down (or puts the brakes on) many aspects of brain nerve transmission. But caffeine weakens its power to do its work, thus allowing artificial stimulation of the brain from the caffeine.

At first, adenosine may seem like a "bad guy." After all, who wants to depress their brain transmission? Perhaps we can see this issue more clearly by looking at an analogy: the importance of good brakes on an automobile. You do not get into your automobile to *stop*—you get into it to *go* somewhere. However, you wouldn't feel comfortable driving a car that did not have the capacity to stop. Good brakes are essential—especially on a vehicle designed to go. Similarly, chemical messengers like adenosine, that have a large role in "putting the brakes on," are very important for balance in the brain.

There are serious concerns in the psychiatric literature about caffeine's role in "unbalancing" the mind. Caffeine has been linked with anxiety, anxiety neurosis, psychosis (a state where a person loses touch with reality), and schizophrenia, the so-called "split personality" disorder.[100] Other researchers add to this list caffeine-induced delirium and anorexia nervosa (an aversion to food).[101]

A chemical messenger called dopamine also rises when you drink a caffeinated beverage.[102,103] This action is worrisome. Some of the most profound psychiatric diseases such as schizophrenia appear to be due in part to excess amounts of dopamine. In fact, standard drug therapy for these serious mental disorders involves the use of dopamine-blocking agents.[104] Consequently, it is not surprising that caffeine—an agent that raises dopamine levels—*increases the risk of certain mental illnesses*, even though it may appear harmless on the surface.

Other psychiatric diseases—with profound frontal lobe effects—may result from the unbalancing of brain metabolism by caffeine. This is particularly true of depression. As we have already seen, decreased frontal lobe function and blood flow appear to be a characteristic of depression.[105,106] Research indicates that caffeine can contribute to these deleterious findings. Researchers have known for years that *caffeine can significantly decrease frontal lobe blood flow*.[107,108] Caffeine has been documented to decrease whole brain blood flow *by as much as 30 percent*.[109] All of this evidence on impaired brain blood flow naturally raises a question: is there any documented connection between caffeine use and depression?

The internationally acclaimed Norwegian research project known as the Tromso Heart Study has provided a partial answer. The Scandinavian researchers assessed 143,000 men and women and *found a significant increase in depression among women who were heavy coffee users* (but not in men who used similar amounts of coffee). The findings are illustrated in **Figure 18**.[110]

In addition to the link with depression, women who used more coffee also had more problems coping with stress. The reason that these effects did not show up in the men is not clear. It may indicate that women are more susceptible to caffeine, or it may reflect caffeine's exploitation of a

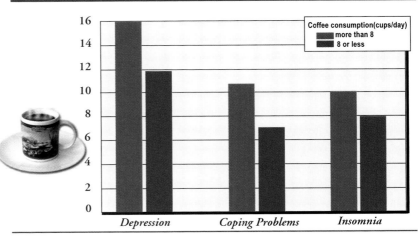

COFFEE CONSUMPTION AND MENTAL PROBLEMS

Coffee consumption(cups/day)
more than 8
8 or less

Figure 18

193

greater female predisposition to depression.

The link between impaired frontal lobe blood flow and depression when coupled with caffeine's effect in robbing the brain's blood flow simply cannot be ignored. When the Tromso Heart Study evidence is added to the puzzle, I think the verdict is clear. If you are seeking to treat or avoid depression, *caffeine should be eliminated from your program.*

The Brain's Adjustment to Caffeine Creates Dependency

If caffeine is so good for us, as some people (even some scientists) would like us to believe, it is interesting to note that the brain puts forth great effort to undo the effects of this popular legal drug. When exposed to caffeine on a daily basis, the brain tries to compensate in at least two ways. First, it decreases its production of *acetylcholine*.[111] This appears to be a way to lessen the impact of the increased acetylcholine levels brought on by caffeine. Sec-

ond, the brain increases its number of *adenosine* receptors.[112] This is likely a response to give adenosine more of an effect in brain communication—in spite of the fact that caffeine is blocking its function to some extent.

Unfortunately, *these brain changes contribute to caffeine dependency.* Brain structure and function become changed and consequently the brain actually comes to expect caffeine's effect on its neurons. This is one of the reasons coffee users are so committed to their morning brew. If they don't get their caffeine, they feel like they are running at less than half-throttle. If coffee users stop using their java, they are likely to develop withdrawal symptoms such as headache in addition to fatigue.

Caffeine Withdrawal and Headaches

Many wonder why headaches occur during caffeine withdrawal. The answer probably resides with either adenosine, acetylcholine, or both of these transmitters. One of the important functions of adenosine (that is blocked in part by caffeine) is relaxation or dilation of blood vessels—particularly those in the heart and brain.

With habitual caffeine consumption, the brain increases the numbers of adenosine receptors in an attempt to offset caffeine's competition. Once caffeine is removed, however, this increased number of receptors is still there for a short time. The now unopposed action of adenosine causes marked blood vessel relaxation. With relaxed blood vessels to the brain, there is increased blood flow that causes congestion in the brain. Many attribute the caffeine withdrawal headache to this mechanism. Interestingly, the brain's attempt to deal with caffeine-induced acetylcholine changes may also predispose to caffeine withdrawal headaches.

The quick *remedy* for caffeine-withdrawal headache is ingesting coffee, caffei-

CAFFEINE IMPAIRS THE BRAIN SEVEN WAYS

- Tends to produce dependence.
- Can cause drug withdrawal reactions.
- Can cause or worsen psychiatric illnesses.
- Impairs physical and mental performance.
- Interferes with sleep.
- May influence the risk of other illnesses that in turn exert frontal lobe effects through physical or mental stress.
- May exert effects that impact on spiritual and social dimensions of character.

Figure 19

nated soda pop, or one of the many over-the-counter headache pills that contain caffeine like *Excedrin.*® None of these options is as good as toughing out the withdrawal. Usually, within two days, the brain adjusts to a normal internal environment without caffeine, the headaches will be gone, and the brain will be well on its way to a better chemical balance. Unfortunately, I have had a few patients that had severe headaches for up to two weeks after caffeine withdrawal. In these cases there may have been an underlying tendency to headache that was triggered by caffeine withdrawal.

In practical terms, caffeine's disruption of brain chemistry sets the stage for more than just caffeine withdrawal problems and the obvious psychiatric illnesses that we have already mentioned. Habitual coffee drinkers can have weakened physical and mental performance even if they have no psychiatric symptoms and are not undergoing withdrawal. According to research, the drug does tend to help people do simple tasks more quickly, but it is "disruptive on more complex tasks of motor reaction time and fine motor coordination."[113]

The decreased production of acetylcholine that results from regular caffeine use also plays a role.[114] Researchers consistently find that a decrease in brain acetylcholine is associated with impaired mental functioning.[115,116] Furthermore, despite common lore, the authors of an extensive medical review on caffeine found no evidence that this drug helped to improve intellectual capacity.[117] A summary of some of the effects of caffeine on the brain appears in **Figure 19**.

It comes as no surprise that caffeine interferes with sleep. Caffeine consumed within six hours of bedtime makes it harder to fall asleep, decreases the total amount of time slept, and significantly worsens sleep quality.[118] Caffeine decreases the deepest, most restorative stages of sleep. *More surprising is that excessive amounts of caffeine can cause severe brain problems, including seizures.*[119] There are even descriptions of *human fatalities due to caffeine.*[120]

So much for the damages caused by caffeine. Next, we look at the effects of another common drug, nicotine.

Nicotine Impairs the Frontal Lobe

Nicotine addiction continues to be a global plague. This pernicious drug has stimulant effects on the nervous system similar to caffeine and should be avoided. Quality of sleep, performance of tasks, and even stress control all suffer while using cigarettes. Smokers are less able to perform complex mental tasks than nonsmokers.[121] This is ironic, since many smokers believe mental function is actually improved by smoking. The catch is that when they quit, these problems worsen initially before getting better. So, shortly after some individuals become nonsmokers, they mistakenly think that smoking was helping them in these areas and they return to their cigarettes after a few days of abstinence.

In addition to short-term mental effects, smoking takes a long-term toll on brain function. Compared to nonsmokers, smokers significantly increase their risk of brain-damaging strokes.[122] Initial reports suggesting that smoking may help decrease the risk of Alzheimer's disease have not stood up to further scrutiny.[123,124] In short, nicotine is a leading cause of lost mental function (stroke) without providing any long-term benefits for brain health. The multiple damages that nicotine inflicts on the frontal lobe are listed in **Figure 20**.

Nicotine's prenatal effects are also important to emphasize. Nicotine used by a pregnant woman impairs brain function in her child, perhaps for life. Research shows mental deficits in children of smokers that can only be explained by the effects of nicotine. One study made a comparison of mental function between three-year-old children of women who smoked throughout their entire pregnancy with the children of those who quit during pregnancy. Children of those who kicked the habit tested significantly better.[125]

Nicotine is Linked to Depression

Nicotine is clearly linked to depression. Epidemiological studies indicate that smokers have an increased risk of depression.[126,127] Furthermore, the more they smoke, the greater their risk.[128] It is possible that smoking increases depression risk through effects similar to that of caffeine—decreases in cerebral blood flow—even though some depression-related brain messenger chemicals may increase. Older studies indicated that cigarette smoking actually increased cerebral blood flow,[129] but newer research has revealed a much more complicated picture.

For example, in research from Japan,[130] Nakamura and colleagues found that after 15 hours of nicotine abstinence, some smokers had increases while others had decreases in brain blood flow. Edward Domino and colleagues at the University of Michigan, Ann Arbor, added further complexity to the nicotine-brain blood flow relationships.[131] They found that nicotine intake in smokers who had been abstinent for 10 hours increased blood flow to some brain areas but decreased blood supply to others. Of concern from the standpoint of depression was a decrease in left-sided brain flow relative to the right in the hippocampal/parahippocampal areas. These areas stimulate the critical orbitomedial prefrontal cortex,[132] and therefore may indicate a nicotine-induced over-dominance of the right frontal lobe—*changes that could predispose to depression.*

Still other researchers assert that smoking probably does not increase the risk for depression. They claim that the reason nicotine use keeps company with depression is because individuals with a depressive tendency tend to medicate themselves with nicotine. Nicotine can raise brain levels of mood-elevating chemicals.[133]

Although the discussions can go back and forth on this subject, several facts remain. First, researchers agree that there is a connection between smoking and depression. Second, no medical practitioner recommends nicotine as a legitimate depression treatment. Therefore, from both the perspective of depression, as well as other nicotine-related brain effects, it is best to leave this addictive chemical out of one's life.

Beware of Meat, Cheese, and Wine

In addition to caffeine, other dietary substances can have a detrimental effect on the frontal lobe. Three that are chemical derivatives of ammonia are found in certain foods such as cheeses, wines, fish, sausages, and certain rich foods. They may also be found in spoilage of poultry and fish, which can occur under prolonged refrigeration. Their names are Tyramine, Tryptamine, and Trimethylamine.

These compounds are associated with depression, a decrease in blood flow to the brain, mind-altering effects, nightmares, hallucinations, and a decrease in brain perfor-

NICOTINE AFFECTS THE FRONTAL LOBE

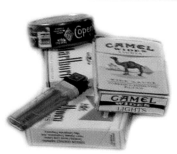

Smoking:

- Reduces the quality of sleep

- Reduces the ability to perform complex mental tasks

- Reduces stress control

- Increases risk of brain-damaging strokes

- Impairs brain function in children of pregnant mothers

- Is linked to depression

Figure 20

mance under stress, such as getting poor test scores due to stress during school examinations. A description of their chemical actions in the brain and the effect on frontal lobe performance are detailed in *Appendix I.*

Hypnosis and the Frontal Lobe

We now move from the field of diet and nutrition to a totally different subject that impacts frontal lobe health. It is a popular method for dealing with things ranging from common bad habits to emotionally devastating childhood trauma. That method is *hypnotism.* Despite the innocent images you see in circus performances, media presentations, comedy routines, and smoking-cessation programs, hypnotism causes serious side effects. *One effect of this popular therapy is frontal lobe impairment.*

The connection between hypnotism and the frontal lobe comes as no surprise to those who understand the technique. Hypnosis, by design, bypasses the frontal lobe as it helps the subject enter a trance-like state. Dr. Freda Morris, a former professor of medical psychology at UCLA, has written several books on hypnosis. In her words, hypnosis is a state characterized by a single-minded focus on only one thing "like a bird watching a snake."[134]

While hypnotized, the subject is unmindful of all other environmental input. How do hypnotists induce such a state? The typical hypnotist will first help the subject remain quiet and still—free from all outside diversions. Next, the hypnotist will help the subject develop a focus "on a certain point." For example, fixing the eyes on a flickering light trains the person to focus on one place, thereby inducing a hypnotic state. Once the subject enters the hypnotic state, he is encouraged to follow the hypnotist's suggestions.

When brain waves are measured with an EEG during this process, we see that the hypnotized person *loses beta wave activity.* Beta activity denotes sound think-

ing and involves dynamic frontal lobe activity. Conversely, in the hypnotized state, an *alpha brain pattern* is active,[135] a state where there is no critical analysis of incoming information.[136] Alpha waves are a lower frequency than beta waves. In this state, an individual will register information and suggestions without interpretation and without frontal lobe filtering.

Hypnosis Short Circuits the Frontal Lobe

During the hypnotic state, individuals can receive information and mentally record the duties the hypnotist asks them to perform. Indeed, their memory works well, their emotions work fine, and they can laugh and cry. But as they continue to focus on a flickering light—or similar object—they do not critically analyze the information they receive.[137] None of the information is filtered according to their sense of values or moral worth. *Their very reasoning powers are bypassed. The frontal lobe has been short-circuited.*

The dangers of hypnotism are listed in **Figure 21**.

Humans have been given large frontal lobes for a good reason. To compromise this

DANGERS OF HYPNOTISM

A hypnotized person:
- Loses thought activity (weak beta brain waves)
- Has a short-circuited frontal lobe
- Has no reasoning power
- Has depressive tendencies
- Has his mind under the control of the hypnotist

Figure 21

control center of the brain, even temporarily, is dangerous. Even worse, *hypnotism alters more than frontal lobe function.* This realization leads us to some insights that will reveal hypnotism's darkest side when it comes to depression.

Hypnotism May Set the Stage for Future Depression

Evidence for years has demonstrated that when people are hypnotized, there is a relative over-dominance of the right side of the brain to the left side.[138,139] As we have seen, this would be expected to cause depressive tendencies. Consequently, hypnotism appears to perpetuate current depression or set the stage for future depression, by decreasing overall frontal lobe activity and by upsetting the balance between the right and left frontal lobes.

Hypnotism may heighten depression risk by changes in brain chemistry that occur even when the person is no longer hypnotized. To fully appreciate this potential, I need to remind you that other areas of the brain are also unbalanced in depression. One of those areas is adjacent to the frontal lobe, called the *parietal lobe*. Interestingly, research has documented a depression-related imbalance in parietal function between the right and left sides. As with the frontal lobes, depressed individuals show greater right parietal lobe activity compared to the left. Of particular relevance, individuals who are highly hypnotizable also have an accentuated right parietal lobe activity.[140] (Some individuals can be more easily hypnotized than others.)

The implication is that individuals who are easy to hypnotize may be at greater risk for depression. Further evidence of such a connection was found in 1998 when researchers in Rome, Italy, found that "high[ly] hypnotizable individuals self-reported greater levels of emotional experiences than did low hypnotizables, especially in terms of negative emotion."[141]

The researchers went on to say that the highly hypnotizable group demonstrated a greater ease of self-generating sad emotions than happy ones. In connection with the sad emotions they demonstrated the expected activation of right-sided brain structures. These characteristics suggest a greater risk of depressive tendencies among highly hypnotizable subjects. Not only does hypnotism undermine frontal lobe function, but it may also permanently alter brain processing in such a way that depressed thoughts are more easily generated.

Despite these very real concerns with hypnotism, it is quite popular. Unknown to many people, hypnotism comes in a variety of forms. There are fairly straightforward medical applications of hypnotism. Medical literature is filled with examples of hypnosis being used for psychiatric and/or behavioral problems, spanning a broad spectrum from traumatic events of childhood to current problems with overeating or nicotine use.

Hypnotism also comes in more subtle forms. Eastern meditation, or yoga, is promoted for stress control. Dr. Freda Morris points out that in many cases it is really a technique of self-hypnosis.[142] For this reason, such meditation is potentially dangerous. The parallels between Eastern meditation and hypnotism, and the differences between Eastern and Christian meditation can be found in *Chapter 8*, "Stress without Distress".

The Home Hypnotist

There may be an object in your home that you unwittingly allow to lead you into a type of hypnotic trance. If you are like the average American, several rooms in your house are equipped with an object that you focus your eyes on. It flickers every few seconds, and can produce a hypnotic-like trance. It is one of the most popular devices of our time—the television set.

More than 96 percent of American

homes have at least one set.[143] Jerry Mander found that although there are many ways to be hypnotized, a number of experts defined hypnotism in such a way that television aptly fits the description. The classic setting for TV watching is similar to a typical environment for hypnotism induction—a darkened room, a flickering light (the TV set) as a single-minded focus, and freedom from outside diversions.[144]

People watch programs provided by TV stations, cable companies, satellite networks, videos, and DVDs. The range of programming is diverse—movies, documentaries, sit-coms, sports, music, education, nature, news, *ad infinitum*. Does what you watch have any effect on your mind and character? It clearly does. From the standpoint of both depression and the frontal lobe, the most disturbing aspects of television relate to the *veritable explosion of both sexual content and violence.*

Television, Sexual Arousal, and Depression

Some adults may argue about whether sensual imagery is increasing on television. Consider the effect the growing amount of televised sexual content is having on American young people. Documentation shows that television's erotic influence is so pervasive that it increases sexual activity in teens and younger children. Studies show that the age of first sexual intercourse significantly decreases due to the influence of TV. The more television watched, the lower the age for that first sexual encounter.[145] Not only do studies show it, children themselves report that television encourages them to take part in sexual activity at a young age.[146]

The growing use of sexuality in the media is viewed with consternation by many segments of the population. More "open-minded" individuals often label those concerns as narrow and puritanical. However, those who are truly concerned

about sexually explicit material—whether it be delivered through the medium of TV, magazines, the internet, sexually suggestive novels, or even a walk on a populated beach—appear to be on very solid footing when it comes to *the effect of sexuality on depression.*

For years, sexual arousal has been linked to stimulation of the right side of the brain.[147] Research suggests that the area particularly stimulated by sexual arousal is the lower part of the right frontal lobe.[148] You will recall that this is probably the last place you would want to stimulate if you want to treat or prevent depression, because depression tends to be characterized by a relatively greater level of activity in the right frontal lobe compared to the left. The three-way relatioinship between TV watching, illicit sexual arousal, and depression is summarized in **Figure 22**.

I will not take the connection between sexual arousal and depression to extremes. I'm not advocating that a husband and wife separate for the time it takes one partner to undergo depression treatment. In such cases, I believe the social and emotional

TV, SEX, AND DEPRESSION

- The age of the first sexual encounter is lower among children who watch TV.

- The more TV watched, the lower the age for the first sexual encounter.

- Children report that TV encourages them to be sexually active at a young age.

- The right frontal lobe is stimulated by sexual arousal.

- A stimulated right frontal lobe is a characteristic of depression.

Figure 22

strain on the relationship would likely be more harmful to emotional recovery than sexual arousal that is restricted in its scope to the marriage relationship.

I do have serious concerns about the very casual attitude that most Americans have taken toward sexually explicit material. The concern is not restricted to nudity. Much of what passes for *acceptable attire* and *acceptable behavior* on primetime shows (and commercials) appears calculated to sexually arouse the viewer. The research is clear as to where the problem lies—it is sexual arousal. Each individual can determine for himself whether that line is being crossed. My guess is that if most of my depressed patients are honest, that line is crossed more than once during the course of a typical evening of television viewing.

Recent research from UCLA revealed that young women exposed to "one or more significant childhood adversities" were more likely to become depressed when exposed to stressors. The childhood adversities included things like family violence, parental mental health problems, and alcoholism.[149] This is not an isolated study. There is a growing body of research linking stressful early life experiences with an increased risk of depression.[150] However, other research indicates that a "significant childhood adversity" may come into the home via the television set.

In 1994, a series of case histories was presented in the *British Medical Journal*. In an initial article and two follow-up letters, seven different children were described *who experienced major psychological trauma after viewing a single disturbing television program* called *Ghostwatch*.[151,152,153] The 90-minute pseudo-documentary was a staged production which featured a family who was being violently victimized by ghosts. The show ended giving the impression that viewers were at risk of similar violence from these spirits.

The seven children viewers described in the *British Medical Journal* consequentially experienced an array of psychological problems that seriously disrupted their lives and the lives of their families. The problems are listed in **Figure 23**.

Among the symptoms and signs described were depressed mood, nightmares, fear of the dark and of sleeping alone, difficulties in concentrating, impaired memory, "persistent intrusive thoughts and images of the traumatic event [the TV show]," raised levels of anxiety, panic attacks, and irritability. I would not be surprised if some of these youngsters later experienced an increased incidence of major depression following this stressful life event.

We do not yet have hard evidence of a connection between violent television viewing and depression. The lines of evidence are in place, but a definitive study has yet to be undertaken to conclusively bring the previous research into a fully congruent picture. The documented connection between life stress and future depression, and the fact that violent television viewing can be a significant stressor, certainly implies the connection between violent television viewing and depression.

Television Poses Other Dangers to the Brain

Although the *content* you view exerts a powerful effect on your mind, the *medium* of television itself also appears to have profound mental effects. Independent of content, evidence suggests that merely watching most television programs is detrimental to the frontal lobe. This deleterious effect appears to be the result of the scene-switching work in most programming.

The technical problem with the filming technique is referred to as a "rapidly changing scene of reference." The average television program (or video or DVD) changes its reference every three to five seconds. The perspective from which you are viewing the event suddenly changes from camera to camera many times each minute, whether you want it to or not. The frequent camera switching and scene changes that the viewer passively experiences is thought to be the critical factor that brings about frontal lobe suppression during the viewing process. This is in sharp contrast to how we normally view the world around us. We see real life scenes from one perspective (where we are located at the time of the event). We can change our perspective only by voluntarily moving, and then we are limited by means of transportation.

Dr. Morris cites television's rapid change of reference as contributing to a hypnotic-type effect.[154] Dr. Thomas Mulholland looked at children's EEGs (brain waves) as they watched their favorite television programs. The researchers assumed that since these programs were their favorite shows, the kids would be mentally involved with what they were viewing and would experience a continual shift between alpha brain wave activity and beta. Instead, after just two or three minutes of the show, they sat back and stayed almost entirely in an alpha pattern. This meant that while they were watching they were "not reacting, not orienting, not focusing, just *spaced-out*."[155]

Very few television programs (less than one percent) are truly educational. Within a minute of watching any television program you can determine if the program will detract or enhance frontal lobe activity. True education will not only convey information but will also enhance particularly the front-middle and left prefrontal cortex of the frontal lobe. If the scene of reference stays the same for thirty seconds or a minute, you can be sure that the program is educational.

Most C-Span programs, some Discovery Channel programs, and many 3ABN programs (specializing in spiritual and health programming) are examples of informational programs conveyed via a slow or perhaps no scene of reference change. This allows full analytical abilities of the viewer to be operative while receiving the

information. One additional benefit of such programming is that the prolonged "eye-focus" associated with hypnosis tends not to occur while receiving this information. Since there is no rapid scene of reference change, the eyes do not have to unnaturally stare at the television, but will often leave the set, and look around the room while still receiving and analyzing the information.

Dr. Herbert Krugman, a brain wave researcher, has gone on record saying, "Television is a communication medium that effortlessly transmits huge quantities of information [to the viewer] not thought about at the time of exposure."[156] Dr. Erik Peper, another influential brain wave researcher and writer, once said, "The horror of television is that the information goes in, but we do not react to it. It goes right into our memory pool and perhaps we react to it later, but we do not know what we are reacting to. When you watch television you are training yourself not to react and so later on, you're doing things without

DAMAGE TO CHILDREN FROM A SINGLE TV PROGRAM

- "Ghostwatch" was a "scary" TV story with violence.
- Seven children who watched were greatly affected.
- They and their families' lives were seriously disrupted.
- Their children had:
  - depressed mood
  - nightmares
  - fear of the dark
  - fear of sleeping alone
  - difficulty in concentrating
  - impaired memory
  - raised level of anxiety
  - panic attacks
  - irritability

Figure 23

knowing why you're doing them or where they came from."[157]

Under the influence of television, the frontal lobe cannot function at its full capacity. The brain does record information: sight, memory, and emotions are all functioning well. Nevertheless, the brain no longer critically analyzes the information. *Terrible scenes can be depicted, but the viewer tends only to laugh or shrug them off.* Normally, if those kinds of events happened in real life the individual would be appalled. Even this is *changing as people become more desensitized through exposure.*

Despite how one responds—whether by laughing, apathetically staring, averting the eyes in disgust, or a hundred other ways—*scenes are indelibly imprinted upon the mind.* When you see a rerun, once it begins you know you have seen it before. The memory is there, although the last time you saw it your frontal lobe was not any more active than it is this time.

Alvin Toffler, author of the '70s best seller

EFFECTS OF CONSTANT STIMULATION OF THE SENSES

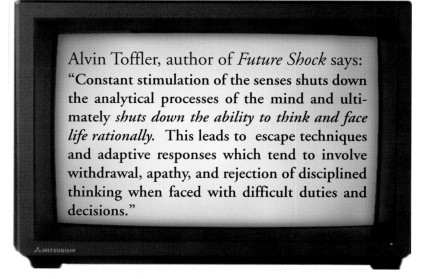

Alvin Toffler, author of *Future Shock* says: "**Constant stimulation of the senses shuts down the analytical processes of the mind and ultimately** *shuts down the ability to think and face life rationally.* **This leads to escape techniques and adaptive responses which tend to involve withdrawal, apathy, and rejection of disciplined thinking when faced with difficult duties and decisions.**"

Figure 24

"Future Shock," gave a particularly lucid account of the effects of artificial stimulation. His words still strike me as an apt description of television's subtle effects. His statement is recited in **Figure 24**.[158]

Well over a decade ago there were more than 3000 scientific studies published on the effects of television on the mind.[159] Research continues on this interrelationship. More than 500 books have been written on the subject. It is one of the most well researched subjects in our culture, yet most people have little awareness of TV viewing's solemn consequences. Television news programs often publicize lifestyle-related scientific studies, but little is said about the studies done on the effects of television on the mind. We cannot expect the television industry to reveal the truth about itself, but *we do not have to remain uninformed.*

The references already cited provide a range of sources dealing with television. Most libraries have books that explain the effects of television on the mind, and university libraries are usually connected to scientific data sources that can put you in touch with hundreds of articles written on the subject. The Internet has made research accessible to most people in their home environment. For example, in December 2000, a Lycos® search using the terms "television" and "mental health" yielded more than 10,000 hits. Six decades after David Sarnoff, President of RCA, unveiled the first television at the 1939 World's Fair, it is time to ask—*what is television doing to our country?* More specifically, *what is television doing to me?*

TV Trains in Non-Reaction

Both the Emerys and Dr. Erik Peper point out that viewing television also trains individuals to be non-reactive, as previously cited. This state of non-reaction describes a passive do-nothing attitude when confronted with needs and problems. Even watching the news day after day tends to induce a non-reactive attitude, which is a protective mechanism.

When you view starving children in a drought-stricken land, you cannot go to the television set and give them food. When you see war-ravaged foreign nations, you cannot lend a helping hand. Yes, you could send money to some humanitarian organization (which may or may not address the problem), but the next evening's news likely presents the same tragedy that you just donated money to help. Even worse, two days later you will probably see another shocking event that, were you present at the scene, would again call for your whole-hearted involvement.

The more we see tragedies that we cannot respond to, the less we tend to react. We learn to be non-reactive. Whether it is on the news, in serial programs, or in full-length movies, when we see suffering repeatedly portrayed without an ability to correct it we become desensitized. The consequence of people becoming non-reactive is seen today when violent crimes are committed while witnesses passively look on, none lifting a finger to intervene. Television and its legacy of non-reaction can lead viewers to regard violence lightly. However, the connections between television and violence involve more than the area of non-reaction.

Can Non-Reaction Affect Lifestyle Choices?

I will mention one other personal concern. I am troubled by the possibility that non-reaction induced by TV may spill over into our personal lifestyle choices. I wonder if individuals who have been trained in non-reaction would be less likely to take the initiative to act on information—even when it affects their own life and health. Are we developing a society of passive watchers who can watch a TV show about healthy lifestyle choices and then give it no more thought than last year's sporting events? And more to the point, are individuals who have grown accustomed to a steady diet of television less

likely to implement the depression-fighting strategies in this book? There are no definite answers, but the connections between television, desensitization, and non-reaction are disturbing as I try to help my patients address the risk factors for depression. The hazard of non-reaction is reviewed in **Figure 25**.

How much television does the average American watch? If we consider television merely from the standpoint of time, it often captivates the few hours of discretionary time that we have in our day. Before television, the three most profound influences on American values were *the family, the church, and the school*. If the amount of time we spend in an activity directly corresponds to its power to shape our values, then in the 1950s television *superseded the church*. In the '60s TV superseded the family. By the '70s it *superseded the school*. Upon graduating from high school, the average American child has spent more time in front of the television set than in the classroom.[160,161] All told, U.S. children spend approximately 20 percent of their waking hours watching television.[162]

THE HAZARD OF NON-REACTION

- "Non-reaction" describes a do-nothing attitude when confronted with needs.

- Watching TV news repetitively may induce non-reactive behavior.

- A non-reactive behavior may prevent a person from acting on vital information.

- Thus, TV addicts may be less likely to implement depression-fighting strategies.

Figure 25

If any are still wavering as to whether TV should be emphasized less in your homes, see the list of 17 deleterious effects of TV watching in *Appendix VI*.

Internet—the New Boob Tube

Alvin Toffler's description of the effects of television you just read in **Figure 24** equally fits what the Internet is doing to so many unfortunate individuals. Many people sit in front of the computer screen while rapidly surfing from one page to another. The mind so rapidly jumps from one scene to the next and one subject to the next that information overload becomes the norm.

Internet addicts spend an average of 30 hours of spare time each week on the Internet, which is more than four hours daily. Researchers found that *79 percent met the criteria for bipolar disorder (manic depression)*, and described the malady as *Internetomania*.[163]

Internet Users Suffer with Depression

Several computer companies funded a two-year study from normal families. They were surprised to find that those who spent only *a few hours a week online* at home experienced *higher levels of depression and loneliness* than when they used it less frequently. Greater use of the Internet was associated with declines in participants' communication with family members in the household, declines in the size of their social circle, and *increases in their depression and loneliness*.[164]

Other harm caused by the Internet include ruined marriages, social isolation, familial discord, academic failure, lost jobs, and lawsuits, all due to the results of the addictive behavior it induces.[165]

Combat Depression with Lifestyle Modifications

Strategies to enhance the health of the frontal lobe will combat depression. There are a number of actions that a depressed person can take that will improve and protect the function of the frontal lobe. Let us start with our thought process.

Cultivating Happy Thoughts

Cultivating positive, happy thoughts may sound like obvious advice to anyone who wants to treat or prevent depression. However, the recommendation to "think on the positive" is advice that has some fascinating support from neuroscience. We now understand that *happy thoughts help to decrease activity in the right frontal lobe, the part of the brain that tends to be over-dominant when a person is depressed*.[166] Thus, a program of overall frontal lobe enhancement, coupled with something that gently puts the brakes on the right frontal lobe relative to the left, would be expected to help enhance mood.

Get Physical Exercise.

As I pointed out in *Chapter 5*, physical exercise is vital to induce and/or maintain healthy emotional balance.[167] Exercise has value when it comes to quelling anxious thoughts. It is also important in improving the mood when a person is depressed. Fron-

SUMMARY OF THE BENEFITS OF MASSAGE

- Decreases anxiety symptoms

- Increases alertness

- Decreases the level of cortisol

- Increases math computation speed and accuracy

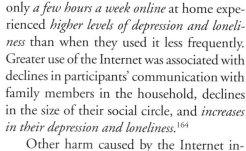

- Helps to balance right frontal lobe activity with the left

- Helpful in a treatment program for depression

Figure 26

tal lobe research has now uncovered another possible explanation as to why exercise benefits those with depression—it improves left frontal lobe function with respect to the right.

Researchers Petruzzello and Landers at the University of Illinois found that *running on a treadmill had an immediate effect on improving activation of the left frontal area with respect to the right*.[168] At the same time, they showed that *the exercisers experienced a decrease in anxiety*. They suggested that the increased stimulation of the left frontal lobe that was helping depression may also be responsible for the decrease in anxiety.

Make Time for Massage Therapy

Although I have attempted to categorize therapies into those that a person can undertake himself in contrast to those provided by a practitioner, massage really does not seem to fit easily into either category. Massage is clearly something that requires a practitioner. However, it is not usually used as a treatment for depression. For this reason, it seems that it often takes more effort for depressed individuals to include massage in their depression treatment program than for the massage therapist to do his work.

Regardless of how it is categorized, it must be included in any list of depression treatments that can favorably influence the frontal lobe. The reason for this is that massage can balance frontal lobe function. Recently, Jones and Field, of Florida Atlantic University, demonstrated that massage could help balance the greater relative right frontal lobe activation that characterizes depression.[169] These same researchers showed similar effects for music therapy—a topic I will later address.

The mental health benefits of massage therapy are not limited to depression per se. Massage has been demonstrated to decrease other symptoms that often accompany depression, such as anxiety. University of Miami researchers Field and colleagues found that 15-minute massages twice weekly for five weeks not only *decreased anxiety levels*, but also *dropped levels of cortisol, the detrimental stress hormone*.[170] Field's group documented other brain performance benefits from this brief massage treatment, including *enhanced alertness* and *increased speed and accuracy on math computations*. The many benefits of massage are condensed in **Figure 26**.

Lessons from Carbohydrates

Even every day foods that are commonly eaten can have an impact in either enhancing or diminishing frontal lobe activity. Other parts of the body can use fat, protein, or carbohydrates for energy, but not the brain. The brain uses glucose, a simple carbohydrate, almost exclusively as its source of energy.[171] Apparently as a result of the brain's very rapid metabolism, it is dependent on minute-to-minute supplies of this simple carbohydrate. This becomes easier to appreciate when you understand that the brain has a metabolic rate 7.5 times greater than the average body tissue.[172] Although it makes up only *2 percent of our body's mass*, the brain accounts for *15 percent of our total metabolism*.

The brain does not have much room to store nutrients. Space is extremely limited by the hard shell of the skull. Only a two-minute supply of glucose is available to the brain cells, and this is in the form of glycogen, the storage form of sugar. For peak performance, the frontal lobe requires blood with a *steady and adequate glucose level*.

Years ago, when scientists first discovered that the brain functioned best with carbohydrate fuel, some people began referring to candy bars as "brain food." Eventually we learned that, for sustained performance, *refined sugar was not brain food at all*. It was just the opposite, as stated in **Figure 27**.

The statement in this figure implies that

reduced amounts of refined sugar in the diet *strengthen the activity of the frontal lobe.* Research has verified the truth of this statement. Children seem to be particularly susceptible to decreased thinking and intellectual function as a result of sugar consumption. Even academically well-prepared children can get poorer grades on their tests if they choose the wrong food for their brains. One study of over forty 5-year-old boys is particularly revealing.[173] *Boys with little sugar in their diet had superior attention spans and more accurate responses than their high-sugar consuming peers.* The difference could not be explained by IQ or the parent's social or education status. When tested, the boys on a low refined-sugar diet performed the equivalent of one whole letter-grade higher in school. This provocative study *suggests that a better diet may help transform a B-student into an A-level scholar.*

Why Does a High Sugar Diet Impair Brain Function?

If sugar is a carbohydrate and carbohydrate is the frontal lobe's preferred fuel, then how does a high sugar diet impair brain function? The sequence of events, beginning with eating foods high in refined sugar, is spelled out in **Figure 28**.

Our bodies were created to eat foods such as fruits and grains in a *natural, unrefined state.* These foods help keep our blood sugar at a *fairly constant level.* However, when refined, sugary foods enter the digestive system, the *blood sugar rises dramatically* and the body reacts as if it was just exposed to a *great volume of natural food.*

In response, the pancreas produces a large amount of insulin. However, the rapid rise in blood sugar is deceptive. Unlike natural plant foods, foods rich in refined sugar are quickly absorbed and the rapid rise in blood sugar is quickly over. With insulin still present and no more sugar coming in via the digestive tract, the blood sugar level is driven down. It is not unusual for the blood sugar to drop well below where it was before the sugary food was eaten. When blood sugar level falls low enough, frontal lobe functions suffer due to inadequate fuel supplies.

To make matters worse, the most common response to hypoglycemia (low blood sugar) is to eat yet another sugary snack. Although this will drive the blood sugar up quickly again, research demonstrates that it takes the brain another 45 to 75 minutes to regain normal intellectual function after the blood sugar returns to normal.[174,175]

In *Proof Positive* I refer to a classic study that lends some support to the preceding explanation. Dr. Haber and colleagues examined the effects of eating apples in each of three different physical forms—as whole apples, as applesauce, and as apple juice.[176] Even though the same number of calories was consumed from each preparation, eating whole apples kept blood sugars steadier than drinking apple juice or using applesauce alone. Within 60 minutes, the apple juice caused *a drop in blood sugar.*

Blood sugars following *whole apple consumption were similar to those before it was consumed.* Blood sugar changes after the

SUGAR AND THE FRONTAL LOBE

Large amounts of sugar in the diet have been demonstrated to impair frontal lobe functions in school-age children.

Figure 27

applesauce fell in a range between the juice and the whole apples. One of the key factors involved is the abundant amount of fiber in whole foods like unprocessed apples. Fiber, especially soluble fiber like pectin and gum, slows the emptying of food from the stomach[177] and helps to slow the absorption of simple sugars by the small intestine.[178]

Some of the most profound research on diet, the frontal lobe, and depression points the finger at other popular American food items that are high in fat and protein. Diets that emphasize such high fat/high protein choices tend to run a life cycle of popularity. Most readers have likely heard of regimens like the Atkins diet, the Zone diet, or other similar eating regimens that avoid carbohydrates. When enough people experience the downsides of such programs these diets inevitably fall out of favor. Then a new generation comes along and again embraces the same programs (that, incidentally, often do lead to some initial weight loss).

High Carbohydrate Intake Increases Serotonin and Reduces Cortisol

The problem with diets that skimp on carbohydrates is that they compromise frontal lobe functioning. It is now well established that one way *to improve brain levels of mood-elevating serotonin is to boost your carbohydrate intake.*[191,192,193] Many patients have learned to adopt a carbohydrate diet in order to gain an emotional lift.[182] On a low protein diet, liberal amounts of carbohydrates raise brain levels of tryptophan, a vital amino acid that is used by the brain to make serotonin. Short-term drops in blood tryptophan levels can actually result in a relapse of depression. In fact, low blood tryptophan states have demonstrated decreased function in a critical frontal lobe area (the orbitofrontal cortex) that is associated with depression.[183]

Ironically, over the long haul, a low carbohydrate diet may not only predispose to depression but to weight gain. The first links in this chain come from fascinating studies conducted in the Netherlands under the direction of Dr. C.R. Markus.[184,185] These European researchers demonstrated that individuals who have a stress-related worsening of depressive symptoms *do remarkably better if they are given a low-protein, high carbohydrate diet.*

Their research lends support to the fact that stress-prone individuals are at greater risk of brain serotonin deficiency and that *carbohydrates may prevent a shortage of serotonin* during stressful situations. Also of interest is their finding that a carbohydrate-rich diet not only blocked a stress-induced rise in depression but also *prevented a rise in cortisol*. In contrast, those very same individuals experienced *heightened depression scores and cortisol increases* if they were eating a *protein-rich, low carbohydrate diet before exposure to stress.*

The remaining links in the chain associating high protein/high fat diets to long term risk of weight gain comes from researchers at the University of California, San Francisco. Dr. Epel and colleagues reported a *connection between stress-related rises in cortisol and increased food consump-*

HIGH SUGAR DIET IMPAIRS BRAIN FUNCTION

- Refined sugar enters the digestive system
- Blood sugar rises rapidly
- Pancreas responds by producing a large amount of insulin
- Overabundant insulin drives blood sugar too low
- Frontal lobe function is impaired.

Figure 28

tion.[186] The picture that emerges shows that avoiding carbohydrates may be particularly harmful for people prone to stress-related overeating. On a low carbohydrate diet such individuals are at greater risk not only for increased depressive tendencies, but also for *rises in cortisol levels that are associated with increased food consumption.* The many benefits of a high-carbohydrate, low-protein diet are recited in **Figure 29**.

The message I take away from this research is that adults as well as school children need a *high carbohydrate diet* if they want to function at *peak mental efficiency* and *decrease their risk of depression* and counterproductive stress-related responses.

Now that we have established the benefits of a high-carbohydrate, low-protein diet in combating depression and increasing the general performance of our brain, it begs a question. What foods should we eat to get these benefits? What changes in our diet do we need to gain these advantages? The answer to these vital questions is very simple: *A liberal supply of fruits, vegetables, and grains, all unrefined, provide the*

best nourishment for the frontal lobe. All of these foods contain a healthy quantity of carbohydrates and are packed with nutrients (including fiber) and sugar in its unrefined form.*

Meat is Devoid of Carbohydrates

Meat is essentially devoid of carbohydrates. If you look at food tables, you will see a recurring theme—whether it is red meat, fish, or chicken—they all score a big zero (or very close to it) in the carbohydrate category.[187] This may be one reason why *meat is associated with subtle frontal lobe impairment.* I recommend beginning each day with a high-quality breakfast that includes a *balanced selection of plant foods.* My family typically chooses a variety of fruits and whole grains along with a few nuts or a nut butter. These items keep the blood sugar in the proper range throughout the entire morning *without a need for snacks.*

There is another bit of irony in all this data. Because the brain is very adaptable and becomes accustomed to your lifestyle, even healthy changes *may cause a short-term decline in brain efficiency* before any improvement occurs. It is comparable to the situation with nicotine that I wrote about in *Proof Positive*. Despite nicotine's deleterious brain effects, when a person stops smoking, sleep quality and mental agility tend to worsen before they get better.

The same is true with diet. Research suggests that when people dramatically change their diets like increasing their intake of fat or even carbohydrates, mental performance can suffer in the short term. However, persevering with the better lifestyle will bring benefits in time. The message is: *no matter how difficult it may be in the short term, develop new health habits and stick with them.*[188]

A Spartan Diet Can Improve Brain Performance

For years researchers have known that animals live longer if they are calorically deprived (i.e., given less to eat than they

BENEFITS OF A HIGH CARBOHYDRATE, LOW PROTEIN DIET

High carbohydrate intake:

- Reduces cortisol
- Fosters peak mental efficiency
- Reduces tendency to overeat and gain weight
- Increases brain levels of tryptophan
  (high tryptophan levels are necessary for the brain to produce serotonin.)

Figure 29

would normally choose).[189] An American research team under the direction of Dr. L.W. Means added new evidence for the benefits of a Spartan diet. Means and his colleagues, by direct measurement, showed *improved brain performance on a lower calorie diet*.[190] Furthermore, their research demonstrated that animals received these brain benefits even if they did not begin such a restricted diet until they were middle-aged.

This is not isolated research. Researchers from Italy first demonstrated the obvious—rats on a normal diet lose mental function as they age. The investigators went on to discover that old rats that had been on a low calorie diet since birth had mental abilities as good as their younger counterparts.

The performance of our brains today can be affected by the number of calories we consumed 15 years ago. Ninety-nine subjects age 75 or older were tested in California for mental performance by taking the Mini-Mental State Examination. Those who consumed more calories in 1976 had lower test scores in 1991. This study indicates that a *higher consumption of calories in middle age accelerates the decline in mental function with aging*.[191]

These studies suggest that overeating (also referred to as "intemperate eating") can impair the whole brain. Such global mental decline would be expected to also compromise the frontal lobe.

When we think of the effect of a properly nourished frontal lobe on the potential for a fuller, richer life, it is encouraging. We do not have to be a statistic of poor mental health. We all have the opportunity to enjoy a *high quality of life with longevity as a bonus*. Nutrition and lifestyle deserve our most serious efforts. The results will be felt day by day and year by year.

Music, Depression, and the Frontal Lobe

Music appears to have both general and specific brain effects. The very act of listening to music—apparently regardless of the type of music—has beneficial effects on balancing frontal lobe function in depression. By actual EEG measurement, music has been demonstrated to help decrease the over-dominance of right frontal lobe activity in chronically depressed individuals.[192,193] However, medical research also suggests that we should have serious concerns about certain types of music.

Few people understand the powerful influence that music has on the frontal lobe. Music enters the brain through its emotional regions as explained in **Figure 30**.[194]

Note the effect of different kinds of music on the brain. Some kinds produce a response of the frontal lobe, and other kinds produce an emotional response. Depending on the type of music, *its net influence can be either beneficial or detrimental*. Music therapists tell us that certain types of music, such as rock with its syncopated

MUSIC AND THE FRONTAL LOBE

- Music enters the brain through its emotional regions, which include the temporal lobe and the limbic system.

- From there, some kinds of music tend to produce a frontal lobe response that influences the will, moral worth, and reasoning power.

- Other kinds of music will evoke very little, if any, frontal lobe response, but will produce a large emotional response with very little logical or moral interpretation.

Figure 30

rhythm, *bypass the frontal lobe and our ability to reason and make judgments about it.* Evidence suggests that it, like television, can produce a hypnotic effect.[195]

For many years some have argued that rock music was ruining America's youth. Some years ago, researchers Schreckenberg and Bird (a neurobiologist and a physicist) teamed up to put this generalization to a test. They designed a study to evaluate the neurological reaction of mice to different musical rhythms.[196] For eight weeks they exposed each of three groups of mice to different music settings. One group heard rock-like disharmonic drum beats playing softly in their environment, a second group heard classical music, while the third heard no music whatsoever.

All the mice went through a standard maze test (in search of food at the end of the maze). On the first day, all three groups performed equally well, groping about the maze until they found the food. By the end of eight weeks the second and third groups had learned the direct path to the food. *The "rock group," however, was still groping about, taking much longer to find the food than the other two groups.*

EFFECTS OF MUSIC ON LABORATORY MICE

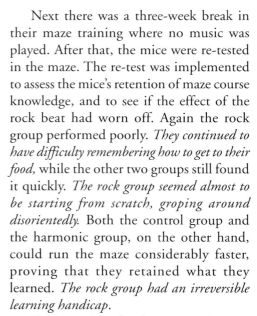

1. Eight weeks of a soft-rock beat permanently impaired their memory.

2. Three weeks after the music stopped, their memory had not come back.

3. Permanent brain damage could be seen.

4. Eight weeks of classical music had no detrimental effect on another group of mice.

Figure 31

Next there was a three-week break in their maze training where no music was played. After that, the mice were re-tested in the maze. The re-test was implemented to assess the mice's retention of maze course knowledge, and to see if the effect of the rock beat had worn off. Again the rock group performed poorly. *They continued to have difficulty remembering how to get to their food,* while the other two groups still found it quickly. *The rock group seemed almost to be starting from scratch, groping around disorientedly.* Both the control group and the harmonic group, on the other hand, could run the maze considerably faster, proving that they retained what they learned. *The rock group had an irreversible learning handicap.*

To determine why the poor performers were having so much trouble, the researchers examined their brains, looking for changes in the hippocampus. Remember, this region lies deep in the brain and affects emotions, memory, and learning. Schreckenberg and Bird found visible evidence of *abnormal branching and sprouting of the nerve cells,* as well as disruptions in the normal amounts of messenger RNA, a chemical crucial to memory storage.

The researchers concluded that the culprit causing memory and learning problems was the *music's rhythm,* not its harmonic or melodic structure. The theory is that *certain musical rhythms help to synchronize natural biological rhythms,* thus enhancing body functions, while *other rhythms tend to clash with, or disrupt internal rhythms.*

This is not surprising. All of our body systems function in rhythm. The study's authors postulated that if these natural rhythms are disrupted by some kind of disharmony, detrimental effects result, including *permanent learning difficulties.* This could help explain why rock music listeners are more prone to use drugs and engage in extramarital sex, and why heavy metal listeners are more likely to contemplate suicide.[197]

One other insight gained from

Schreckenberg and Bird's research is pertinent to our discussion. Not only did the disharmonic rock-like music cause damage to the hippocampus, it also caused *shrinking of the frontal lobe*. This would be expected to *affect moral values, learning, and reasoning power*. This research is summarized in **Figure 31**.

Harmonious types of hymns and symphonies, on the other hand, can produce a very beneficial frontal lobe response. This is the kind of musical environment in which our children should be raised—music that can produce a positive rather than a negative effect. Classical music has been demonstrated to help college students understand spatial relationships in geometry.[198] A study showed that listening to Mozart piano sonatas significantly increased spatial-temporal reasoning.[199] Interestingly, Mozart began composing music at the age of four.

In a follow-up of the Mozart study, one group of children three to five years of age received eight months of group singing and keyboard lessons. Another group in the same pre-school did not receive any music lessons. The music group *scored significantly higher on an assembly task* which required frontal lobe function. The task involved arranging pieces of a puzzle to form a meaningful whole.[200] Another study showed that musicians who possess perfect pitch were soundly exposed to music before the age of seven.[201]

The impact of music on *shaping the character* (and hence the frontal lobe) was recognized at least 23 centuries ago. Aristotle, the Greek philosopher of the fourth century B.C., recognized that music can be either beneficial or detrimental to our character, depending on the kind of music we expose ourselves to. He wrote, "Music directly represents the passions or states of the soul—gentleness, anger, courage, temperance, and their opposites and other qualities. Hence, when one listens to music that imitates a certain passion he

becomes imbued with the same passion. If over a long time he habitually listens to the kind of music that rouses ignoble [degraded or vulgar] passions, his whole character will be shaped to an ignoble form. In short, if one listens to the *wrong kind of music* he will become the *wrong kind of person*; conversely, if he listens to the *right kind of music* he will tend to become the *right kind of person*."[202] Aristotle unwittingly referred to the frontal lobe, where we now know the seat of our character resides. These statements are so profound and so applicable to our current social ills that they deserve to be highlighted. They appear in **Figure 32** and are an unwitting reference to the frontal lobe.

Certainly from the studies we have reviewed, most television programming and rock-like music fits into Aristotle's category of music that shapes character "to an ignoble form." If our young people could grow up in a positive, supportive environment, imagine how many of them would become wholesome, ethical individuals who might then be numbered among the greatest men and women of our day.

MUSIC CAN INSPIRE OR CORRUPT THE CHARACTER

"If one listens to the wrong kind of music, he will become the wrong kind of person; conversely, if one listens to the right kind of music, he will tend to become the right kind of person."

— *Aristotle*

Figure 32

Studies Show that Prayer Improves Health

Even honest skeptics are being forced to conclude that prayer has unique benefits that Eastern meditation cannot provide. A case in point is provided by Larry Dossey, M.D., an internal medicine specialist trained at the prestigious Southwestern Medical School in Dallas. Dr. Dossey was raised in the evangelical Protestant tradition of the *Bible Belt*. He became a self-proclaimed agnostic while in college.[203] Some years later he became interested in Eastern philosophies like Buddhism and Taoism, and began to practice meditation.

His spiritual perspective was shattered when he found that there is a host of *scientific studies showing that prayer for patients could actually improve their health*. As Dossey described his initial reaction to the compelling data, he wanted nothing to do with "talking to God." Ultimately, he came to the opposite conclusion: "I decided that not to employ prayer with my patients was the equivalent of withholding a potent drug or surgical procedure."[204] Dossey, convinced by the power of prayer, was no longer content to meditate in the Eastern fashion. He made it a daily practice to commune with the

IMPACT OF PRAYER ON RECOVERY FROM ILLNESS

- Prayer for patients may improve their health.

- The key in prayer is "giving oneself totally to the will of God."

Figure 33

Absolute Source of Power.

Dossey's experience does not address the effect of prayer on the frontal lobe. However, it does demonstrate that from the perspective of thinking scientists, *prayer has benefits that extend beyond mere meditation*. Dossey does, however, make profound connections between prayer and the frontal lobe in his book, *Healing Words: The Power of Prayer and the Practice of Medicine*. The theme of the book is remarkable, because Dossey is not a religious zealot who is trying to promote a particular sect. He comes across as an honest scientist who was *forced to acknowledge the power of prayer* despite his preconceived biases. Although my understanding of prayer differs from Dossey's, I believe he has pulled together some valuable insights that are relevant to this chapter.

One of the interesting frontal lobe connections is brought to light when Dossey links prayer with one of the most baffling occurrences for secular physicians, the spontaneous regression of cancer (SRC). In SRC, *a person with a fatal cancer survives without undergoing any treatment*. The individual may actually be cured and totally free of cancer, or there may still be evidence of the cancer's presence without it taking any toll on the person.

Dossey quotes the research of Yujiro Ikemi in Japan on cancer regression, and makes the following observation. "Often a prayerful, prayer-like attitude of devotion and acceptance—not robust aggressive prayer for specific outcomes, including eradication of the cancer—precedes the cure."[205] Interestingly, it may be the frontal lobe's connection with God through prayer—and a resulting acceptance of ill health or adversity that helps to pave the way for healing. Later in his book, when Dossey again discusses Ikemi's research, he points out that "all the patients [who experienced SRC] gave themselves totally to the will of God after learning they had cancer."[206]

Investigations of the impact of prayer on recovery from illness are summarized in

Figure 33.

There is evidence that *typical meditation or relaxation training can short circuit this process and be detrimental*. A study of stress hormones in surgery patients before, immediately following, and two days after surgery, seems to support these contentions. Dossey points out that British researchers found the immune-weakening stress hormones significantly increased only in those who had formal relaxation training. Those who addressed their anxieties and fears—without using relaxation techniques—did not show the rise in stress hormones.[207] Prayer's focus is not on denial or dealing with symptoms, but to bring the praying person in touch with God.

Prayer at times can be primarily receptive—consenting to God's will. At other times, prayer can be extremely active. Examples include struggling with God for answers to difficult questions, or seeking to know His will in a perplexing situation. In this latter context, prayer can be viewed as one of the ultimate frontal lobe activities. It could be argued that without a frontal lobe that is sound and intact, we cannot optimally pray such active, focused prayers.

Defying Your Moral Code is Dangerous

Since the frontal lobe is the seat of morality, habitually going against your moral code may cause frontal lobe suppression, quieting the voice of conscience and possibly making you feel better for the short term. Consider the story of Elijah, a prophet of God.

Even the most faithful prophets of God were not immune to depression. Elijah had spent what must have been the most exhilarating day of his life on Mount Carmel, leading out in a contest between the God of Israel and the god Baal. There he watched as the prophets of Baal spent most of a day wildly exhorting their lifeless god

to accept their sacrifice by sending fire to consume it. After Baal failed to answer their noisy rituals, Elijah quietly knelt before his offering and spoke a short, simple prayer that God answered immediately with a majestic display of fire from heaven. It consumed his offering and even the altar on which it was held.

He then prayed for God to end the years of drought that had plagued the land. God answered his persistent prayer that evening and Elijah ran in front of King Ahab's chariot in a downpour, leading him a great distance through the dark, back to the safety of the palace. How much greater an evidence of God's power and presence could Elijah have experienced—and all in one day?

But that night he received a warning that Jezebel was out to kill him. Elijah apparently forgot about God's mighty power and how he had just been protected from 450 priests of Baal and the King of Israel. He panicked at the threat of a heathen woman. After the exhausting day he had just experienced, he jumped up and ran a day's journey into the wilderness, collapsed under a juniper tree, and cried for the Lord to take his life. "It is enough; now, O Lord, take away my life; for I am not better than my fathers."[208]

At this point God sent an angel to feed Elijah—*an angel!* How much more clearly could God's favor be expressed? Yet, Elijah continued his flight for more than a month until he came to a cave, where he settled down in a mood of despair. God asked him what he was doing there and Elijah answered, "I have been very jealous for the Lord God of hosts: for the children of Israel have forsaken thy covenant, thrown down thine alters, and slain thy prophets with the sword; and I, even I only, am left: and they seek my life, to take it away."[209]

Elijah had allowed his mind to be controlled by despondency, which in turn disheartened him to the point of *losing his faith and trust in the God who had so majestically revealed His presence*. Instead of standing firm for God against a human queen, Elijah's mind was captivated by negative thoughts he allowed to take hold. God had planned for Elijah to lead a great revival in Israel. Instead, Elijah went against God's will, and gave in to depression.

Have you ever gone against God's will for your life? Are you doing it now? Can you take the chance of having the seat of your morality compromised by rebellion against what you know to be right? Can you take the chance of having to make daily choices with a brain that is no longer in communion with God? Your frontal lobe is your connection to God's network. Keep it connected by *doing His will*.

The Frontal Lobe: Making it Practical

In this chapter I have presented, in my judgment, much vital and useful information about the frontal lobe. It deserves a summary list of insights to help us protect and enhance the function of the "Crown of the Brain." An eight-point summary is listed in **Figure 34**.

TREAT YOUR FRONT BRAIN WITH CARE

1. *Protect it from physical injury.*
2. *Prevent or control underlying diseases that may damage your frontal lobe.*
3. *Avoid drugs and toxins that can impair brain performance.*
4. *Give it an adequate supply of oxygen from the blood.*
5. *Supply it with good nutrition by eating the best foods and avoiding the harmful ones.*
6. *Get adequate sunshine.*
7. *Exercise both your body and mind.*
8. *Provide proper inputs by controlling what you see, hear, and experience.*

Figure 34

1. Protect Your Frontal Lobe from Physical Injury

Physical injury can inflict permanent brain damage. Boxing, football, and motorcycle riding are examples of high-risk activities. Blows to the head while boxing frequently damage the tiny blood vessels, particularly in the frontal lobe. A boxer with these injuries is sometimes referred to as being "punch drunk." Other sports can lead to similar injuries. All such activities are best avoided by those who want to maintain good frontal lobe function.

Frontal lobe injury by physical means is not limited to sports participants. Head injuries from automobile collisions can inflict frontal lobe damage. For this reason, car seat belts and *shoulder harnesses* are a must. Furthermore, work place injuries are not confined to the Phineas Gages of yesteryear. Take all reasonable safety precautions on the job.

2. Prevent Diseases That May Damage Your Frontal Lobe

The proper use of preventive medicine principles can also help you preserve frontal lobe function. A number of diseases can lead to loss of frontal lobe capacity. Many of these maladies are preventable. Stroke is among the most worrisome; happily, controlling risk factors such as high blood pressure can often prevent it. Independent risk factors for stroke in people between the ages of 16 and 60 include high blood pressure, diabetes, current tobacco use, heart disease, and alcohol consumption (within 24 hours preceding the onset of the stroke).[210] Women can add oral contraceptives to this stroke risk factor list.[211]

High blood pressure and strokes are not the only conditions that can jeopardize the frontal lobe. Physical conditions often affect brain performance. Heart conditions can lead to problems that later affect the brain. Nervous system disorders of many sorts compromise brain function. In fact, being ill with any serious disease will have measurable effects on the brain. The bottom line is to follow a healthful lifestyle that addresses your body's total needs.

3. Avoid Drugs and Toxins that Can Impair Brain Performance

In addressing causes of frontal lobe dysfunction, I must reemphasize the association made with drugs and toxins. Clearly, if we want to give ourselves the best advantage to prevent and/or treat depression—as well as to enhance frontal lobe function in general—we will avoid all mind-altering drugs. That list includes "legal drugs" like caffeine, nicotine, and alcohol, as well as street drugs.

4. Improve the Quality of Your Brain's Blood Supply

Enhancing the quality of the brain's blood supply is important. Again, this improvement stands to help the entire brain, not just the frontal lobe. What can you do? Breathe clean, fresh, well-oxygenated air. In *Proof Positive* I review the body of research suggesting that negatively charged ions in fresh air enhance mental performance.

In addition to the quality of air, our habits of breathing may also make a difference. In a classroom or office setting, most of us do not realize that we tend to take shallow breaths. This may be one reason we may find it somewhat more difficult to concentrate after 30 minutes. Shallow breathing has the deleterious effects of allowing our blood oxygen level (called "oxygen saturation") to dip below the level necessary for optimal frontal lobe performance.[212] Consciously taking deep breaths periodically may help to counter this tendency. By taking deep breaths, particularly of fresh air, we may be able to boost oxygen saturation sufficiently to improve frontal lobe function. In addition to taking deep breaths while sitting, regular aerobic exercise (preferably outdoors) will cause the heart to pump vital, oxygenated blood to the brain.

5. Provide Good Nutrition

I have focused a significant portion of this chapter on the role of good nutrition in optimal frontal lobe function. An abundance of fruits, vegetable, whole grains, and nuts, while avoiding meat and cheese is the best diet to improve the ability of our front brains. Nursing infants should be breast-fed.

6. Get Adequate Sunshine

Sunlight has beneficial effects on the mood in general and the frontal lobe in particular. Among other things, sunshine is capable of increasing serotonin production in the daytime. This, in turn, helps prevent depression and fatigue.[213] Animal research further indicates that exposure to natural daylight results in significantly higher evening melatonin levels than an equal amount of exposure to artificial light.[214]

The role of melatonin, in turn, promotes sound sleep and may help to boost frontal lobe function the following day. Of further relevance, an autopsy series of suicide victims found significantly less melatonin in their brains than in the brains of others who died at the same age and the same time of day.[215] Some of the relationship with suicide may be explained by the loss of the effect of melatonin in relieving stress. The work of Georges Maestroni and his Swiss collaborators provides evidence that melatonin plays a role in decreasing the impact of stress on the body.[216]

7. Exercise Both Your Body and Mind

We discussed the importance of physical exercise to both improve and balance brain function. *Physical exercise* is a neglected strategy for mental health and depression treatment. Also, *mental exercise* is very important! Just as our muscles shrivel if we do not use them, so it is with our frontal lobe. The challenge of mental tasks will help maintain our mental acuity by stimulating the frontal lobe. Serious reading, the study of nature, asking questions about the vast world surrounding us, and other wholesome uses of our mental capacities tend to stimulate the frontal lobe. One recent study found that imagining a certain activity stimulated 80 percent of the brain circuitry that would be used to physically perform the very task imagined.[217] Such mental practice strengthens the brain cell connections, and when the time comes to execute the activity, the individual is better prepared.

Mental activity in children and teenagers is especially important in enhancing the ability to learn. Scientists have now discovered the first strong evidence that *intellectual stimulation can significantly increase the number of brain cells in a crucial region of the brain*. Previously, it was thought that the number of active brain cells was more-or-less set early in childhood. This landmark study was performed at the Salk Institute for Biological Studies.[218]

There, young mice were provided with an enriched environment, with more games and toys, and room to roam in extra large cages. When the results were in, those mice had developed 15 percent more brain cells in a key part of the brain responsible for memory and learning than genetically identical mice living in sparse surroundings. The extra brain cells enabled them to negotiate complex mazes faster and more efficiently. Researchers say that there is every reason to suppose that similar results would hold true for humans. The important conclusion is that *the environment we provide for our children and teenagers may actually influence their number of brain cells and their ability to learn.*

Ellen White describes the effects of challenging the brain, as quoted in **Figure 35**.[219]

8. Control What We See, Hear, and Experience

The final point on the list is related to the previous point. Dwelling on *happy, positive themes* and exposing our minds to *great inspirational material* aids in combating depression as well as *enlarging our minds* and *strengthening our intellects*. And do not forget the frontal lobe balancing effects of a good massage! Massage therapy's growth in popularity has ensured access to qualified professionals in most areas of our country.

Negatively, *many sensory inputs have the ability to compromise our front brain function*. This is true whether we consciously give someone permission to bypass our frontal lobe (as in hypnosis) or unconsciously compromise our frontal lobe function and balance (through activities like watching entertainment television or listening to rock music). Since spirituality, morality, and the will are centered in the frontal lobe of the brain, the optimal choices for input seem to be inspirational material chosen to appeal to our spiritual and moral natures. In

EXERCISING THE BRAIN WILL EXPAND IT

1. "The understanding adapts itself to the dimensions of the subjects with which it is required to deal.

2. If occupied with trivial, commonplace matters only, never summoned to earnest effort to comprehend great and eternal truths, it becomes dwarfed and enfeebled.

3. Hence, the value of the Scriptures as a means of intellectual culture."

Figure 35

READ THE BIBLE AND STRENGTHEN THE INTELLECT

1. "The Bible, just as it reads, is to be your guide."

2. "Nothing is so calculated to enlarge the mind and strengthen the intellect as the study of the Bible."

3. "No other study will so elevate the soul and give vigor to the faculties as the study of the living oracles . . . ."

4. "As the mind is brought to the study of God's Word, the understanding will enlarge and the higher power will develop for the comprehension of high and ennobling truth."

Figure 36

my experience, the study of the Word of God fills this requirement like no other can.

Ellen White outlined the impact of studying the Scriptures on the mind, soul, and intellect, as quoted in **Figure 36**.[220]

I have used considerable space in this chapter making the point that proper physical and mental habits are important for optimal frontal lobe function. Clearly, *right mental habits* promote mental excellence. At the same time, "*right physical habits* promote mental superiority."[221] These are the laws of nature, laws that the Creator has put into our being. "Intellectual power, physical strength, and longevity depend upon immutable laws. There is no happenstance, no chance, about this matter. Heaven will not interfere to preserve men from the consequences of the violation of nature's laws."[222]

Conclusion

God has provided each of us with the power to freely choose how we will live. And He usually does not interfere, even when we make bad choices. Truly, "there is much truth in the adage that every person is the architect of his own fortune."[223] In view of this tremendous power that you have been given to shape your own future, please take some time today to look seriously at your lifestyle.

I challenge you to reflect on your current health habits and ask yourself if you can take what you have learned from this chapter and improve them. Identify some concrete steps that you will take within the next week to help protect and enhance your frontal lobe—and with it your entire body.

A healthful lifestyle makes sense. Do not merely follow your old ways of doing things just because they are comfortable, or "because everyone else is doing it." In the words of Scripture, "*Be not conformed* to this world: but *be ye transformed* by the *renewing of your mind*, that ye may prove what is that good, and acceptable, and perfect, will of God." Romans 12:2 (italics supplied).

References—

[1] Details on the life of Phineas Gage were obtained from the following sources:Constantian HM. *The Country Doctor and His Illustrious Patient*. Worchester Medical News, Sept-Oct. 1972.
Damasio H, Grabowski T, et al. *The return of Phineas Gage*: clues about the brain from the skull of a famous patient. Science 1994 May 20;264(5162):1102-1105.
Fuster J. *The Prefrontal Cortex, Anatomy, Physiology, and Neuropsychology of the Frontal Lobe—2nd edition*. New York: Raven Press, 1989 p. 126.
Koskoff Y, Goldhurst. Prologue. In: *The dark side of the house*. New York: The Dial Press, 1968 p. I-XXII.
Damasio H, Grabowski T, et al. The return of Phineas Gage: clues about the brain from the skull of a famous patient. Science 1994 May 20;264(5162):1102-1105.
[2] Robinson RG, Szetela B. Mood change following left hemispheric brain injury. *Ann Neurol* 1981;9:447-453.
[3] Robinson R, Kubos K, et al. Mood disorders in stroke patients: Importance of location of lesion. *Brain* 1984;107:81-93.
[4] Bench C, Friston K, et al. The anatomy of melancholia—focal abnormalities of cerebral blood flow in major depression. *Psychol Med* 1992;22:607-615.
[5] Baxter L Jr, Schwartz J, et al. Reduction of prefrontal cortex glucose metabolism common to three types of depression. *Arch Gen Psychiatry* 1989;46:243-250.
[6] Sarazin M, Pillon B, et al. Clinicometabolic dissociation of cognitive functions and social behavior in frontal lobe lesions. *Neurology* 1998 Jul;51(1):142-148.
[7] *Tasman: Psychiatry*, 1st ed. W. B. Saunders Company. 1997 p. 491-492.
[8] Galynker I, Cai J, et al. Hypofrontality and negative symptoms in major depressive disorder. *J Nucl Med* 1998 Apr 39(4):608-612.
[9] Videbech P. PET measurements of brain glucose metabolism and blood flow in major depressive disorder: A critical review. *Acta Psychiatr Scand* 2000 Jan;101(1):11-20.
[10] Luria A. *Higher cortical functions in man*. New York: Basic Books,

1966.

[11] Dubois B, Levy R, et al. Experimental approach to prefrontal functions in humans. In: Grafman J, Boller F, Holyoak KJ, eds. *Structure and functions of the human prefrontal cortex*. Ann NY *Acad Sci* 1995;179:41-60.

[12] Damasio A, Tranel D, Damasio H. Somatic markers and the guidance of behavior: Theory and preliminary testing. In: Levin HS, Eisenberg H, Benton A, eds. *Frontal lobe function and dysfunction*. Oxford: Oxford University Press, 1991:217-229.

[13] Stuss D, Benson D. The frontal lobes. New York: Raven Press, 1986.

[14] Lhermitte F, Pillon B, Serdaru M. Human autonomy and the frontal lobes. Part I: Imitation and utilization behaviors: A neuro-psychological study of 75 patients. *Ann Neurol* 1986;19:326-334.

[15] Dubois B, Levy R, et al. Experimental approach to prefrontal functions in humans. In: Grafman J, Boller F, Holyoak KJ, eds. *Structure and functions of the human prefrontal cortex*. Ann NY *Acad Sci* 1995;179:41-60.

[16] Damasio A, Tranel D, Damasio H. Somatic markers and the guidance of behavior: Theory and preliminary testing. In: Levin HS, Eisenberg H, Benton A, eds. *Frontal lobe function and dysfunction*. Oxford: Oxford University Press, 1991:217-229.

[17] Sarazin M, Pillon B, et al. Clinicometabolic dissociation of cognitive functions and social behavior in frontal lobe lesions. *Neurology* 1998 Jul;51(1):142-148.

[18] Kim J, Choi-Kwon S. Poststroke depression and emotional incontinence: Correlation with lesion location. *Neurology* 2000;54(9):1805-1810.

[19] Hirono N, Mori E, et al. Frontal lobe hypometabolism and depression in Alzheimer's disease. Neurology 1998 Feb;50(2):380-383.

[20] Drevets W. Prefrontal cortical-amygdalar metabolism in major depression. Ann N Y *Acad Sci* 1999 Jun 29; 877:614-637.

[21] Steingard R, Yurgelun-Todd D, et al. Increased orbitofrontal cortex levels of choline in depressed adolescents as detected by in vivo proton magnetic resonance spectroscopy. *Biol Psychiatry* 2000 Dec 1;48(11):1053-1061.

[22] Lane R, Reiman E, Ahern GL, et al.. Neuroanatomical correlates of happiness, sadness, and disgust. *Am J Psychiatry* 1997;154:926-933.

[23] Bench C, Friston J, et al. Regional cerebral blood flow in depression measured by positron emission tomography: The relationship with clinical dimensions. *Psychol Med* 1993;23:579-590.

[24] Bench C, Frackowiak R, Dolan R. Changes in regional cerebral blood flow on recovery from depression. *Psychol Med* 1995 Mar;25(2):247-261.

[25] Drevets W. Functional anatomical abnormalities in limbic and prefrontal cortical structures in major depression. *Prog Brain Res* 2000;126:413-431.

[26] Steingard R, Renshaw P, et al. Structural abnormalities in brain magnetic resonance images of depressed children. *J Am Acad Child Adolesc Psychiatry* 1996 Mar;35(3):307-11.

[27] Sapolsky R. Glucocorticoids and hippocampal atrophy in neuropsychiatric disorders. *Arch Gen Psychiatry* 2000;57:925-935.

[28] Drevets W. Prefrontal cortical-amygdalar metabolism in major depression. Ann N Y *Acad Sci* 1999 Jun 29;877:614-637.

[29] Drevets W. Functional anatomical abnormalities in limbic and prefrontal cortical structures in major depression. *Prog Brain Res* 2000;126:413-431.

[30] Parashos I, Tupler L, et al. Magnetic-resonance morphometry in patients with major depression. *Psychiatry Res* 1998 Nov 9;84(1):7-15.

[31] Drevets W. Prefrontal cortical-amygdalar metabolism in major depression. Ann N Y *Acad Sci* 1999 Jun 29;877:614-637.

[32] Price B, Daffner KR, et al. The compartmental learning disabilities of early frontal lobe damage. *Brain* 1990 Oct;113(Pt 5):1383-1393.

[33] Stuss D, Benson D. *The Frontal Lobes*. New York: Raven Press, 1986 p. 5, 204.

[34] Fulton J, editor. *The Frontal Lobes*. New York: Hafner Publishing. Company, 1966 p. 27,59.

[35] Moore K. *Clinically Oriented Anatomy*. Baltimore, MD: Williams and Wilkens, 1980 p. 935.

[36] Baldwin B. The Front-Brain. *Journal of Health and Healing* 1983;9(1):8-10,26,27,30.

[37] Price B, Daffner K, et al. The compartmental learning disabilities of early frontal lobe damage. *Brain* 1990 Oct;113(Pt 5):1383-1393.

[38] Fuster J. *The prefrontal cortex, anatomy, physiology, and neuropsychology of the frontal lobe* 2nd edition. New York: Raven Press, 1989 p. 129,154.

[39] Guyton A. *Textbook of medical physiology* 6th edition. Philadelphia: WB Saunders Company, 1981 p. 689-690.

[40] Best C, Taylor N. *The physiological basis of medical practice* 5th edition. Baltimore, MD: Williams and Wilkins Company, 1950 p. 1023,1024.

[41] Baldwin B. The front brain. *Journal of Health and Healing* 1983;9(1):9.

[42] George M, Ketter TA, Post RM. SPECT and PET imaging in mood disorders. *J Clin Psychiatry* 1993 Nov;54 Suppl:6-13.

[43] Robert, J. Behavioural disorders are overdiagnosed in U.S. *British Medical Journal* 1996 March 16;312(7032):657.

[44] Stuss D, Benson D. *The frontal fobes*. New York: Raven Press, 1986 p. 243.

[45] Baldwin B. The front brain and the minister. *Ministry Magazine* 1990 Jan:20-23.

[46] Sarazin M, Pillon B, et al. Clinicometabolic dissociation of cognitive functions and social behavior in frontal lobe lesions. *Neurology* 1998 Jul;51(1):142-148.

[47] Grafman J, Schwab K, et al. Frontal lobe injuries, violence, and aggression: A report of the Vietnam Head Injury Study. *Neurology* May 1996;46(5):1231-1238.

[48] Asnis G, Kaplan M, et al. Violence and homicidal behaviors in psychiatric disorders. *Psychiatric Clinics of North America* June 1997;20(2):405-425.

[49] Jordan K, Schlenger W, Fairbank J, et al. Prevalence of psychiatric disorders among incarcerated women: II. Convicted felons entering prison. *Arch Gen Psychiatry* 1996;53:513-519.

[50] Arango V, Underwood M, et al. Localized alterations in pre- and postsynaptic serotonin binding sites in the ventrolateral prefrontal cortex of suicide victims. *Brain Res* 1995;688:121-133.

[51] Mann J, Huang Y, et al. Serotonin transporter gene promoter polymorphism (5-HTTLPR) and prefrontal cortical binding in major depression and suicide. *Arch Gen Psychiatry* 2000;57:729-738.

[52] Arango V, Underwood M, et al. Localized alterations in pre- and postsynaptic serotonin binding sites in the ventrolateral prefrontal cortex of suicide victims. *Brain Res* 1995;688:121-133.

[53] Mann J. Violence and aggression. In: Bloom FE, Kupfer DJ, eds. *Psychopharmacology*: The fourth generation of progress. New York, NY: Raven Press; 1995:1919-1928.

[54] Weiner R. Retrograde amnesia with electroconvulsive therapy: characteristics and implications *Arch Gen Psychiatry* 2000 June;57(6):591,592.

55 Kelly K, Zisselman M. Update on electroconvulsive therapy (ECT) in older adults. *J Am Geriatr Soc* 2000 May;48(5):560-566.

56 Nobler M, Sackeim HA, et al. Regional cerebral blood flow in mood disorders, III: Treatment and clinical response. *Arch Gen Psychiatry* 1994;51:884-897.

57 Fink M, Kellner CH. Certification in ECT. *J ECT* 1998;14:1-4.

58 Weiner R. Retrograde amnesia with electroconvulsive therapy: characteristics and implications *Arch Gen Psychiatry* 2000 June;57(6):591,592.

59 Squire L, Slater PC, Miller PL. Retrograde amnesia and bilateral electroconvulsive therapy: Long-term follow-up. *Arch Gen Psychiatry* 1981;38:89-95.

60 Squire L. Amnesia for remote events following electroconvulsive therapy. *Behav Biol* 1974;12:119-125.

61 Weiner R, Rogers HJ, et al. Effects of stimulus parameters on cognitive side effects. *Ann N Y Acad Sci* 1986;462:315-325.

62 Squire L, Slater PC. Electroconvulsive therapy and complaints of memory dysfunction: A prospective three-year follow-up study. *Br J Psychiatry* 1983;142:1-8.

63 Lisanby S, Maddox JH, et al. The effects of electroconvulsive therapy on memory of autobiographical and public events. *Arch Gen Psychiatry* 2000;57:581-590.

64 Kelly K, Zisselman M. Update on electroconvulsive therapy (ECT) in older adults. *J Am Geriatr Soc* 2000 May;48(5):560-566.

65 George MS, Lisanby SH, Sackeim HA. Transcranial Magnetic Stimulation: Applications in neuropsychiatry. *Arch Gen Psychiatry* 1999;56:300-311.

66 Menkes D, Bodnar P, et al. Right frontal lobe slow frequency repetitive transcranial magnetic stimulation (SF r-TMS) is an effective treatment for depression: A case-control pilot study of safety and efficacy. *J Neurol Neurosurg Psychiatry* 1999 Jul;67(1):113-115.

67 Galynker I, Cai J, et al. Hypofrontality and negative symptoms in major depressive disorder. *J Nucl Med* 1998 Apr; 39(4):608-612.

68 Bench C, Friston KJ, et al. Regional cerebral blood flow in depression measured by positron emission tomography: The relationship with clinical dimensions. *Psychol Med* 1993;23:579-590.

69 Bench C, Frackowiak R, Dolan R. Changes in regional cerebral blood flow on recovery from depression. *Psychol Med* 1995 Mar;25(2):247-261.

70 Pascual-Leone A, Rubio B, et al. Beneficial effect of rapid-rate transcranial magnetic stimulation of the left dorsolateral prefrontal cortex in drug resistant depression. *Lancet* 1996;348:233-237.

71 Teneback C, Nahas Z, et al. Changes in prefrontal cortex and paralimbic activity in depression following two weeks of daily left prefrontal TMS. *J Neuropsychiatry Clin Neurosci* 1999 Fall;11(4):426-435.

72 George M, Wassermann EM, et al. Daily repetitive transcranial magnetic stimulation (rTMS) improves mood in depression. *Neuroreport* 1995;6:1853-1856.

73 Figiel GS, Epstein C, et al. The use of rapid rate transcranial magnetic stimulation (rTMS) in refractory depressed patients. *J Neuropsychiatry Clin Neurosci* 1998;10:20-25.

74 Menkes D, Bodnar P, et al. Right frontal lobe slow frequency repetitive transcranial magnetic stimulation (SF r-TMS) is an effective treatment for depression: a case-control pilot study of safety and efficacy. *J Neurol Neurosurg Psychiatry* 1999 Jul;67(1):113-115.

75 Klein E, Kreinin I, et al. Therapeutic efficacy of right prefrontal slow repetitive transcranial magnetic stimulation in major depression: A double-blind controlled study. *Arch Gen Psychiatry*. 1999 Apr;56(4):315-320.

76 George M, Lisanby SH, Sackeim HA. Transcranial magnetic stimulation: Applications in neuropsychiatry. *Arch Gen Psychiatry* 1999;56:300-311.

77 George MS, Lisanby SH, Sackeim HA. Transcranial magnetic stimulation: Applications in neuropsychiatry. *Arch Gen Psychiatry* 1999;56:300-311.

78 Grunhaus L, Dannon PN, et al. Repetitive transcranial magnetic stimulation is as effective as electroconvulsive therapy in the treatment of nondelusional major depressive disorder: An open study. *Biol Psychiatry* 2000 Feb 15;47(4):314-324.

79 Pascual-Leone A, Rubio B, et al. Beneficial effect of rapid-rate transcranial magnetic stimulation of the left dorsolateral prefrontal cortex in drug-resistant depression. *Lancet* 1996;348:233-237.

80 Segman R, Shapira B, et al. Onset and time course of antidepressant action: Psychopharmacological implications of a controlled trial of electroconvulsive therapy. *Psychopharmacology* 1995;119:440-448.

81 Nobler MS, Sackeim HA, et al. Quantifying the speed of symptomatic improvement with electroconvulsive therapy: Comparison of alternative statistical methods. *Convulsive Ther* 1997;13:208-221.

82 Grunhaus L, Dannon P, Schrieber S. Effects of transcranial magnetic stimulation on severe depression: Similarities with ECT [abstract]. *Biol Psychiatry* 1998;43:76.

83 Conca A, Koppi S, et al. Transcranial magnetic stimulation: A novel antidepressive strategy? *Neuropsychobiology* 1996;34:204-207.

84 Saypol JM, Roth BJ, et al. A theoretical comparison of electric and magnetic stimulation of the brain. *Ann Biomed Eng* 1991;19:317-328.

85 Fink M. *Convulsive Therapy: Theory and Practice*. New York, NY: Raven Press; 1979.

86 George MS, Lisanby SH, Sackeim HA. Transcranial magnetic stimulation: Applications in neuropsychiatry. *Arch Gen Psychiatry* 1999;56:300-311.

87 Pascual-Leone A, Hallett M. Induction of errors in a delayed response task by repetitive transcranial magnetic stimulation of the dorsolateral prefrontal cortex. *Neuroreport* 1994;5:2517-2520.

88 Grafman J, Pascual-Leone A, et al. Induction of a recall deficit by rapid-rate transcranial magnetic stimulation. *Neuroreport* 1994;5:1157-1160.

89 Little JT, Kimbrell TA, et al. Cognitive effects of 1- and 20-hertz repetitive transcranial magnetic stimulation in depression: Preliminary report. *Neuropsychiatry Neuropsychol Behav Neurol* 2000 Apr;13(2):119-124.

90 Pascual-Leone A, Catala M, et al. Lateralized effect of rapid-rate transcranial magnetic stimulation of the prefrontal cortex on mood. *Neurology* 1996 Feb;46(2):499-502.

91 Mosimann UP, Rihs TA, et al. Mood effects of repetitive transcranial magnetic stimulation of left prefrontal cortex in healthy volunteers. *Psychiatry Res* 2000 Jul 17;94(3):251-256.

92 George MS, Wassermann EM, et al. Changes in mood and hormone levels after rapid-rate transcranial magnetic stimulation (rTMS) of the prefrontal cortex. *J Neuropsychiatry Clin Neurosci* 1996 Spring;8(2):172-180.

93 Ahlbom A, Day N, et al. A pooled analysis of magnetic fields and childhood leukaemia. *Br J Cancer* 2000 Sep;83(5):692-698.

94 Monitoring the future survey. Released December 20, 1996 by Donna Shalala, Secretary Department of Health and Human Services. Also National Parents Research Institute for Drug Education (PRIDE) survey, September, 1996. Atlanta GA.

95 Mathias R. Studies show cognitive impairments linger in heavy marijuana users. NIDA notes (National Institute on Drug Abuse) May/June 1996;11(3):1,4,9.

96 Fried PA, Gray R, Watkinson B. A follow-up study of attentional behavior in 6-year-old children exposed prenatally to marihuana, cigarettes, and alcohol. *Neurotoxicology & Teratology* 1992 Sep-Oct;14(5):299-311.

97 Wang GJ, Volkow ND, et al. Functional importance of ventricular enlargement and cortical atrophy in healthy subjects and alcoholics as assessed with PET, MR imaging, and neuropsychologic testing. *Radiology* 1993 Jan;186(1):59-65.

98 Parker DA, Parker ES, et al. Alcohol use and cognitive loss among employed men and women. *Am J Public Health* 1983 May;73(5):521-526.

99 Zador PL. Alcohol-related relative risk of fatal driver injuries in relation to driver age and sex. *J Stud Alcohol* 1991 Jul;52(4):302-310.

100 Kruger A. Chronic psychiatric patients' use of caffeine: Pharmacological effects and mechanisms. *Psychol Rep* 1996 Jun;78(3 Pt 1):915-923.

101 Edelmann RJ, Moxon S. The effects of caffeine on psychological functioning. *Nutr Health* 1985;4(1):29-36.

102 Ferre S, Popoli P, et al. Postsynaptic antagonistic interaction between adenosine A1 and dopamine D1 receptors. *Neuroreport* 1994 Dec 30;6(1):73-76.

103 Ferre S, O'Connor WT, et al. Antagonistic interaction between adenosine A2A receptors and dopamine D2 receptors in the ventral striopallidal system. Implications for the treatment of schizophrenia. *Neuroscience* 1994 Dec;63(3):765-773.

104 Baldessarini RJ. Drugs and the treatment of psychiatric disorders. In: Gilman AG, Goodman LS, et al, editors. Goodman and Gilman's *The Pharmacologic Basis of Therapeutics* 7th edition. New York, NY: MacMillan Publishing Company, 1985 p. 396-397,595.

105 George MS, Ketter TA, Post RM. SPECT and PET imaging in mood disorders. *J Clin Psychiatry* 1993 Nov;54 Suppl():6-13.

106 Passero S, Nardini M, Battistini N. Regional cerebral blood flow changes following chronic administration of antidepressant drugs. *Prog Neuropsychopharmacol Biol Psychiatry* 1995 Jul;19(4):627-636.

107 Mathew RJ, Barr DL, Weinman ML Caffeine and cerebral blood flow. *Br J Psychiatry* 1983 Dec;143:604-8.

108 Mathew RJ, Wilson WH. Caffeine induced changes in cerebral circulation. *Stroke* 1985 Sep-Oct;16(5):814-817.

109 Cameron OG, Modell JG, Hariharan M. Caffeine and human cerebral blood flow: A positron emission tomography study. *Life Sci* 1990;47(13):1141-1146.

110 Jacobsen BK , Hansen V. Caffeine and health. *Br Med J* (Clin Res Ed) 1988 Jan 23;296(6617):291.

111 Lin Y, Phillis JW. Chronic caffeine exposure enhances adenosinergic inhibition of cerebral cortical neurons. *Brain Res* 1990 Jun 18;520(1-2):322-323.

112 Shi D, Nikodijevic O, et al. Chronic caffeine alters the density of adenosine, adrenergic, cholinergic, GABA, and serotonin receptors and calcium channels in mouse brain. *Cell Mol Neurobiol* 1993 Jun;13(3):247-261.

113 Curatolo PW, Robertson D. The health consequences of caffeine. *Ann Intern Med* 1983 May;98(5 Pt 1):641-653.

114 Lin Y, Phillis JW. Chronic caffeine exposure enhances adenosinergic inhibition of cerebral cortical neurons. *Brain Res* 1990 Jun 18;520(1-2):322-323.

115 Moriyama T, Uezu K, et al. Effects of dietary phosphatidylcholine on memory in memory deficient mice with low brain acetylcholine concentration. *Life Sci* 1996;58(6):PL111-118.

116 Floyd EA, Young-Seigler AC, et al. Chronic ethanol ingestion produces cholinergic hypofunction in rat brain. *Alcohol* 1997 Jan-Feb;14(1):93-98.

117 Curatolo PW, Robertson D. The health consequences of caffeine. *Ann Intern Med* 1983 May;98(5 Pt 1):641-653.

118 Curatolo PW, Robertson D. The health consequences of caffeine. *Ann Intern Med* 1983 May;98(5 Pt 1):641-653.

119 Rall TW. Central nervous system stimulants [continued]: The Methylxanthines . In: Gilman AG, Goodman LS, et al, editors. Goodman and Gilman's *The Pharmacologic Basis of Therapeutics* 7th edition. New York, NY: MacMillan Publishing Company, 1985 p. 595-596.

120 Edelmann RJ, Moxon S. The effects of caffeine on psychological functioning. *Nutr Health* 1985;4(1):29-36.

121 Smoke gets in your brain. Science News 1993 Jan 16;143(3):46-47.

122 Boden-Albala B, Sacco RL Lifestyle factors and stroke risk: Exercise, alcohol, diet, obesity, smoking, drug use, and stress. *Curr Atheroscler Rep* 2000 Mar;2(2):160-166.

123 Doll R, Peto R, et al. Smoking and dementia in male British doctors: Prospective study. *BMJ* 2000 April 22;320:1097-1102.

124 Tyas SL, Pederson LL, Koval JJ. Is smoking associated with the risk of developing Alzheimer's disease? Results from three Canadian data sets. *Ann Epidemiol* 2000 Oct;10(7):409-16.

125 Fox NL, Hebel JR, Sexton M. Prenatal exposure to tobacco: II. Effects on cognitive functioning at age three. *Int J Epidemiol* 1990 Mar;19(1):72-77.

126 Breslau N. Psychiatric comorbidity of smoking and nicotine dependence. *Behav Genet* 1995 Mar;25(2):95-101.

127 Breslau N, Kilbey M, Andreski P Nicotine dependence, major depression, and anxiety in young adults. *Arch Gen Psychiatry* 1991 Dec;48(12):1069-1074.

128 Kendler KS, Neale MC, et al. Smoking and major depression. A causal analysis. *Arch Gen Psychiatry* 1993 Jan;50(1):36-43.

129 Wennmalm A Effect of cigarette smoking on basal and carbon dioxide stimulated cerebral blood flow in man. *Clin Physiol* 1982 Dec;2(6):529-535.

130 Nakamura H, Tanaka A, et al. Activation of fronto-limbic system in the human brain by cigarette smoking: Evaluated by a CBF measurement. *Keio J Med* 2000 Feb;49 Suppl 1:A122-124.

131 Domino EF, Minoshima S, et al. Nicotine effects on regional cerebral blood flow in awake, resting tobacco smokers. *Synapse* 2000 Dec 1;38(3):313-321.

132 Othmer E, Othmer JP, Othmer SC. Brain functions and psychiatric disorders: A clinical view. *Psychiatric Clinics of North America* 1998 Sept 21(3):517-s566.

133 Quattrocki E, Baird A, Yurgelun-Todd D. Biological aspects of the link between smoking and depression. *Harvard Rev Psychiatry* 2000;8:99-110.

134 Mander J. *Four Arguments for the Elimination of Television*. New York, NY: Quill, 1977 p. 195-202.

135 Jerry Mander quoting Merrelyn and Fred Emery, then at the Center for Continuing Education, Australian National University at Canberra. In: Mander J. *Four Arguments for the Elimination of Television*. New York, NY: Quill, 1977 p. 205-211.

136 Guyton AC. *Textbook of Medical Physiology* 8th edition. Philadel-

phia: WB. Saunders Company, 1991 p. 662-663.

[137] Mander J. *Four Arguments for the Elimination of Television*. New York, NY: Quill, 1977 p. 196.

[138] Frumkin LR, Ripley HS, Cox GB. Changes in cerebral hemispheric lateralization with hypnosis. *Biol Psychiatry* 1978 Dec;13(6):741-750.

[139] Crawford H, Crawford K, Koperski BJ. Hypnosis and lateral cerebral function as assessed by dichotic listening. *Biol Psychiatry* 1983 Apr;18(4):415-427.

[140] Crawford H, Clarke SW, Kitner-Triolo M. Self-generated happy and sad emotions in low and highly hypnotizable persons during waking and hypnosis: Laterality and regional EEG activity differences. *Int J Psychophysiol* 1996 Dec;24(3):239-66.

[141] De Pascalis V, Ray WJ, et al. EEG activity and heart rate during recall of emotional events in hypnosis: Relationships with hypnotizability and suggestibility. *Int J Psychophysiol* 1998 Aug;29(3):255-275.

[142] Morris, F as quoted in Mander J. *Four Arguments for the Elimination of Television*. New York, NY: Quill, 1977 p. 208.

[143] Zuckerman D, Zuckerman B. Television's impact on children. *Pediatrics* 1985 Feb;75(2):233-240.

[144] Mander J. *Four Arguments for the Elimination of Television*. New York, NY: Quill, 1977 p. 194-196.

[145] Peterson J, Moore K, Furstenberg F Jr. Television viewing and early initiation of sexual intercourse: Is there a link? *J Homosex* 1991;21(1-2):93-118.

[146] Hundt, Reed E. Chairman, Federal Communications Commission. Delivered before the National Press Club, Washington, D, July 27, 1995.

[147] Tucker D, Dawson S. Asymmetric EEG changes as method actors generated emotions. *Biol Psychol* 1984 Aug;19(1):63-75.

[148] Stoleru S, Gregoire MC, et al. Neuroanatomical correlates of visually evoked sexual arousal in human males. *Arch Sex Behav* 1999 Feb;28(1):1-21.

[149] Hammen C, Henry R, Daley S. Depression and sensitization to stressors among young women as a function of childhood adversity. *J Consult Clin Psychol* 2000 Oct;68(5):782-787.

[150] Daley S, Hammen C, Rao U Predictors of first onset and recurrence of major depression in young women during the 5 years following high school graduation. *J Abnorm Psychol* 2000 Aug;109(3):525-533.

[151] Simons D, Silveira WR. Post-traumatic stress disorder in children after television programmes. *BMJ* 1994 Feb 5;308:389-390.

[152] Forbes F, McClure I. The terror of television: Made worse by family stress *BMJ* 1994 Mar 12;308:714.

[153] Baillie M, Thompson A, Kaplan C. The terror of television. Anxious children at greater risk. *BMJ.* 1994 Mar 12;308(6930):714.

[154] Morris, F as quoted Mander J. *Four Arguments for the Elimination of Television*. New York, NY: Quill, 1977 p. 197.

[155] Mander J. *Four Arguments for the Elimination of Television*. New York, NY: Quill, 1977 p. 210.

[156] Krugman, H as cited in Mander J. *Four Arguments for the Elimination of Television*. New York, NY: Quill, 1977 p. 209.

[157] Peper, E. as cited in Mander J. *Four Arguments for the Elimination of Television*. New York, NY: Quill, 1977 p. 211.

[158] Toffler A. *Future Shock*. New York, NY: Random House Inc., 1970.

[159] Rubinstein E. Television and behavior. Research conclusions of the 1982 NIMH Report and their policy implications. *American Psychologist,* 1983 p. 820-825.

[160] Zuckerman D, Zuckerman B. Television's impact on children. *Pediatrics* 1985 Feb;75(2):233-240.

[161] Dietz W, Gortmaker S. TV or not TV: Fat is the question. *Pediatrics* 1993 Feb;91(2):499-501.

[162] Lyle J, Hoffman H. Children's Use of Television and Other Media. In: Rubinstein EA, Comstock GA, Murray JP, editors. Television and Social Behavior, 4: Television in Day-to-Day Life: Patterns of Use. Washington, DC: U.S. Government Printing Office, 1972.

[163] Shapira N. Psychiatric features of individuals with problematic internet use. *J Affect Disord* 2000 Jan-Mar; 57 (1-3):267-72.

[164] Kraut R, et al. Internet paradox. A social technology that reduces social involvement and psychological well-being? *Am Psychol* 1998 Sep; 53(9):1017-1031.

[165] Young K. Psychology of computer use: XL. Addictive use of the Internet: A case that breaks the stereotype. *Psychol Rep* - 1996 Dec; 79 (3 Pt 1): 899-902.

Young K. Internet addiction affects lives and marriages. Annual meeting of the American Psychological Association, August 1999, Boston, MA.

[166] George M, Ketter T, et al. Brain activity during transient sadness and happiness in healthy women. *Am J Psychiatry* 1995 Mar;152(3):341-351.

[167] Byrne A, Byrne D. The effect of exercise on depression, anxiety and other mood states: A review. *J Psychosom Res* 1993 Sep;37(6):565-574.

[168] Petruzzello S, Landers D. State anxiety reduction and exercise: Does hemispheric activation reflect such changes? *Med Sci Sports Exerc* 1994 Aug;26(8):1028-1035.

[169] Jones N, Field T. Massage and music therapies attenuate frontal EEG asymmetry in depressed adolescents. *Adolescence* 1999 Fall;34(135):529-534.

[170] Field T, Ironson G, et al. Massage therapy reduces anxiety and enhances EEG pattern of alertness and math computations. *Int J Neurosci* 1996 Sep;86(3-4):197-205.

[171] Guyton A. T*extbook of Medical Physiology* 8th edition. Philadelphia: WB. Saunders Company, 1991 p. 684-685.

[172] Guyton A. *Textbook of Medical Physiology* 8th edition. Philadelphia: WB. Saunders Company, 1991 p. 684-685.

[173] Prinz R, Riddle D. Associations between nutrition and behavior in 5-year-old children. *Nutr Rev* 1986 May;44 Suppl:151-158.

[174] Blackman J, Towle V, et al. Hypoglycemic thresholds for cognitive dysfunction in humans. *Diabetes* 1990 Jul;39(7):828-835.

[175] Ryan C, Atchison J, et al. Mild hypoglycemia associated with deterioration of mental efficiency in children with insulin-dependent diabetes mellitus. *J Pediatr* 1990 Jul;117(1 Pt 1):32-38.

[176] Haber G, Heaton KW, et al. Depletion and disruption of dietary fiber. Effects on satiety, plasma-glucose, and serum-insulin. *Lancet* 1977 Oct 1;2(8040):679-682.

[177] Beaser R. *Outsmarting diabetes: A dynamic approach for reducing the effects of insulin-dependent diabetes.* (Joslin Diabetes Center Boston, MA). Minneapolis, MN: Chronimed Publishing, 1994 p. 87.

[178] Jenkins D. Carbohydrates: (B) Dietary fiber. In: Shils M, Young V, editors. *Modern Nutrition in Health and Disease* 7th edition. Philadelphia, PA: Lea and Febiger, 1988 p. 61-63.

[179] Fernstrom J. Diet-induced changes in plasma amino acid pattern: Effects on the brain uptake of large neutral amino acids, and on brain serotonin synthesis. *J Neural Transm Suppl* 1979;(15):55-67.

[180] Fernstrom J. Dietary amino acids and brain function. J *Am Diet Assoc* 1994 Jan;94(1):71-77.

[181] Wurtman R, Wurtman J. Do carbohydrates affect food intake via neurotransmitter activity? *Appetite* 1988;11 Suppl 1:42-47.

[182] Wurtman RJ, Wurtman JJ. Brain serotonin, carbohydrate-craving, obesity and depression. *Obes Res* 1995 Nov;3 Suppl 4:477S-480S.

[183] Bremner J, Innis R, Salomon R, et al. Positron emission tomography measurement of cerebral metabolic correlates of tryptophan depletion-induced depressive relapse. (Yale Univ, New Haven, Conn; Natl ctr for posttraumatic stress disorder, West Haven, Conn) *Arch Gen Psychiatry* 54:364-374, 1997.

[184] Markus C, Panhuysen G, et al. Does carbohydrate-rich, protein-poor food prevent a deterioration of mood and cognitive performance of stress-prone subjects when subjected to a stressful task? *Appetite* 1998 Aug;31(1):49-65.

[185] Markus R, Panhuysen G, et al. Effects of food on cortisol and mood in vulnerable subjects under controllable and uncontrollable stress. *Physiol Behav* 2000 Aug-Sep;70(3-4):333-342.

[186] Epel E, Lapidus R, et al. Stress may add bite to appetite in women: a laboratory study of stress-induced cortisol and eating behavior. *Psychoneuroendocrinology* 2001 Jan;26(1):37-49.

[187] Pennington J. Supplementary tables: Sugars. In: Bowes and Church's Food Values of Portions Commonly Used, Fifteenth Edition. Philadelphia, PA: JB Lippincott Company, 1989.

[188] Lloyd H, Green M, Rogers P. Mood and cognitive performance effects of isocaloric lunches differing in fat and carbohydrate content. *Physiol Behav* 1994 Jul;56(1):51-57.

[189] Beauchene R, Bales C, et al. Effect of age of initiation of feed restriction on growth, body composition, and longevity of rats. *J Gerontol* 1986 Jan;41(1):13-19.

[190] Means L, Higgins J, Fernandez T. Mid-life onset of dietary restriction extends life and prolongs cognitive functioning. *Physiol Behav* 1993 Sep;54(3):503-508.

[191] Fraser G, Singh P, Bennett H. Variables associated with cognitive function in elderly California Seventh-day Adventists. *Am J Epidemiol* 1996 Jun 15;143(12):1181-1190.

[192] Field T, Martinez A, et al. Music shifts frontal EEG in depressed adolescents. *Adolescence* 1998 Spring;33(129):109-116.

[193] Jones NA, Field T. Massage and music therapies attenuate frontal EEG asymmetry in depressed adolescents. *Adolescence* 1999 Fall;34(135):529-534.

[194] McElwain J. Personal Communication. Retired Chair of Music Therapy Department, Phillips University. Enid, OK.

[195] McElwain J. Personal Communication. Retired Chair of Music Therapy Department, Phillips University. Enid, OK.

[196] Schreckenberg G, Bird HH. Neural plasticity of MUS musculus in response to disharmonic sound. The Bulletin, *New Jersey Acad of Science* 1987 Fall;32(2):77-86.

[197] Scheel K, Westefeld J. Heavy metal music and adolescent suicidality: An empirical investigation. *Adolescence* 1999 Summer;34(134):253-273.

[198] Rauscher F, Shaw G, Ky KN. Listening to Mozart enhances spatial-temporal reasoning: Towards a neurophysiological basis. Neuroscience netter 1995;185:44-47.

[199] Rauscher F, Shaw G, Ky K. Listening to Mozart enhances spatial-temporal reasoning: Towards a neurophysiological basis. *Neuroscience Letter* 1995;185:46.

[200] Rauscher F, Shaw G, et al. Music and Spatial Task Performance: A causal relationship. Presented at the American Psychological Association 102nd Annual Convention in Los Angeles, CA, August 12-16, 1994.

[201] Schlaug G, Jancke L, et al. In vivo evidence of structural brain asymmetry in musicians. Science 1995 Feb 3;267(5198):699-701.

[202] Grout D. *A History of Western Music* 3rd edition. New York: W.W.Norton & Company, 1980.

[203] Dossey L. *Healing Words: The Power of Prayer and the Practice of Medicine*. New York, NY: HarperCollins Publishers, 1993 p. xvi-xix.

[204] Dossey L. *Healing Words: The Power of Prayer and the Practice of Medicine*. New York, NY: HarperCollins Publishers, 1993 p. xviii.

[205] Dossey L. *Healing Words: The Power of Prayer and the Practice of Medicine*. New York, NY: HarperCollins Publishers, 1993 p. 30-32.

[206] Dossey L. *Healing Words: The Power of Prayer and the Practice of Medicine*. New York, NY: HarperCollins Publishers, 1993 p. 241.

[207] Dossey L. *Healing Words: The Power of Prayer and the Practice of Medicine*. New York, NY: Harper Collins Publishers, 1993 p. 62-63.

[208] I Kings 19:4. *The Holy Bible*. KJV.

[209] I Kings 19:10. *The Holy Bible*. KJV.

[210] Haapaniemi H, Hillbom M, Juvela S. Lifestyle-associated risk factors for acute brain infarction among persons of working age. *Stroke* 1997 Jan;28(1):26-30.

[211] Haapaniemi H, Hillbom M, Juvela S. Lifestyle-associated risk factors for acute brain infarction among persons of working age. *Stroke* 1997 Jan;28(1):26-30.

[212] Moss M, Scholey A. Oxygen administration enhances memory formation in healthy young adults. *Psycopharmacology* 1996 Apr 124:255-260.

[213] Rao M, Muller-Oerlinghausen B, et al. The influence of phototherapy on serotonin and melatonin in non-seasonal depression. Pharmacopsychiatry 1990 May;23(3):155-158.

[214] Laakso M, Porkka-Heiskanen T, et al. Twenty-four-hour patterns of pineal melatonin and pituitary and plasma prolactin in male rats under 'natural' and artificial lighting conditions. *Neuroendocrinology* 1988 Sep;48(3):308-313.

[215] Stanley M, Brown G. Melatonin levels are reduced in the pineal glands of suicide victims. *Psychopharmacol Bull* 1988;24(3):484-488.

[216] Maestroni G , Conti A. Anti-stress role of the melatonin-immuno-opioid network: Evidence for a physiological mechanism involving T cell-derived, immunoreactive beta-endorphin and MET-enkephalin binding to thymic opioid receptors. *Int J Neurosci* 1991 Dec;61(3-4):289-298.

[217] Stephan K, Fink G, et al. Functional anatomy of the mental representation of upper extremity movements in healthy subjects. *J Neurophysiol* 1995 Jan;73(1):373-386.

[218] Rodriguez-Esteban C, Schwabe J, et al. Radical fringe positions the apical ectodermal ridge at the dorsoventral boundary of the vertebrate limb. *Nature* 1997 Mar 27;386(6623):360-366.

[219] White E. The Bible a means of both mental and moral culture. In: *Advent Review and Sabbath Herald*, 1883 Sept 25, p. 25. Found In: Ellen G. White Estate. The Published Writings of Ellen G. White. Version 2.0 (CD-ROM), 1995.

[220] White E. Mind, *Character, and Personality*. Hagerstown, MD: Review and Herald Publishing Association, 1977 p.93.

[221] White E. *Counsels on Diet and Foods*. Hagerstown, MD: Review and Herald Publishing Association, 1976 p. 29.

[222] White E. *Reflecting Christ*. Hagerstown, MD: Review and Herald Publishing Association, 1985 p. 142.

[223] White E. *Reflecting Christ*. Hagerstown, MD: Review and Herald Publishing Association, 1985 p. 142.

CHAPTER TEN

The Twenty-Week Cure

Instead of starting this chapter with another wonderful success story of a previously depressed patient, I want to dedicate this chapter to you, the reader. Chances are that you picked up this book because either you or someone dear to you is suffering from depression. You (or your loved one) are not alone. At least a third of all individuals are likely to experience an episode of depression during their lifetime.[1] Sadly, most of these individuals will either not recognize that they have the condition, or will not conquer their depression because of a lack of a proper treatment strategy.[2,3]

Those who recognize their depression may feel forced into taking drug medications for life.[4] They may attempt to get off the medication, but each time the attempt is made a dramatic worsening of the mental state occurs, often with a sense of unexplainable deep sadness or emptiness. Eventually, they resort to taking their daily antidepressant pill as if taking a necessary daily vitamin. Even while taking the medication, they often do not feel completely well.[5] They may be able to function in the family and at the workplace. They may not actively contemplate suicide—but they still do not feel complete, whole, happy, and goal-oriented. For such individuals, I have good news! I have saved the best for last! You are likely just twenty weeks away from a lasting cure for depression if the strategy outlined in this chapter is followed!

An Individual Approach is Required

Many people hope for a simple cookbook approach to follow that will cure their depression in a short period of time. Unfortunately, there is no such one-size-fits-all, cookie-cutter approach to treating this condition. This should come as no surprise, since diseases that are even more understood, such as congestive heart failure (the number one disease requiring hospital admission), do not have a *simple cookbook approach to bring about a quick and lasting cure to their condition in a short period of time*. What works for one patient may not be of benefit to another. It may even be damaging.

Each depressed individual has a unique set of underlying causes that must be discovered. These causes can then be used as a basis for determining an individualized treatment program to bring about the best results. The goal of this chapter is twofold: 1) to enable the reader to *discover the causes* of his or her depression (or the depression of a loved one), 2) to enable the reader to *use these causes for laying out a tailor-made strategy for conquering the depression.*

To lay the groundwork for this exercise, I would encourage you to read at least *Chapters 1, 3, 4, 5,* and *9* before proceeding. For those who have a large amount of stress or anxiety, I would also encourage the reading of *Chapters 7* and *8.* If you (or your loved one) are taking an herb or medication, I encourage you to study at least the principles involved in taking and withdrawing from medication in *Chapter 6.* You should also read what I say about your particular medication in *Chapter 6.*

While you are reading these chapters, I encourage you to take notes regarding the principles, causes, and treatments that likely apply to you or your loved one. This will help you later to devise you or your loved one's own particular treatment regimen. Now you are ready to return to this chapter and apply the information.

How to Find the Specific Causes of Your Depression

As you begin this section, I will assume that you know that you (or someone dear to you) are genuinely suffering from depres-sion. For purposes of illustration, let us assume it is you, the reader. To find the causes for your condition, we divide the possible causes into 10 "hit" categories. They are listed in **Figure 1**.

As you examine the list of these 10 "hit" categories, you may find several that you think may apply to you. As I stated in the Conclusion of *Chapter 3*, the brain can often sustain "hits" (or causes) in three "hit" categories and still function quite well. *Once a fourth "hit" category is sustained, depression or another mental disorder will likely result.* It is important for you to identify as many causes of your condition as you possibly can. This will enable you to devise a more effective personal treatment program to follow.

Before asking you to select which hit categories apply to you, each one is broken down into one or more causes of depres-sion, as laid out in **Figure 2**.

To illustrate how **Figure 2** is used, let's look at an example. Note that the "Genetic Hit Category" (the first one on the list in **Figure 2**) lists one specific cause, which is "Family history of depression or suicide." If that applies to you, you count that as one "hit." The second category, "Developmen-tal Hit," has four causes. If none of them apply to you, go to the next category. If any one of them does apply, you have another "hit."

If you have two causes *in the same hit category,* such as "History of Depression in Adolescence" and "Not being raised by both biological parents," it still counts as only one "hit."

As you go through this exercise, you will be able to identify most of the hit catego-ries that apply. However, some hit items may require certain background informa-tion such as obtained by a directed history and physical with some blood tests or other tests performed by a knowledgeable health care provider. Areas that such a health care provider could help identify include some nutritional hits, toxic hits, and medical con-dition hits. However, you may have four or

TEN "HIT" CATEGORIES OF POSSIBLE CAUSES OF DEPRESSION

1. *Genetic*

2. *Developmental*

3. *Nutrition*

4. *Social*

5. *Toxic*

6. *Circadian rhythm*

7. *Addiction*

8. *Lifestyle*

9. *Medical condition*

10. *Frontal lobe*

Figure 1

DEPRESSION CAUSES IN EACH HIT CATEGORY

Genetic Hit Category
- Family history of depression or suicide

Developmental Hit Category
- Early puberty in girls (begin menstruation by age 11 or younger)
- History of depression in adolescence
- Not being raised by both biological parents
- Suffered severe sexual abuse

Nutrition Hit Category
- Low dietary tryptophan
- Low omega-3 fat intake
- Low folic acid intake
- Low vitamin B intake
- Diet high in cholesterol, saturated fat, and sugar
- Marked anorexia and weight loss

Social Hit Category
- Absence of social support
- Negative, stressful life events
- Low social class
- Grandparents who raise grandchildren
- Immediate family member is an alcoholic or drug addict

Toxic Hit Category
- High lead levels
- High mercury levels
- High arsenic, bismuth, or other toxin levels

Circadian Rhythm Category
- Regular insomnia
- Sleeping more than 9 hrs/day routinely
- Sleeping less than 6 hrs/day routinely
- Not having regular hours for sleeping and eating

Addiction Hit Category
- Alcohol
- Smoker or tobacco user
- Heavy caffeine user
- Illicit drug user (such as marijuana)

Lifestyle Hit Category
- Not on a regular exercise program
- Not regularly being in daylight 30 minutes a day
- Rarely breathing fresh air

Medical Condition Hit Category
- Hepatitis C
- Recent head injury
- Stroke
- Heart disease
- Terminal cancer
- Parkinson's disease
- Uncontrolled diabetes
- Postpartum severe stress
- Premenstrual tension syndrome
- Inadequately treated thyroid disease
- Lupus
- Inadequately treated adrenal gland disease

Frontal Lobe Hit Category
- On low carbohydrate diet
- On high meat or high cheese diet eating lots of rich food
- Regular entertainment TV viewer or movie goer
- Entertainment internet or chat internet addiction
- Frequent sexual arousal outside of marriage
- MTV (or other rock/country music)viewer
- Undergoing hypnosis or Eastern meditation
- No regular Bible study or abstract thinking
- Going against your conscience

TOTAL NUMBER OF CAUSES=51

Figure 2

more hits without having to get this information.

It is important to realize that **Figure 2** is not an exhaustive list of causes of depression. Only the more common causes are listed. Some uncommon causes mentioned in *Chapter 3* are not in the figure (such as the Borna disease virus or sick building syndrome in the "Medical Condition" category). It is not necessary to go through the time and expense to search for such uncommon causes if enough causes listed in the figure are found to apply.

I also do not routinely search for toxic causes unless the history and physical of the patient leads me to suspect a possible toxin. One exception would be if only two hit categories are identified in a person with major depression. That usually means that at least one and probably two hit categories have yet to be identified. Undergoing a toxic work-up (sending off blood, hair, and possibly nail samples) and checking for undiagnosed medical conditions (such as lupus, diabetes, or a frontal lobe stroke)

would then be helpful.

Singular Causes of Depression

Importantly, we must recognize that there can be a single cause in a single category that can cause major depression alone, even if there are no hits in any other category. These causes are listed in **Figure 3.**

Designing a Treatment Program

Once you have successfully determined the cause or causes of your depression, it is now time to plan the treatment program. Many depressed individuals will have four or more hit categories with multiple causes under each one. For instance, under the "Addiction hit category" in **Figure 2**, a person may be a smoker, an alcoholic, *and* a heavy caffeine user. Under the "Circadian Rhythm" hit category, a person may regularly get less than 6 hours of sleep, have insomnia frequently, *and* lack a regular schedule for eating and sleeping. Under the "Frontal Lobe" hit category, a person may be an entertainment television addict, an MTV viewer, never study the Bible or engage in abstract thought, *and* be on a heavy meat diet. *The proper treatment program is one that should work on all of the modifiable causes under each hit category.*

Although some depressed individuals are willing and able to address all of their modifiable causes *simultaneously*, others are not. A step-by-step approach will also work well in combating depression—but will take a longer period of time to reach complete success. I often have my depressed patients work on one modifiable hit catagory each month until all causes are corrected. This may be only a three-month process, since some causes are often not modifiable (genetic, developmental, and some medical causes). It is important for the depressed patient to attempt correction of all of the causes in a hit category simultaneously during that month. This may sound "impossible" for some depressed people to fathom,

SINGULAR CAUSES OF DEPRESSION

- Thyroid disease
- Parkinson's disease
- Uncontrolled diabetes
- Certain strokes
- Chronic insomnia
- Chronic low carbohydrate diet
- Chronic low tryptophan diet
- Chronic complete absence of social support
- Very high toxin levels

Figure 3

but I have found that it is not only possible, but often *easier* to attack all causes in a hit category at the same time.

Addiction Hits—Conquering Multiple Addictions at the Same Time

A person who is a smoker, an alcoholic, and a heavy caffeine user may think it is impossible to give up all of these addictions at once. The good news is that long-term abstinence may be greater if all such additions are dealt with at the same time. See **Figure 4**.[6,7]

An alcoholic who has been drinking large amounts of alcohol for a long period of time should "play it safe" and enter into a detoxification program or a lifestyle live-in treatment program. During this time, his intention to give up tobacco and caffeine should also be made known. His treatment supervisors will likely be glad to help him with these addictions as well—recognizing that this will improve their chances of success with this individual.

While a depressed person is working on the focused category (such as addictions) he should not completely ignore the other categories—but should see what cause in another hit category he might easily work on during the month as well—such as readily incorporating a daytime brisk walk, etc. Some causes, such as a heavy meat diet, may be so ingrained that an attempt to change it while overcoming tobacco and caffeine may not be practical. It may set the depressed person up for disappointment. Thus, some (and maybe many) items in some hit categories will have to be addressed during a subsequent month.

Nutrition Hits—Changes in Diet

In a step-by-step program, I usually reserve the correction of nutrition hits for the second or third month. One exception would be a depressed anorexic patient who would need immediate nutritional attention. Be sure and review the nutrition areas in *Chapters 3, 4*, and *9*. To help you adopt improvements in your diet, you will find recipes in *Appendix X* that assist in addressing the problems of a low omega-3, low tryptophan, and low folate diet.

When working on the nutrition month, it is also good to work on items in other categories that have to do with nutrition, such as the Frontal Lobe Hit Category of **Figure 2**. Cutting down on or eliminating meat while increasing natural carbohydrates in the diet can assist in promoting other nutritional changes. Meatless dishes that are high in nutrients can elevate mood. Recipes for such dishes are also found in *Appendix X*.

Social Hits May Require Getting Involved

Some social hits are more modifiable than others. For instance, most grandpar-

CONQUERING MULTIPLE ADDICTIONS SIMULTANEOUSLY

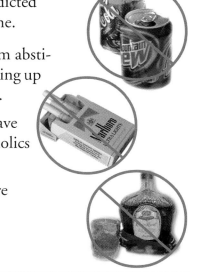

- A depressed person may be addicted to tobacco, alcohol, and caffeine.

- There is evidence that long-term abstinence may be improved by giving up all addictions at the same time.

- Alcohol treatment programs have better success rates when alcoholics give up tobacco.

- Smoking cessation programs are more successful if alcohol and caffeine are given up at the same time.

Figure 4

ents who are raising their grandchildren are only doing so because the parents are not available or are incapable of raising them. These circumstances cannot be modified. *Social isolation is more modifiable.* Making new friends or even getting closer to old acquaintances can be helpful. This is often best accomplished by becoming involved in a respected volunteer project that assists the community.

A close friendship is often developed by working with others toward a common goal. Becoming involved in an active local church that fosters community projects may be the answer. A person may honestly try these suggestions and give them time to work—but still does not develop close friends. The next step may be cognitive behavioral therapy with an experienced counselor, who may help you discover what you can do differently to overcome social isolation.

Circadian Rhythm Hits Require Scheduled Sleep Hours

This area is often best addressed by addressing hits in the lifestyle category at the same time. *A self-imposed sleep schedule is a "must" during this month.* This means watching the clock often, especially during the first two weeks of the month, until sleep regularity becomes more of a habit. Should you use alarm clocks during this time? Most definitely, but after you get up by an alarm clock every morning at the same time without fail—you will not need an alarm clock for very long.

Taking *a hot bath before bedtime* as described in *Chapter 5* will help you sleep, along with the other measures mentioned. Regular aerobic physical exercise, particularly if performed in the morning or during daytime hours outdoors in fresh air, will help the circadian rhythm. A summary of the solution to circadian rhythm problems is given in **Figure 5**.

Toxic and Medical Condition Hits

These will require diagnosis by a health care provider and will be best treated in concert with a health care provider's recommendations and treatment. However, there are often parts that you should play in helping to treat these conditions yourself. For instance, if mercury levels in your blood are high, you will definitely want to change your diet to eliminate fish and seafood. If you have been diagnosed with diabetes, you will want to get on a diet that is best for not only controlling your blood sugars, but also preventing the complications of the disease. I devote an entire chapter to controlling diabetes through nutrition and lifestyle improvements in the book ***Proof Positive***.

Frontal Lobe Hits

This is one of the most common problem areas in depressed patients today. I tend to have the patient overcome these problems in the second or third month. Many people who are addicted to entertainment television, the movie theater, the internet, MTV, or repeated sexual arousal outside of the marriage relation actually believe that their life will no longer be "fun" without

SOLVING THE CIRCADIAN RHYTHM PROBLEM

- Establish a self-imposed sleep schedule.

- An alarm clock is necessary.

- Take a hot bath before retiring.

- Participate in regular aerobic exercise.

Figure 5

their particular habit. After one month with the absence of the hit or hits on the frontal lobe of the brain, every person I know who has overcome has told me that their *enjoyment of life is actually much better now than before.* If you wonder how you can have recreation without these hits you may want to pick up a copy of **Proof Positive**. I discuss over 30 recreational activities that can enhance left and middle frontal lobe functions in *Chapter 13* in a section entitled "What To Do After Pulling the Plug."

Even cutting out the evening television news can be helpful. Most do not realize that the evening news actually just gives a few headlines but very little useful information. If you were to see a transcript of an average network television 30-minute news program, you would see less than six pages of written information. A newspaper or news magazine will give much more information in the same period of time, with an additional advantage—you will not be subjected to information that is not useful or interesting to you. You can glance at the headline, know it's not for you, and move on. You will learn much more that is relevant to your personal life in 30 minutes by reading the newspaper than by viewing hours of TV news.

One activity that will enhance frontal lobe action is serious personal daily Bible study. Reading a chapter in the book of Proverbs, or doing a topical study in the Bible on the subject of "faith" or another spiritual theme will provide health to the frontal lobe.

Dealing With Multiple Hits

Some individuals will live a long portion of their life with three ongoing hit categories. Then a series of events or lifestyle patterns will occur that will suddenly increase the hit categories to five or six, bringing about a major depression. If all of these areas are changeable they should be addressed. Since I usually have the patient at-

tack only one category per month, a few depressed individuals may require up to 24 or 28 weeks to achieve a lasting cure.

It is not absolutely necessary to have zero active hit categories to achieve a lasting cure. As I pointed out earlier, some categories cannot be changed, such as genetic or developmental hit categories. Although zero hit categories are ideal, many patients will improve dramatically if they reduce them to one or two. However, a gray area may be entered if there are four or more active hit categories that are reduced to three. Most patients with this amount of reduction will eventually feel better and become more functional; however, many will need to continue to take an herb or medication long-term, at least until they further reduce their active hit categories. Thus, I strongly encourage that all changeable active hit categories be removed to give the patient the best chance for achieving a lasting cure without the need of drugs.

Some depressed patients ultimately fail to effectively reduce their hit areas. Undergoing counseling in which cognitive behavioral therapy is applied by an experienced therapist may then be necessary to achieve success. It is important to let the counselor know exactly what hits you desire to change so that the therapy sessions can be efficient and directed toward lasting results.

Some people who have previously failed to reduce their hit categories will find lasting success by enrolling in a live-in lifestyle center as previously mentioned. In such a facility, all of the active changeable hit categories will be dealt with at once so the setup for success can be achieved in three weeks or less! Lasting success occurs once the patient implements his new lifestyle in his home environment.

The Lasting Cure

I have found that most patients can achieve a lasting cure from depression just by knowing the causes of their condition and undergoing the lifestyle changes necessary to eliminate them. Their motivation springs from their true desire to feel better, function better, think better, and their desire to be more useful to their loved ones, as emphasized in **Figure 6.**

Such patients are *absolutely thrilled* to experience their new life—especially without the use of drugs and with the elimination of side effects. They agree with the statement written by the author of Hebrews, recited in **Figure 7**.[8]

Those who have overcome depression will often state that *they feel much better than they did before they were depressed.* Yes, their depression grieved them, but as a result of that grieving they found the cause and changed their diet and lifestyle ("straight paths for the feet") and were healed. Now they experience joy, fulfillment, and peace such as they have never known before.

Lasting Cure Failures

Although some failures occur due to the reasons stated previously under the section "Multiple Hit Categories," others will occur simply because the person does not have a true desire to feel better, function better, think better, and may not have a desire to be more useful to their loved ones. Such

individuals usually reason that they are somehow gaining from their disease—a process referred to as "secondary gain." Such "gain" may be the thought that they would no longer experience the love and attention from their family, fellow employees, counselor, or doctor if they are cured.

Others might feel they experience "gain" by the "good conversation piece" that depressed feelings bring to their friends; once cured, they may not be as interesting to converse with—and may lose friends. They are "glorying in their infirmities." There can be a host of other reasons that a person may feel that he is gaining from continuing his depressed state. Whatever the reason, I have found it useful to ask the patient what he feels he is gaining by continuing to practice a lifestyle that is known to cause depression. Once the reason is acquired, I can then help the patient identify his *false needs* and *true needs* and can help him see which thoughts are irrational and must be overcome. Such a process often requires a counselor experienced in cognitive behavioral therapy. Once irrational thinking is corrected, the behavior and feelings are positively affected, and a lasting cure can result.

A Case Study

Victoria, age 45, had lost twenty pounds in two months and had not had a good night's sleep for over ten weeks. She had cried at least once every day for the last two months, often without apparent reason. She had seriously contemplated suicide, but realized those thoughts were irrational and did not feel suicidal at present. Her first office visit with me revealed that she had major depression. She was given **Figure 2** in this chapter in the form of a checklist to attempt to find the cause and to see which specific areas needed to be analyzed in her blood. She was positive for six out of the ten possible hit categories.

She had no family history of depression, but she was a victim of severe sexual abuse

MOTIVATION FOR A LASTING CURE

- Feel better

- Think better

- Function better

- Be more useful to loved ones

Figure 6

by her uncle until the age of 9. Her diet was low in omega-3 fat. The last two months she had hardly been eating at all and even went entire days without eating any calories. Socially, she now felt isolated. Her husband had fallen in love with another woman one year prior to her office visit. She had been very close to her 20-year-old daughter, who was getting married to a man who lived out of state. Her 14-year-old daughter was choosing to live with her father because of his "anything goes" permissive attitude.

Fortunately, Victoria was not addicted to alcohol or drugs, and had not turned to them in order to "cope" with her feelings of depression. She had an indoor job and had no regular exercise for one year. She watched entertainment television regularly and had turned to internet chat rooms to help her cope with feelings of social isolation. Fortunately, she had no medical maladies and her blood analysis did not reveal any other disease states. Her hit categories were developmental, nutrition, social, circadian rhythm, lifestyle, and frontal lobe.

Because of severe depression and no appetite, I encouraged her to begin taking the medication Remeron® (an antidepressant drug medicine) every evening while we addressed the hit categories one month at a time. She had experienced adverse reactions to medication in the past and pleaded with me to begin the diet and lifestyle approach aggressively in hopes of avoiding medication. I permitted this approach only with her agreement that if she did not improve significantly by the end of one week, that she would try the medication. I placed her on a diet high in tryptophan and in omega-3 fat (flaxseed and walnuts) and high in folic acid with no cholesterol. She was to get 30 minutes of sunlight near the noon hour daily, while exercising (brisk walking or swimming). She was to go to bed no later than 9 p.m. and take a 30-minute hot bath prior to retiring. The internet chat rooms and entertainment television were to be

stopped abruptly.

The only potentially changeable category that remained was her social situation. I could not see how I could get her husband and daughters to return. She previously had close acquaintances in a church that she had attended in the past. She could possibly re-establish an active friendship with some people dear to her in this church—and I encouraged her to pursue this, while also pursuing an active daily Bible study and prayer program.

Because she wanted to try a treatment approach apart from medication, I told her that immediate implementation of the entire treatment program would bring about the best results if she thought she could accomplish these multiple changes simultaneously. She thought it was possible and was willing to try. Try she did—successfully accomplishing the entire program at once. In one week, she had actually gained two pounds, her appetite had improved, she was sleeping 7 to 8 hours every night, and had

THE PEACEABLE FRUITS OF RIGHTEOUSNESS

"No chastening for the present seemeth to be joyous, but grievous: nevertheless, afterward it yieldeth the peaceable fruit of righteousness unto them which are exercised thereby.

"Wherefore lift up the hands which hang down, and the feeble knees; And make straight paths for your feet, lest that which is lame be turned out of the way; but let it rather be healed." —Hebrews 12:11,12

Figure 7

not cried even once during the previous four days. She was thoroughly enjoying her renewed spiritual life with private devotions and in studying with her old friends. She obviously did not need the medication.

Weeks later, no relapse has occurred and she is feeling better than ever—while continuing her diet and lifestyle program. Yes, she still misses her husband and daughters, but she trusts God to work out in His timing His plan for the rest of her life. She feels she has been given a wonderful opportunity to be open to His continued leading.

This abbreviated case report does not mean that the approach that worked for Victoria is for everyone. As previously stated, the treatment program needs to be planned *according to the specific causes and needs of each individual patient*. If this patient had an addiction, it would likely have been dealt with during the first four weeks before implementing the rest of the program—which may have made antidepressant medication mandatory (depending on the kind of addiction). The case demonstrates again the *vital connection of diet and lifestyle to optimal mental health*.

Withdrawal From Medication

Because of vulnerability to relapse, depressed patients are typically advised to continue antidepressant medications for nine to twelve months before withdrawal is advised.[9] Most individuals who come to me with depression are already on antidepressant medication. Although it usually has helped their condition somewhat, they often are still depressed and are suffering physical symptoms from their condition. I usually have them overcome all of their changeable hit categories, wait a month longer to be sure that they have achieved success in these areas, and then begin the process of withdrawing their medication. The withdrawal process is described in *Chapter 6*. Within one month the withdrawal process is successful in approximately 90 percent of patients. The patient is no longer depressed, and is no longer dependent on medication.

Conclusion

This chapter is designed to serve as a guideline for anyone who wants to conquer depression. A five-point summary is shown in **Figure 8**.

Depression should not be tolerated as a lifelong condition with its miserable effects. I encourage you to begin the process that will result in a lasting cure for depression. Find the cause or causes of your depression. Reverse as many changeable causes as possible through a program that addresses nutrition, lifestyle, social factors, and a renewed spiritual life. The words of the apostle John, quoted in **Figure 9**, ring true today.[10]

"To be in health" means optimal physical, mental, social, and spiritual health. You can have genuine, invigorating health of body, mind, and soul.

SUMMARY OF CHAPTER 10

1. There is no such thing as a "standard" case of depression.

2. Each victim of depression has a unique set of causes.

3. Most cases of depression have more than one cause. Many have four or more.

4. Each cause must be identified before a strategy for conquering the disorder can be laid out.

5. A depressed person can often determine his own causes from a list of 51 possibilities.

Figure 8

"Beloved, I wish above all things that thou mayest prosper and be in health, even as thy soul prospereth."

—3 John 2

Figure 9

References—

[1] Rorsman B, Gräsbeck A, Hagnell O, Lanke J, Öhman R, Öjesjö L,Otterbeck L. A prospective study of first-incidence depression: The lundby study, 1957-72.*Br J Psychiatry.*1990;156:336-342.

[2] Freeling P, Rao BM, Paykel ES, Sireling LI, Burton RH. Unrecognised depression in general practice. *Br Med J* (Clin Res Ed). 1985;290:1880-1883.

[3] Hirschfeld RMA, Keller MB, Panico S, Arons BS, Barlow D, Davidoff F, Endicott J, Froom J, Goldstein M, Gorman JM, Guthrie D, Marek RG, Maurer TA, Meyer R, Phillips K, Ross J, Schwenk TL, Sharfstein SS, Thase ME, Wyatt RJ. The National Depressive and Manic-Depressive Association consensus statement on the undertreatment of depression. *JAMA.* 1997;277:333-340.

[4] One study showed recurrence of depression in nearly 80% of patients switched to a placebo as quoted by Kupfer DJ, FrankE, Perel JM, Cornes C, Mallinger AG, Thase ME, McEachran AB, Grochocinski VJ. Five-year outcome for maintenance therapies in recurrent depression. *Arch Gen Psychiatry* 1992 Oct;49(10):769-73.

[5] National Depressive and Manic-Depressive Association. Most patients report troublesome side effects, modest inprovement using cuent anti-depression treatments: New survey also shows satisfaction with treatment and care among people with depression. Press Release. Nov 30, 1999. http://www.ndmda.org/deptreat.htm.

[6] Hurt RD, et al. Chapter 15—Treating Nicotine Addiction in Patients with Other Addictive Disorders, in *Nicotine Addiction: Principles and Managment* (Orleans CT, Slade J, editors), Oxford, England: Oxford University Press, 1993, p.310-326.

[7] DeRose DJ, et al. Alternative and complementary therapies for nicotine addiction. *Complementary Health Practice Review* 2000 Fall;6(1)98.

[8] Hebrews 12:11-13 *The Holy Bible,* KJV.

[9] Gruenber AM, Goldstein RD. Chapter 54 - Depressive Disorders in *Tasman Psychiatry, 1st edition* (Tasman A, Kay J, Lieberman JA, editors), Philadelphia, PA: Harcourt Brace & Company, 1997, p.1005.

[10] 3 John 2 *The Holy Bible,* KJV.

APPENDIX I
BRAIN COMMUNICATIONS
and BRAIN CHEMISTRY

The structure of a neuron is shown in **Figure 1.**

A neuron has a cell body that contains the genetic material and much of the neuron's energy-producing machinery. Emerging from the body are the dendrites, which are branches that are the most important receptive surfaces of the neurons in the line of communication. These dendrites, depending on the type and location of the neuron, have a great many shapes and sizes. The output of the neuron usually follows a single branch called the axon, which often branches out into many terminals on its end, as illustrated in **Figure 1.**

An enlarged sketch of a neuron terminal and its communication system is shown in **Figure 2.**

Communications in the brain occur at small, specialized membrane structures called synapses (pronounced si-nap'sees) located between the neurons, as shown in the figure. The usual form of communication involves electrical signals that travel within neurons, that give rise to chemical signals that cross the synapses. These, in turn, are transformed into new electrical signals in one or more of the connecting neurons. Each neuron, on average, makes more than 1000 connections with other neurons through synapses.

It is estimated that there are at least 100 trillion synapses in the entire brain, but there could be even 10 or more times this amount.[1] These synapses are not positioned randomly, but arranged in patterns known as circuits. If a circuit is stimulated by a neurosurgeon's probe, it can result in a memory, a thought, or even a movement of the arm, hand, and index finger, depending on where the probe was placed in the brain. An additional complexity is that a single neuron can be part of more than one circuit.

The complexity of the physical structure of the human brain is amazing to say the least. Superimposed on this physical structure is the brain chemistry, which is not any less amazing. When an electrical signal travels down an axon it then turns into a chemical signal. These chemical signals are molecules known as neurotransmitters. These are shown in **Figure 2.** There are more than 100 different types of neurotransmitters in the brain.[2] Some are small chemicals such as serotonin, dopamine, acetylcholine, and norepinephrine. Others are larger chemicals made out of protein chains.

Let us consider three kinds of

STRUCTURE OF A NEURON

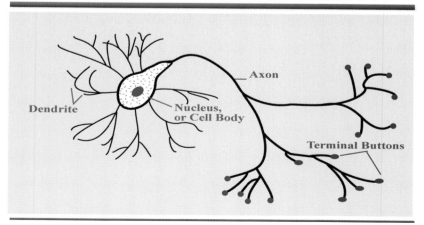

Dendrite

Nucleus, or Cell Body

Axon

Terminal Buttons

Figure 1

neurotransmitters:

1. Excitatory – triggers an electrical excitation in a neuron
2. Inhibitory – inhibits a neuron from producing an electrical signal
3. Modulating – modulates an existing electrical signal from a neuron.

An example of an excitatory neurotransmitter is the chemical glutamate. The chemicals glycine and gamma aminobutyric acid are examples of inhibitory neurotransmitters.

Most neurotransmitters are neither excitatory nor inhibitory, but act to produce complex modulation of the electrical signal. Serotonin, dopamine, and the protein chains fit this category of neurotransmitters. To illustrate how these neurotransmitters work together, consider an example of a musical instrument such as a flute. To get music from a flute, we must first have the instrument available, followed by wind to produce sound, and then keys to control or modulate the sound. A neuron is the flute, an excitatory neurotransmitter is the wind, and a modulating neurotransmitter is the array of keys that provide or alter the melody.

Each modulating neurotransmitter is made by a relatively small number of neurons clustered in a limited number of areas in the brain. For instance, dopamine is made by only about 500,000 neurons, which is only one out of every 200,000 cells. Dopamine neurons are clustered only in areas deep within the brain. Each of these neurons sends its axons branching throughout the brain, so that in each case, when a small number of these neurons fire in unison almost the entire brain is influenced.

One type of neuron (called a Purkinje cell, sketched in **Figure 3**) can make up to 200,000 connections with other neurons.

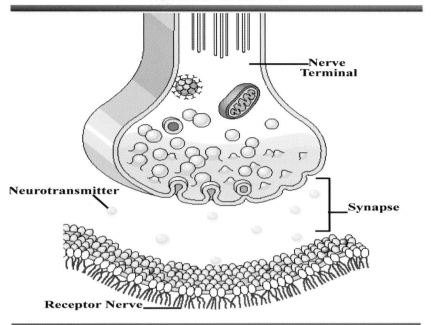

NEURON COMMUNICATION SYSTEM

Nerve Terminal

Neurotransmitter

Synapse

Receptor Nerve

Figure 2

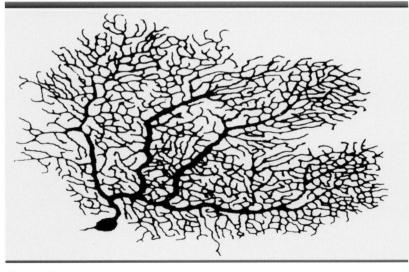

THE PURKINJE CELL

Figure 3

References—

[1] Mental Health:A Report of the Surgeon General Department of Health & Human Services, National Institutes of Health, Nation Institutes of Mental Health. 1999, p.33.

[2] Mental Health: A Report of the Surgeon General Department of Health & Human Services, National Institutes of Health, Nation Institutes of Mental Health. 1999, p.36.

APPENDIX II

THE LIMBIC SYSTEM: EMOTIONAL CENTER OF THE BRAIN

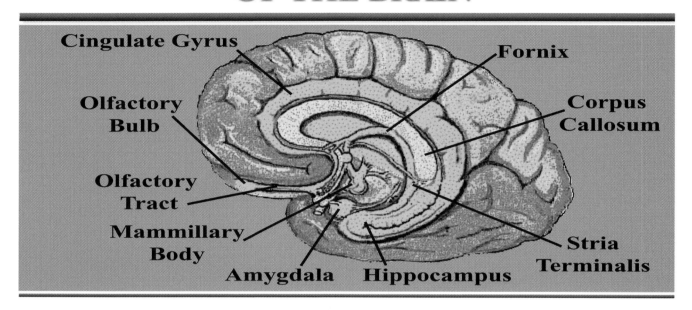

This diagram is a cross section of the brain made by dividing the brain in half, to allow viewing of the limbic system components.

APPENDIX III
OFFICIAL PSYCHIATRIC SYMPTOMS OF DEPRESSION

A. Five (or more) of the following symptoms have been present during the same 2-week period and represent a change from previous functioning; at least one of the symptoms is either (1) depressed mood or (2) loss of interest or pleasure.

NOTE: Do not include symptoms that are clearly due to a general medical condition, or mood incongruent delusions or hallucinations.

(1) depressed mood most of the day, nearly every day, as indicated by either subjective report (e.g., feels sad or empty) or observation made by others (e.g., appears tearful). **Note:** In children and adolescents, can be irritable mood.

(2) markedly diminished interest or pleasure in all, or almost all, activities most of the day, nearly every day (as indicated by either subjective account or observation made by others).

(3) significant weight loss when not dieting or weight gain (e.g., a change of more than 5% of body weight in a month), or a decrease or increase in appetite nearly every day. **Note:** In children, consider failure to make expected weight gain.

(4) insomnia or hypersomnia nearly every day.

(5) psychomotor agitation or retardation nearly every day (observable by others, not merely subjective feelings or restlessness or being slowed down).

(6) fatigue or loss of energy nearly every day.

(7) feelings of worthlessness or excessive or inappropriate guilt (which may be delusional) nearly every day (not merely self-reproach or guilt about being sick).

(8) diminished ability to think or concentrate, or indecisiveness, nearly every day (either subjective account or as observed by others).

(9) recurrent thoughts of death, not just fear of dying; recurrent suicidal thoughts without a specific plan, or a suicide attempt or a specific plan for committing suicide.

B. The symptoms do not meet criteria for a mixed episode.

C. The symptoms cause clinically significant distress or impairment in social, occupational, or other important areas of functioning.

D. The symptoms are not due to the direct physiological effects of a substance (e.g., drug of abuse, or medication) or a general medical condition (e.g., hypothyroidism).

E. The symptoms are not better accounted for by bereavement, i.e., after the loss of a loved one; the symptoms persist for longer than 2 months or are characterized by marked functional impairment, morbid preoccupation with worthlessness, suicidal thoughts, psychotic symptoms, or psychomotor retardation.

American Psychiatric Association (1994). *Diagnostic and Statistical Manual of Mental Disorders (4th ed).* Washington, D.C.

APPENDIX IV

OFFICIAL PSYCHIATRIC SYMPTOMS OF DYSTHYMIA

A.   Depressed mood for most of the day, for more days than not, as indicated either by subjective account or observation by others, for at least 2 years. NOTE: In children and adolescents, mood can be irritable and duration must be at least 1 year.

B.   Presence, while depressed, of two (or more) of the following:

 (1) poor appetite or overeating
 (2) insomnia or hypersomnia
 (3) low energy or fatigue
 (4) low self-esteem
 (5) poor concentration or difficulty making decisions
 (6) feelings of hopelessness

C.   During the 2-year period (1 year for children or adolescents) of the disturbance, the person has never been without the symptoms in Criteria A and B for more than 2 months at a tme.

D.   No major depressive episode has been present during the first 2 years of the disturbance (1year for children and adolescents); i.e., the disturbance is not better accounted for by chronic major depressive disorder or major depressive disorder in partial remission.

 NOTE: There may have been a previous major depressive episode provided there was a full remission (no significant signs or symptoms for 2 months) before development of the dysthymic disorder. In addition, after the initial 2 years (1 year for children or adolescents) of dysthymic disorder, there may be superimposed episodes of major depressive disorder, in which case both diagnoses may be given when the criteria are met for a major depressive episode.

E.   There has never been a manic episode, a mixed episode, or a hypomanic episode, and criteria have never been met for cyclothymic disorder.

F.   The disturbance does not occur exclusively during the course of a chronic psychotic disorder such as schizophrenia or delusional disorder.

G.   The symptoms are not due to the direct physiological effects of a substance (e.g., an abuse of a drug or medication) or a general medical condition (e.g., hypothyroidism).

H.   The symptoms cause clinically significant distress or impairment in social, occupational, or other important areas of functioning.

American Psychiatric Associaton (1994), *Diagnostic and Statistical Manual of Mental Disorders (4th ed.)* Washington, D.C.

APPENDIX V
BIPOLAR DISORDER

Bipolar Disorder, not too long ago, was known by the term *Manic Depression*. People diagnosed with this problem swung from deeply depressive moods to wildly manic (high) moods. However, closer study into the disorder has provided insights that show people can have many different levels and intensities of their mood swings. It's not as narrowly definable a problem as once thought.

Hippocrates was one of the first to characterize *melancholia* (depressive) and manic states to be a result of biological processes in the body and mind[1] instead of the infiltration of supernatural forces. In the 19th century efforts were made to narrow the definitions of mania and melancholy, and the use of the term *depression* came into being. Medicine considered the disorders to be caused by defects in personality and not in intellect. German psychiatrist Emil Kraeplin closely studied the disorders and came to the conclusion that though they were at far ends of the behavioral spectrum, they were alternate manifestations of the same illness.[2]

Kraeplin described mania as a state of extreme flight of ideas, exalted mood, and a whirl of activity. He saw depression as a sad or anxious moodiness and sluggishness of thought and action. He saw the illness as a continuum that ranged through swings from mild to intense states of both ends of the spectrum. Depending on intensity, the swings could go from no disruption of normal function to wildly intense moods of mania and depression that could be debilitating.

A person in the grip of a manic episode can be in a state of pure euphoria or extreme irritability. Their thought patterns can be grand with whatever they are doing, seen as the best or greatest ever, or paranoid, imagining aliens monitoring their every move. While their thought processes are racing, ideas come and go with the speed of light, yet they are easily distracted and have trouble concentrating. Other symptoms include poor judgment, offensive behavior, promiscuity, spending sprees, reckless behavior, increased energy and activity, and a reduced need for sleep.

To be diagnosed with bipolar disorder, the patient must currently (or very recently) be in a manic episode, must have had one previous major depressive, manic, or mixed episode which cannot be accounted for by some other schizoid, psychotic, or delusional disorder.[3] The criteria for diagnosing a manic episode are shown in **Figure 1**.[4]

Investigations suggest that approximately 30 percent of depressed patients under treatment may have bipolar illness.[5,6] Almost two percent of the entire adult population in the U.S. suffer from the affliction.[7] A review of many studies shows that 25 to 50 percent of bipolar patients attempt suicide at least once.[8] A follow-up showed that 15 percent succeeded, 30 times the rate found in the general population.[9]

Numerous areas of the brain may be involved in bipolar disorder. Instead of going into technical details, I will tell you they include the amygdala, hippocampus, thalamus, cerebellum, prefrontal cortex, striatum, and pallidus. (See *Chapter 1* for brain structure.)

There are two main circuits thought to be involved in mood disorders. Mood disorders like mania and depression can result from dysfunction of the connections in these regions among their various circuits.[10]

Researchers are beginning to study the physical structure of the brain to see if there are differences between a normal brain and the brain of a bipolar patient. Early studies with MRI suggest there may be abnormalities in the structure and blood flow of these particular areas of the brain, but there have not yet been enough studies with the proper controls to come to a definite conclusion.[11,12,13,14] What we do know is that serotonin and dopamine play critical roles in these networks, and any disturbance can play a part in mood disorders.

Treatment for this disease most likely involves being on medication for life, which

CRITERIA FOR MANIC EPISODE

A. A distinct period of abnormally and persistently elevated, expansive, or irritable mood occurs that lasts at least 1 week (or any duration of hospitalization is necessary).

B. During the period of mood disturbance, three (or more) of the following symptoms have persisted (four if the mood is only irritable) and have been present to a substantial degree:

- Inflated self-esteem or grandiosity

- Decreased need for sleep (e.g., feels rested after only 3 hours of sleep)

- More talkative than usual or pressure to keep talking

- Flight of ideas or subjective experience that thoughts are racing

- Distractibility (i.e., attention too easily drawn to unimportant or irrelevant external stimuli)

- Increase in goal-directed activity (socially, at work or school, or sexually) as psychomotor agitation

- Excessive involvement in pleasurable activities that have a high potential for pain consequences (e.g., unrestrained buying sprees, sexual indiscretions, or foolish business investments).

C. The symptoms do not meet the criteria for a mixed episode.

D. The mood disturbance is sufficiently severe to cause marked impairment in occupational functioning or in usual social activities or relationships with others or to necessitate hospitalization to prevent harm to self or others or there are psychotic features present.

E. The symptoms are not due to the direct physiological effects of a substance (e.g., a drug of abuse, a medication, or other treatment) or a general medical condition (e.g., hyperthyroidism).

Figure 1

would tend to lend credence to the idea that perhaps there is some type of permanent change or difference in the bipolar's brain structure and circuitry. The types of medication that are currently found to be the most effective are the antidepressants bupropion (Wellbutrin®) and the SSRIs (selective serotonin reuptake inhibitors). MAOIs (monoamine oxidase inhibitors) can also be used, but tricyclics are rarely used and have been little studied for this disorder.

Care must be taken when administering antidepressants for depression, as they can actually produce mania in certain individuals. Hence, treating a bipolar person most often requires the use of a mood stabilizer—lithium being the standard medication—in combination with the antidepressant to prevent the patient from shifting into a manic phase.[15] Mania is caused by the neurotransmitter systems in the parts of the brain we mentioned above, being overactive or misfiring. Mood stabilizers appear to inhibit excessive neuronal signals and also help keep unnecessary signals from starting up.[16,17,18,19]

Other medications have recently been found to work well as an option to lithium for mood stabilization. These drugs are anticonvulsants and must be used with care. They include valproate (Depakote®), lamotrigine (Lamictal®), gabapentin (Neurontin®), topiramate (Topamax®), and olanzapine (Zyprexa®). All of these can cause weight gain (among numerous other more severe side effects), except Topamax,® which can actually cause weight loss.

Another recent nutritional discovery is the possibility that omega-3 may help ease the symptoms of bipolar patients and work as an alternative to lithium as a mood stabilizing agent by inhibiting neuronal signals.[20] Currently in the U.S. and Western Europe, the diet has almost been depleted of omega-3 fatty acids, compared to the pre-industrial age or countries like Japan,[21,22] leading to indirect evidence that it may play a part in the increasing incidence of depression. Rates of major depression have increased and the age of onset has decreased in every decade of the last century.[23] During the last 100 years, omega-3 has been almost entirely replaced by omega-6 fatty acids, which may increase the incidence of coronary artery disease. In *Chapter 4* we further examine omega-3 and its nutritional value.

Though currently the most popular source of omega-3 is fish oil, we know that flaxseed oil can be a superior source, and early tests show it has promise as an alternative to fish oil. For example, in tests with bipolars, the omega-3 content of fish oil required that patients take 30 capsules a day to get the needed amount, which proved to be a chore. Flaxseed oil is concentrated enough to require only a few capsules each day. The fish oil capsules also proved to be *distasteful* to the patients in more ways than one, as the number of capsules was intimidating and the fish taste was overwhelming to many.

Results of the tests with fish oil capsules found that 64 percent treated with omega-3 responded to treatment, and remained in remission much longer after termination of the supplement than those in the control group.[24] Studies have only begun on flaxseed oil, but may prove to provide a superior source of omega-3 in treating bipolar disorder.

Finally, electroconvulsive therapy (ECT) is used especially for severely ill patients and has the fastest and probably highest response rates of all the therapies.[25] It may be the best initial treatment for those who are delusional or at a high risk for suicide.[26] Its downside is a relatively high relapse rate.

Unfortunately, bipolar disorder requires a lifetime of treatment with medications at this time. However, with a proper diet including omega-3, the maintenance of bipolar disorder may be easier and more effectively accomplished.

References—

[1] Georgotas A, Cancro R, eds. *Depression and Mania*. New York, NY:Elsevier Science Inc;1988:4-6.

[2] Kraeplin E, ed. *Manic-Depressive Insanity and Paranoia*. Edinburgh, Scotland:ES Livingstone;1921.

[3] American Psychiatric Association. *Diagnostic and Statistical Manual of Mental Disorders*, 4th ed. Washington, DC. American Psychiatric Association; 1994: p. 356.

[4] American Psychiatric Association. *Diagnostic and Statistical Manual of Mental Disorders, 4th ed*. Washington, DC. American Psychiatric Association; 1994: p. 332.

[5] Cassano G, Akiskal H, et al. Proposed subtypes of Bipolar II a related disorder: With hypomanic episodes (or cyclothymia) and with hyperthymic temperment. *J Affect Dis* 1992;26:127-140.

[6] Rao A, Nammalvar N. The course and outcome in depressive illness: A follow-up study of 122 cases in Mandurai, India. *Br J Psychiatry* 1977;130:392-396.

[7] U.S. Department of Health and Human Services. Mental Health: *A Report of the Surgeon General*. Rockville, MD: U.S Department of Health and Human Services, Substance Abuse and Mental Health Services Administration, Center for Mental Health Services, National Institutes of Health, National Institute of Mental Health, 1999.

[8] Compton M, Nemeroff C. The treatment of bipolar depression. *J Clin Psychiatry* 2000;61(suppl 9):57-67.

[9] Goodwin F, Jamison K. *Manic-Depressive Illness*. New York, NY: Oxford University Press: 1990.

[10] Soares J, Mann JJ. The functional neuroanatomy of mood disorders. *J Psychiat Res* 1997;31(4):393-432.

[11] Soares J, Mann J. The functional neuroanatomy of mood disorders. *J Psychiat Res* 1997;31(4):393-432.

[12] Norris S, Krishnan R, Ahearn E. Structrual changes in the brain of patients with bipolar affective disorder by MRI: A review of the literature. *Prog Neuro-Psychopharmacol & Biol Psychiat* 1997 Sep;21:1323-1337.

[13] Strakowski S, DelBello, M, et al. Brain magnetic resonance imaging of structural abnormalities in bipolar disorder. *Arch Gen Psychiatry* 1999 Mar;56:254-259.

[14] Pearlson, G. Structural and functional brain changes in bipolar disorder: A selective review. *Schizophrenia Research* 1999;39:133-140.

[15] Frances A, Kahn D, et al. The expert consensus guidelines for treating depression in bipolar disorder. *J Clin Psychiatry* 1998;59(suppl 4):73-79.

[16] Stoll A, Severus E. Mood stabilizers: shared mechanisms of action at post-synaptic signal transduction and kindling processes. *Harvard Review of Psychiatry* 1996;4:77-89.

[17] Leviel V, Naquet R. A study of the action of valproic acid on the kindling effect. *Epilepsia* 1977;18:229-234.

[18] Wurpel J, Iyer S. Calcium channel blockers verapamil and nimodipine inhibit kindling in adult and immature rats. *Epilepsia* 1994;35:443-449.

[19] O'Donnel R, Miller A. The effect of lamotrigine upon development of cortical kindled seizures in the rat. *Neuropharmacology* 1991;30:253-258.

[20] Stoll A, Locke C, et al. Omega-3 fatty acids and bipolar disorder: A review. *Prostaglandins, Leukotrienes and Essential Fatty Acids* 1999;60(5&6):330-331.

[21] Leaf A, Weber P. A new era for science in nutrition. *Am J Clin Nutr* 1987;43:1048-1053.

[22] Hibbeln J. Fish consumption and major depression. *Lancet* 1998;351:1213.

[23] Weissman M, Bland R, et al. Cross-national epidemilogy of major depression and bipolar disorder. *JAMA* 1996;276:293-299.

[24] Stoll A, Locke C, et al. Omega-3 fatty acids and bipolar disorder: A review. *Prostaglandins, Leukotrienes and Essential Fatty Acids* 1999;60(5&6):334.

[25] Frances A, Kahn D, et al. The expert consensus guidelines for treating depression in bipolar disorder. *J Clin Psychiatry* 1998;59(suppl 4):73-79.

[26] Goodwin F, Jamison K. *Manic-Depressive Illness*. New York, NY:Oxford University Press; 1990.

APPENDIX VI

MEDICAL CONDITIONS ASSOCIATED WITH DEPRESSION

Syndrome	Disorders
Neurologic	Dementias, hydrocephalus, Huntington's chorea, infectious (including HIV, neurosyphilis), migraines, multiple sclerosis, myasthenia gravis, Parkinson's disease, seizure disorders, stroke, trauma, tumors, vasculitis, Wilson's disease
Endocrine	Addison's disease, Cushing syndrome, diabetes mellitus, hyperparathyroidism, hyperthyroidism, hypoparathyroidism, hypothyroidism, menses-related depression, postpartum depression
Metabolic/nutrition	Folate deficiency, hypercalcemia, hypocalcemia, hyponatremia, pellagra, porphyria, uremia, vitamin B_{12} deficiency
Infectious/inflammatory	Influenza, hepatitis, mononucleosis, pneumonia, rheumatoid arthritis, Sjogren's disease, systemic lupus erythematosus, tuberculosis
Other	Anemia, cardiopulmonary disease, neoplasms (including gastrointestinal, lung, pancreatic), sleep apnea

Milner K. *Psychiatr Clin North Am* -1999 Dec; 22(4): 755-77

APPENDIX VII
MEDICATIONS ASSOCIATED
WITH DEPRESSION

*Asterisk denotes that at least three percent of patients on medication reported depression

Accupril (Quinapril Hydrochloride)
Accuretic (Hydrochlorothiazide, Quinapril Hydrochloride)
Accutane (Isotretinoin)
Aceon (Perindopril Erbumine)
Aciphex (Rabeprazole Sodium)
*Actimmune (Interferon Gamma-1B)
Activella (Estradiol, Norethindrone Acetate)
*Actonel (Risedronate Sodium)
Adalat (Nifedipine)
Aerobid (Flunisolide)
*Agenerase (Amprenavir)
Agrylin (Anagrelide Hydrochloride)
Aldoclor (Chlorothiazide, Methyldopa)
Aldomet (Methyldopate Hydrochloride)
Aldoril (Hydrochlorothiazide, Methyldopa)
Alesse- (Ethinyl Estradiol, Levonorgestrel)
Alferon (Interferon alfa-N3 (Human Leukocyte Derived))
Alphagan (Brimonidine Tartrate)
Altace (Ramipril)
Ambien (Zolpidem Tartrate)
AmBisome (Amphotericin B)
Amerge (Naratriptan Hydrochloride)
*Androderm (Testosterone)
Andro (Testosterone)
*Android (Methyltestosterone)
Arava (Leflunomide)
*Aricept (Donepezil Hydrochloride)
*Arimidex (Anastrozole)
*Aromasin (Exemestane)
Arthrotec (Diclofenac Sodium, Misoprostol)
Asacol (Mesalamine)
Atacand (Candesartan Cilexetil)
Ativan (Lorazepam)
Avalide (Hydrochlorothiazide, Irbesartan)
Avapro (Irbesartan)
Avelox (Moxifloxacin Hydrochloride)
Avonex (Interferon Beta-1a)
Aygestin (Norethindrone Acetate)
Azmacort (Triamcinolone Acetonide)
Azulfidine (Sulfasalazine)
Bactrim (Sulfamethoxazole, Trimethoprim)
Baycol (Cerivastatin Sodium)
Beclovent (Beclomethasone Dipropionate)
Beconase (Beclomethasone Dipropionate Monohydrate)
Betagan (Levobunolol Hydrochloride)
Betaseron (Interferon Beta-1b)
Betoptic (Betaxolol Hydrochloride)
Blocadren (Timolol Maleate)

Brevibloc (Esmolol Hydrochloride)
Brevicon (Ethinyl Estradiol, Norethindrone)
Captopril (Captopril)
Betapace (Sotalol Hydrochloride)
Carbatrol (Carbamazepine)
Cardizem (Diltiazem Hydrochloride)
*Carnitor (Levocarnitine)
Carteolol Hydrochloride (Carteolol Hydrochloride)
Cartrol (Carteolol Hydrochloride)
*Casodex (Bicalutamide)
Cataflam (Diclofenac Potassium)
Catapres (Clonidine Hydrochloride)
Celebrex (Celecoxib)
Celestone (Betamethasone Acetate, Betamethasone Sodium Phosphate)
Celexa (Citalopram Hydrobromide)
*CellCept (Mycophenolate Mofetil)
Celontin (Methsuximide)
*Cenestin (Estrogens, Conjugated, Synthetic A)
Cerebyx (Fosphenytoin Sodium)
Chibroxin (Norfloxacin)
Cipro (Ciprofloxacin)
Claritin (Loratadine, Pseudoephedrine Sulfate)
Climara (Estradiol)
Clinoril (Sulindac)
Clomid (Clomiphene Citrate)
Clorpres (Chlorthalidone, Clonidine Hydrochloride)
Clozaril (Clozapine)
Cogentin (Benztropine Mesylate)
*Cognex (Tacrine Hydrochloride)
Colazal (Balsalazide Disodium)
Colocort (Hydrocortisone)
Combipres (Chlorthalidone, Clonidine Hydrochloride)
Concerta (Methylphenidate Hydrochloride)
Copaxone (Glatiramer Acetate)
Coreg (Carvedilol)
Cortenema (Hydrocortisone)
Cortone Acetate (Cortisone Acetate)
Corzide (Bendroflumethiazide, Nadolol)
Cosopt (Dorzolamide Hydrochloride, Timolol Maleate)
Cozaar (Losartan Potassium)
*Crinone (Progesterone)
Crixivan (Indinavir Sulfate)
Cylert (Pemoline)
Cytovene (Ganciclovir)
Danocrine (Danazol)
Dantrium (Dantrolene Sodium)

Daranide (Dichlorphenamide)
*DaunoXome (Daunorubicin Citrate)
Daypro (Oxaprozin)
DDAVP (Desmopressin Acetate)
Decadron (Dexamethasone)
Delatestryl (Testosterone Enanthate)
Demser (Metyrosine)
Demulen (Ethinyl Estradiol, Ethynodiol Diacetate)
*Depacon (Valproate Sodium)
*Depakene (Valproic Acid)
*Depakote (Divalproex Sodium)
Depo-Provera (Medroxyprogesterone Acetate)
Desmopressin Acetate (Desmopressin Acetate)
Desogen (Desogestrel, Ethinyl Estradiol)
Diastat (Diazepam)
Didronel (Etidronate Disodium)
Dilaudid Ampules (Hydromorphone Hydrochloride)
Diovan (Valsartan)
Dipentum (Olsalazine Sodium)
Diprivan Injectable Emulsion (Propofol)
Dolobid (Diflunisal)
*Dostinex (Cabergoline)
Doxil (Doxorubicin Hydrochloride)
Duraclon (Clonidine Hydrochloride)
*Duragesic (Fentanyl)
Duranest (Etidocaine Hydrochloride)
Dynabac (Dirithromycin)
*Effexor (Venlafaxine Hydrochloride)
8-MOP (Methoxsalen)
Eldepryl (Selegiline Hydrochloride)
Elmiron (Pentosan Polysulfate Sodium)
Elspar Asparaginase
Enbrel (Etanercept)
Ergamisol (Levamisole Hydrochloride)
Esclim (Estradiol)
Estinyl (Ethinyl Estradiol)
Estrace (Estradiol)
Estratab (Estrogens, Esterified)
Estratest (Estrogens, Esterified, Methyltestosterone)
Estring (Estradiol)
Estrostep (Ethinyl Estradiol, Norethindrone Acetate)
Eulexin (Flutamide)
*Evista (Raloxifene Hydrochloride)
Evoxac (Cevimeline Hydrochloride)
*Exelon (Rivastigmine Tartrate)
Fareston (Toremifene Citrate)
*Felbatol Oral Suspension (Felbamate)

APPENDIX

Feldene (Piroxicam)

Femara (Letrozole)

*Femhrt (Ethinyl Estradiol, Norethindrone Acetate)

Flagyl (Metronidazole)

Flexeril (Cyclobenzaprine Hydrochloride)

*Flolan (Epoprostenol Sodium)

Flovent (Fluticasone Propionate)

Floxin (Ofloxacin)

Fludara (Fludarabine Phosphate)

Flumadine (Rimantadine Hydrochloride)

Fortovase (Saquinavir)

*Foscavir (Foscarnet Sodium)

*Gabitril (Tiagabine Hydrochloride)

Gastrocrom (Cromolyn Sodium)

Gengraf (Cyclosporine)

*Gliadel (Carmustine (BCNU))

Glucotrol (Glipizide)

Halcion (Triazolam)

Haldol Decanoate (Haloperidol Decanoate)

*Herceptin (Trastuzumab)

Hivid (Zalcitabine)

Hydrocortone Acetate (Hydrocortisone Acetate)

Hytrin (Terazosin Hydrochloride)

Hyzaar (Hydrochlorothiazide, Losartan Potassium)

Imdur (Isosorbide Mononitrate)

Imitrex (Sumatriptan Succinate)

Indapamide (Indapamide)

Inderal (Propranolol Hydrochloride)

Inderide (Hydrochlorothiazide, Propranolol Hydrochloride)

Indocin (Indomethacin)

*Infergen (Interferon Alfacon-1)

*Intron (Interferon alfa-2B, Recombinant)

Invirase (Saquinavir Mesylate)

Iopidine (Apraclonidine Hydrochloride)

Kadian (Morphine Sulfate)

*Keppra (Levetiracetam)

Kerlone (Betaxolol Hydrochloride)

*Klonopin (Clonazepam)

*Lamictal (Lamotrigine)

Lanoxicaps (Digoxin)

Lanoxin (Digoxin)

Lariam (Mefloquine Hydrochloride)

Lescol (Fluvastatin Sodium)

Levaquin (Levofloxacin)

Levlen (Ethinyl Estradiol, Levonorgestrel)

Levo-Dromoran (Levorphanol Tartrate)

Levora (Ethinyl Estradiol, Levonorgestrel)

Lexxel (Enalapril Maleate, Felodipine)

Lidoderm (Lidocaine)

Lipitor (Atorvastatin Calcium)

Lodine (Etodolac)

Loestrin (Ethinyl Estradiol, Norethindrone Acetate)

Lomotil (Atropine Sulfate, Diphenoxylate Hydrochloride)

Lo/Ovral (Ethinyl Estradiol, Norgestrel)

Lopid (Gemfibrozil)

Lotronex (Alosetron Hydrochloride)

Low-Ogestrel (Ethinyl Estradiol, Norgestrel)

*Lupron Depot (Leuprolide Acetate)

Luvox (Fluvoxamine Maleate)

LYMErix (Lyme Disease Vaccine (Recombinant OspA))

Macrobid (Nitrofurantoin Monohydrate)

Macrodantin (Nitrofurantoin)

Marinol (Dronabinol)

Matulane (Procarbazine Hydrochloride)

Maxair (Pirbuterol Acetate)

Maxalt-MLT (Rizatriptan Benzoate)

Maxaquin (Lomefloxacin Hydrochloride)

Maxzide (Hydrochlorothiazide, Triamterene)

Mebaral (Mephobarbital)

Megace (Megestrol Acetate)

Menest (Estrogens, Esterified)

*Meridia (Sibutramine Hydrochloride Monohydrate)

Merrem (Meropenem)

Metadate (Methylphenidate Hydrochloride)

Methylin (Methylphenidate Hydrochloride)

Metro (Metronidazole)

Mevacor (Lovastatin)

Mexitil (Mexiletine Hydrochloride)

Miacalcin (Calcitonin-Salmon)

Micardis (Telmisartan)

Midamor (Amiloride Hydrochloride)

Migranal (Dihydroergotamine Mesylate)

Minipress (Prazosin Hydrochloride)

Minizide (Polythiazide, Prazosin Hydrochloride)

Mintezol (Thiabendazole)

Mirapex (Pramipexole Dihydrochloride)

Mithracin (Plicamycin)

Moban (Molindone Hydrochloride)

Mobic (Meloxicam)

Modicon (Ethinyl Estradiol, Norethindrone)

Moduretic (Amiloride Hydrochloride, Hydrochlorothiazide)

Monopril (Fosinopril Sodium)

Motofen (Atropine Sulfate, Difenoxin Hydrochloride)

Motrin (Ibuprofen, Pseudoephedrine Hydrochloride)

MS Contin (Morphine Sulfate)

MSIR (Morphine Sulfate)

Mykrox (Metolazone)

*Mylotarg (Gemtuzumab ozogamicin)

Nadolol (Nadolol)

Nalfon (Fenoprofen Calcium)

Naprelan (Naproxen Sodium)

Naropin (Ropivacaine Hydrochloride)

Nasacort (Triamcinolone Acetonide)

Necon (Ethinyl Estradiol, Norethindrone)

Neoral (Cyclosporine)

Nesacaine (Chloroprocaine Hydrochloride)

Neurontin (Gabapentin)

Nicotrol (Nicotine)

*Nilandron (Nilutamide)

Nimotop (Nimodipine)

*Nipent (Pentostatin)

Nizoral (Ketoconazole)

Nolvadex (Tamoxifen Citrate)

Nordette (Ethinyl Estradiol, Levonorgestrel)

Norinyl 1 + 35 (Ethinyl Estradiol, Norethidrone)

Norinyl 1 + 50 (Mestranol, Norethindrone)

Normodyne (Labetalol Hydrochloride)

Noroxin (Norfloxacin)

Norvasc (Amlodipine Besylate)

Norvir (Ritonavir)

Novarel (Chorionic Gonadotropin)

Nubain (Nalbuphine Hydrochloride)

Numorphan (Oxymorphone Hydrochloride)

Ocupress (Carteolol Hydrochloride)

Ogen (Estropipate)

Ogestrel (Ethinyl Estradiol, Norgestrel)

OptiPranolol (Metipranolol)

Oramorph (Morphine Sulfate)

*Orap (Pimozide)

Orlaam (Levomethadyl Acetate Hydrochloride)

Ortho Tri-Cyclen (Ethinyl Estradiol, Norgestimate)

Ortho-Cept (Desogestrel, Ethinyl Estradiol)

Ortho-Cyclen (Ethinyl Estradiol, Norgestimate)

Ortho-Est (Estropipate)

Ortho-Novum (Ethinyl Estradiol, Norethindrone)

*Ortho-Prefest (Estradiol, Norgestimate)

Orudis (Ketoprofen)

Oruvail (Ketoprofen)

Ovcon (Ethinyl Estradiol, Norethindrone)

Ovral (Ethinyl Estradiol, Norgestrel)

Ovrette (Norgestrel)

Oxandrin (Oxandrolone)

Oxsoralen (Methoxsalen)

OxyContin (Oxycodone Hydrochloride)

Paxil (Paroxetine Hydrochloride)

Pediazole (Erythromycin Ethylsuccinate, Sulfisoxazole Acetyl)

Penetrex (Enoxacin)

Pentasa (Mesalamine)

Pepcid (Famotidine)

*Permax (Pergolide Mesylate)

*Plavix (Clopidogrel Bisulfate)

Plendil (Felodipine)

Ponstel (Mefenamic Acid)

Pravachol (Pravastatin Sodium)

Pregnyl (Chorionic Gonadotropin)

Prelone (Prednisolone)

Premarin (Estrogens, Conjugated)

Premphase (Estrogens, Conjugated, Medroxyprogesterone Acetate)

*Prempro (Estrogens, Conjugated, Medroxyprogesterone Acetate)

Prevacid (Lansoprazole)

PREVPAC (Amoxicillin, Clarithromycin, Lansoprazole)

Prilosec (Omeprazole)

Prinivil (Lisinopril)

Prinzide (Hydrochlorothiazide, Lisinopril)

Procanbid (Procainamide Hydrochloride)

Procardia (Nifedipine)

Profasi (Chorionic Gonadotropin)

*Prograf (Tacrolimus)

Proleukin (Aldesleukin)

*Prometrium (Progesterone)

ProSom (Estazolam)

Protonix (Pantoprazole Sodium)

Proventil (Albuterol Sulfate)

Provera (Medroxyprogesterone Acetate)

*Provigil (Modafinil)

Prozac (Fluoxetine Hydrochloride)

Pulmicort (Budesonide)
Quinaglute (Quinidine Gluconate)
Quinidex (Quinidine Sulfate)
Quinidine Gluconate (Quinidine Gluconate)
*Rapamune (Sirolimus)
*Rebetron (Interferon alfa-2B, Recombinant, Ribavirin)
Reglan (Metoclopramide Hydrochloride)
Relafen (Nabumetone)
Remeron (Mirtazapine)
Remicade (Infliximab)
Requip (Ropinirole Hydrochloride)
Retrovir (Zidovudine)
*ReVia (Naltrexone Hydrochloride)
Rhinocort (Budesonide)
Rilutek (Riluzole)
Risperdal (Risperidone)
Ritalin (Methylphenidate Hydrochloride)
*Rituxan (Rituximab)
*Roferon (Interferon alfa-2A, Recombinant)
Romazicon (Flumazenil)
Rythmol (Propafenone Hydrochloride)
Salagen (Pilocarpine Hydrochloride)
Sandimmune (Cyclosporine)
*Sandostatin (Octreotide Acetate)
Sectral (Acebutolol Hydrochloride)
Sedapap (Acetaminophen, Butalbital)
Sensorcaine-MPF with Epinephrine (Bupivacaine Hydrochloride, Epinephrine Bitartrate)
Sensorcaine-MPF (Bupivacaine Hydrochloride)
Septra (Sulfamethoxazole, Trimethoprim)
Serophene (Clomiphene Citrate)
*Serostim (Somatropin)
Serzone (Nefazodone Hydrochloride)
*Simulect (Basiliximab)
Sinemet (Carbidopa, Levodopa)
Solu-Medrol (Methylprednisolone Sodium Succinate)
Sonata (Zaleplon)
*Soriatane (Acitretin)
Sporanox (Itraconazole)
Stadol (Butorphanol Tartrate)
Sular (Nisoldipine)
Sustiva (Efavirenz)
Symmetrel (Amantadine Hydrochloride)
*Synarel (Nafarelin Acetate)
Tagamet (Cimetidine)
Talacen (Pentazocine Hydrochloride)
Talwin (Aspirin, Pentazocine Hydrochloride)
Talwin Nx (Naloxone Hydrochloride, Pentazocine Hydrochloride)
Tambocor (Flecainide Acetate)
Targretin (Bexarotene)
Tasmar (Tolcapone)
Tegretol (Carbamazepine)
*Temodar (Temozolomide)
Tenex (Guanfacine Hydrochloride)
*Tenoretic (Atenolol, Chlorthalidone)
*Tenormin (Atenolol)
Tequin (Gatifloxacin)
Testoderm (Testosterone)
Testred (Methyltestosterone)
Teveten (Eprosartan Mesylate)

Thalomid (Thalidomide)
Tiazac (Diltiazem Hydrochloride)
Tigan (Trimethobenzamide Hydrochloride)
Timolide (Hydrochlorothiazide, Timolol Maleate)
Timoptic (Timolol Maleate)
Tolectin (Tolmetin Sodium)
Tonocard (Tocainide Hydrochloride)
*Topamax (Topiramate)
Toprol (Metoprolol Succinate)
Toradol (Ketorolac Tromethamine)
Tranxene (Clorazepate Dipotassium)
Trecator (Ethionamide)
Trental (Pentoxifylline)
Tricor Micronized (Fenofibrate)
Tri-Levlen (Ethinyl Estradiol, Levonorgestrel)
Triphasil (Ethinyl Estradiol, Levonorgestrel)
Trivora (Ethinyl Estradiol, Levonorgestrel)
Trovan (Trovafloxacin Mesylate)
Ultram (Tramadol Hydrochloride)
Uniretic (Hydrochlorothiazide, Moexipril Hydrochloride)
Valium (Diazepam)
Valtrex (Valacyclovir Hydrochloride)
Vanceril (Beclomethasone Dipropionate)
Vascor (Bepridil Hydrochloride)
Vaseretic (Enalapril Maleate, Hydrochlorothiazide)
Vasotec (Enalaprilat)
Velban (Vinblastine Sulfate)
*Vesanoid (Tretinoin)
Viagra (Sildenafil Citrate)
Vicoprofen (Hydrocodone Bitartrate, Ibuprofen)
Vioxx (Rofecoxib)
Viracept Nelfinavir Mesylate)
Vistide (Cidofovir)
Vivelle (Estradiol)
Voltaren (Diclofenac Sodium)
Wellbutrin (Bupropion Hydrochloride)
Winstrol (Stanozolol)
*Xanax (Alprazolam)
Xenical (Orlistat)
Zagam (Sparfloxacin)
Zanaflex (Tizanidine Hydrochloride)
Zantac (Ranitidine Hydrochloride)
Zarontin (Ethosuximide)
Zaroxolyn (Metolazone)
Zebeta (Bisoprolol Fumarate)
*Zenapax (Daclizumab)
Zestoretic (Hydrochlorothiazide, Lisinopril)
Zestril (Lisinopril)
Ziac (Bisoprolol Fumarate, Hydrochlorothiazide)
Zocor (Simvastatin)
*Zoladex (Goserelin Acetate)
Zoloft (Sertraline Hydrochloride)
Zomig (Zolmitriptan)
*Zonegran (Zonisamide)
Zosyn (Piperacillin Sodium, Tazobactam Sodium)
Zovia (Ethinyl Estradiol, Ethynodiol Diacetate)
Zyban (Bupropion Hydrochloride)
Zyprexa (Olanzapine)
Zyrtec (Cetirizine Hydrochloride)

APPENDIX

APPENDIX VIII
COMPARISON OF
OMEGA-3 AND OMEGA-6

Food Item	Amount	Omega-3 ÷ Omega-6	Omega-3	Omega-6
Jack Mackerel	1 cup	8.0	2,639	329
Spinach (canned)	1 cup	5.3	353	66
Flaxseed/Linseed Oil	1 Tbsp.	4.1	7,540	1,822
Canola Oil	1 Tbsp.	0.4	1,266	2,776
Walnuts, English	¼ cup	0.2	2,043	9,540
Walnuts, Black	¼ cup	0.1	1,031	10,468

APPENDIX IX
SUMMARY OF 17 HARMFUL EFFECTS OF TV WATCHING

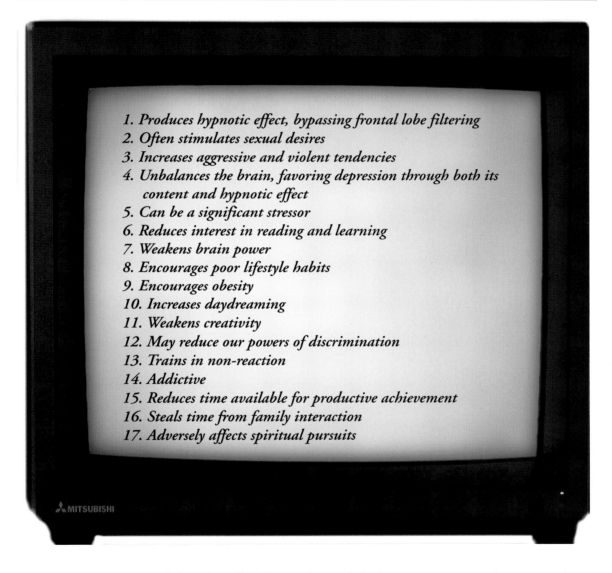

1. *Produces hypnotic effect, bypassing frontal lobe filtering*
2. *Often stimulates sexual desires*
3. *Increases aggressive and violent tendencies*
4. *Unbalances the brain, favoring depression through both its content and hypnotic effect*
5. *Can be a significant stressor*
6. *Reduces interest in reading and learning*
7. *Weakens brain power*
8. *Encourages poor lifestyle habits*
9. *Encourages obesity*
10. *Increases daydreaming*
11. *Weakens creativity*
12. *May reduce our powers of discrimination*
13. *Trains in non-reaction*
14. *Addictive*
15. *Reduces time available for productive achievement*
16. *Steals time from family interaction*
17. *Adversely affects spiritual pursuits*

These harmful effects collectively build a strong case for personal action—today. Clearly, television is doing much more than worsening depressive tendencies. The very moral conscience of you and your family—residing in your frontal lobes—may be hanging in the balances.

Reference: Nedley N. *Proof Positive: How to Reliably Combat Disease and Achieve Optimal Health through Nutrition and Lifestyle.* Ardmore, OK: Nedley Publishing, 1999 pp. 280-287.

APPENDIX X
RECIPES TO IMPROVE MOOD

Walnut Jam Muffins

Muffins make a healthy breakfast choice, especially for morning commuters that need to eat on the go. And this recipe already has the jam added to the muffin! The flax seed meal in this recipe replaces the eggs, resulting in a cholesterol free muffin, and increasing the omega-3 content of the recipe.

You Will Need

1½ cup	flour (*1 cup whole wheat pastry + ½ cup white*)
⅓ cup	Sucanat or brown sugar
2 tsp	Rumford baking powder
¼ tsp	salt
1 cup	Tofutti sour cream
2 Tbsp	flaxseed meal
¼ cup	hot water
1 tsp	vanilla
¼ cup	walnuts, chopped
½ cup	jam (*100% Fruit*) apricot or strawberry flavor

Step by Step

1. Preheat oven to 375°. Coat muffin pans with non-stick spray. Recipe makes 24 miniature or 12 large muffins.

2. In a medium size bowl mix all the dry ingredients.

3. In a small cup mix water with flax meal and let it sit for 2 to 3 minutes. In a small bowl, measure sour cream and vanilla. Stir in the flax meal mixture.

4. Add the sour cream mixture and nuts to dry ingredients and mix well with a fork. The batter is heavy, more like dough. Drop dough by spoonfuls in muffin pans.

5. Fill each mold about 2/3 full with batter. With the back of a teaspoon, make a small well on top of batter. Add about 1/2 teaspoon of jam in each well.

6. Bake for 12-15 minutes until muffins are golden brown.

If Tofutti sour cream is not available, you can subsitute. In a blender, place 1cup Mori-Nu silken tofu, firm, 1/4 cup canola oil, 1/4 cup honey, 1 tsp. lemon juice, vanilla and blend until smooth. Then follow the recipe as presented.

Walnut Granola

Granola makes an excellent breakfast addition and a wonderful snack at home or on the road. I have served granola many times as a light supper with a smoothie or fresh fruit. My children also enjoy the crunchy clusters of this recipe. Walnut granola is high in omega-3, fiber, melatonin and tryptophan.

You Will Need

½ cup	water
1 cup	dates, sliced to remove pits
½ cup	Welch's White Grape Juice concentrate
¼ cup	canola oil
1 Tbsp	vanilla extract
1½ tsp	salt
6 cups	old fashion rolled oats
1 cup	unsweetened coconut flakes
1 cup	walnuts, coarsley chopped
1 cup	almonds, coarsley chopped
1 cup	raw wheat bran
½ cup	flaxseed meal

Step by Step

1. In the microwave, heat water and dates. Place in a blender with white grape juice concentrate, oil, vanilla, and salt. Blend until smooth.

2. In a large bowl combine all dry ingredients. Pour blender mixture into bowl and mix with hands until dry ingredients are well-coated.

3. Spread about 1/2 inch thick on 2 double-insulated cookie sheets. Rotate cookie sheets during baking.

4. Two basic methods for cooking granola are:
   1) Bake overnight at 150°. In the morning bake 10-15 minutes, or until golden brown at 200°.
   2) Or bake at 225° for about 1 hours, until golden brown. Stir every 15 minutes.

If you don't have the flax seed meal, take 1/4 cup of whole flax seed and grind it in a coffee grinder to give you 1/2 cup of meal.

Morning Parfait

Use soy yogurt and granola along with fresh fruit for a quick breakfast.

In a parfait glass, alternate layers of granola, your favorite flavor of soy yogurt, and fresh fruit. Repeat layers. Serve immediately.

251

Green Soy Salad

Crunchy is the best description of this very colorful salad. The green soybeans are high in omega-3 and that is what inspired me to develop this recipe. You can add green soybeans to your favorite salad; just partially thaw them.

You Will Need

1	12 oz. pkg. frozen green soybeans
1	16 oz. pkg. frozen shoepeg white corn
1	8 oz. can water chestnuts
²/₃ cup	celery, finely chopped
¹/₃ cup	green onion, thinly sliced
¹/₄ cup	red sweet pepper, diced
5 Tbsp	lemon juice, freshly squeezed
1¹/₂ tsp	honey
1¹/₂ tsp	salt
1 Tbsp	fresh parsley, finely chopped
1	clove garlic, pressed
¹/₈ tsp	dill weed
¹/₄ tsp	sweet basil

You can find green soybeans in the frozen section of health food stores and some large supermarkets. I recommend using the shelled green soybeans.

Step by Step

1. Slice chestnuts in thin strips.
2. In a large bowl combine all vegetables.
3. In a small jar, combine remaining ingredients, cover, and shake well. Chill at least 2 hours. Serve on lettuce leaves and garnish with fresh mint.

Tofu

Tofu is made from soy beans in much the same way that cheese is made from milk. Its bland flavor gives it a remarkable versatility. You can purchase it in several different forms. These range from silken tofu (the softest form) to hard pressed tofu, which is very dense and firm, the form I prefer to use in the Baked Tofu Strips recipe. Fresh water packed tofu is my favorite, it has a fresh and delicate scent. Look for the expiration date on the package to make sure it is fresh. It keeps in the refrigerator up to a week, submerged in cold water, changing the water every other day to keep it fresh. If not used within the week, I freeze the tofu. That drastically changes its consistency, becoming spongy with a meaty and chewy texture. I thaw it, squeezing out the water before marinating and using it in dishes to substitute for meat. There is also the Mori-Nu silken tofu which has a long extended shelf life. I like to keep it in the pantry and use it in creams, sauces and puddings, because of its light, silky and creamy texture.

Baked Tofu Strips

You Will Need

1 lb	fresh firm tofu
1 Tbsp	Braggs Aminos or soy sauce
1 Tbsp	McKay's chicken seasoning

Step by Step

1. To prepare the tofu cut into ¼ by ¼ inch strips.

2. Sprinkle Braggs Aminos and McKay's seasoning over strips and stir gently.

3. Spread in a single layer on a cookie sheet and bake at 350° for 30 minutes or until golden brown. Stir once during the baking time. The strips can be used in stir-fry or in burritos with a non-dairy mayonnaise and vegetables.

This is my children's favorite dish! They have learned to make it themselves. Tofu, the highest source of tryptophan, is a soybean product that doesn't have much flavor when eaten plain; however, it can be seasoned to substitute in many fish, dairy, and poultry dishes. In order for this recipe to work, you need to use the fresh extra firm tofu.

Melty Cheese

You Will Need

2 cups	water, divided
1 cup	raw cashews
1	4 oz. jar of pimiento
1 cup	nutritional yeast
1 tsp	salt
1 tsp	onion powder
1 tsp	garlic powder
3 Tbs	cornstarch
1 Tbs	lemon juice
1 Tbs	sesame tahini

If using this recipe for pizza, in order to give more of the Mozzarella flavor and color, omit the pimiento and increase the amount of sesame tahini to 2 tablespoons.

Step by Step

1. In a blender place *one cup* of water and cashews; blend until creamy. Add all other ingredients and blend again until smooth. Add last cup of water (hot water will shorten cooking time) and blend briefly.

2. Heat in a heavy saucepan, stirring constantly, and cook until hot and bubbly.

This recipe is a mild, but tasty substitute for soft, melting English cheese. It has endless options without the tyramine found so abundantly in the regular cheeses. Use this cheese as a dip (use mild green chili for extra flavor when served with baked corn chips), on burritos, enchiladas, pizzas, vegetables, or anywhere you would use melted cheese.

Oat Burger

This savory burger is high in omega-3 and melatonin and makes a tasty vegetarian sandwich. I like to make a whole bunch and freeze the leftover, if any! My children like the burgers plain, just like patties, and those burgers disappear fast! You can serve as patties with your favorite gravy or with tomato sauce over pasta.

You Will Need

4 cups	water
½ cup	Braggs Aminos or soy sauce
¼ cup	nutritional yeast flakes
2 Tbsp	canola oil
1 Tbsp	flaxseed meal
1 Tbsp	dried sweet basil
2 tsp	garlic powder
2 tsp	onion powder
1 tsp	Bakon seasoning
1 tsp	ground coriander
1 tsp	dried sage
1 cup	walnuts, finely chopped
4 cups	rolled oats

To give the look of a hamburger use the lid of a large-mouth canning jar. Fill and pat the burger mixture into the lid and then push the lid through the ring with your thumb. See picture to the right.

Step by Step

1. Place a 2 quart pan on a burner over medium heat and add the ingredients in the given order except the rolled oats.

2. Bring the water to a slow boil, quickly stir in rolled oats and immediately remove from heat. Cover and set aside to cool.

3. Preheat oven to 350°.

4. Form oat mixture into three-inch patties and place on oiled baking sheets.

5. Bake for 20 minutes on each side. Serve with whole wheat buns, soy mayonnaise, lettuce, onions, tomato and pickles.

Bowtie Pasta with Avacado

A high carbohydrate dish increases the serotonin level and can make a filling meal. This recipe includes avocado with its monounsaturated fat, thus greatly reducing the amount of oil added to many pasta dishes. The tomato and onion add a refreshing taste to this one-dish meal.

You Will Need

1	12 oz. bowtie pasta
½ Tbsp	olive oil
2	avocados, diced
2½ Tbsp	lemon juice
½ tsp	garlic powder
1½ tsp	salt, or to taste
2	large Roma tomatoes, diced
2	green onions, chopped
1 Tbsp	fresh parsley, finely chopped
	sweet basil, sprinkle

Pasta is available in many sizes and shapes. It is also available made from grains other than wheat.
Health food stores often carry corn, rice and buckwheat pasta. Using the whole grain will give a higher fiber content.

Step by Step

1. In a large pot bring about one gallon of salted water to a boil. Add the pasta and cook until done (do not overcook).

2. Cut the avocado in half. Remove the pit, then cut in two again, making four pieces. Pull the peel off the avocado and cut in thin slices. Place slices in a bowl and sprinkle with lemon juice, garlic powder, and salt.

3. Drain pasta, add olive oil, and stir gently. Transfer to a serving platter.

4. Pour avocado mixture and tomatoes and onions over pasta, then toss gently. Garnish with diced parsley and/or basil if so desired.

Corn Flake Nut Dressing

Make this dressing the center piece of an appetizing main meal. High in omega-3, it also has an increased amount of minerals and vitamins, including B_{12} from the cornflake cereal. Serve with gravy, mashed potatoes, and colorful vegetables of your choice.

You Will Need

2 cups	onion, chopped
2	cloves garlic, minced
2	large stalks celery, diced
2 Tbsp	oil
¼ cup	flour
1½ cup	soy milk or water
1 Tbsp	McKay's chicken seasoning
2 Tbsp	flaxseed meal
1 tsp	sage, ground
½ tsp	salt
1 Tbsp	parsley
1 cup	walnuts, chopped
3 cups	corn flakes, slightly crushed

Step by Step

1. Sauté onion, garlic, and celery in oil for 10 minutes. Add flour and stir. Add water or milk and stir. Bring to a boil and continue boiling for 2 to 3 minutes to thicken.

2. Add remaining ingredients in the given order, mixing after each one.

3. Pour in a loaf pan that is well coated with non-stick spray.

4. Bake at 375° for 45 minutes or until brown. If using the miniature loaf pan bake for 20 minutes.

5. Let set for 10 minutes on a rack. Turn out of loaf pan on to a serving dish.

I like using individual small loaf pans or a mini-multi-loaf pan for faster baking, an easier and more elegant way to present this recipe. I prefer Kellogg's brand corn flakes. However, for an increased amount of minerals and vitamins Total corn flake cereal would be desired. The main difference is the sugar content; Total being sweeter creates a slightly sweeter loaf.

Walnut Maple Cookies

These mouth watering cookies are so easy to make and are healthy for you. Very high in omega-3, they are made without butter and eggs. Maple syrup adds a delicious touch of natural sweetness and replaces all the sugar found in most cookies.

You Will Need

2½ cups	walnuts, ground in food processor
⅔ cup	whole wheat pastry flour
1 tsp	salt
⅓ cup	flaxseed meal
⅓ cup	carob chips
½ cup + 2 Tbsp	maple syrup
2 tsp	vanilla

The cookies can burn easily and become hard if too dark. Use a double insulated cookie sheet for baking and bake on the middle rack of the oven.

Step by Step

1. In a small bowl add all the ingredients in the given order. Mix well.

2. Spray a large cookie sheet and preheat the oven to 350°.

3. Drop dough on cookie sheet with a spoon and flatten with a fork.

4. Bake for 10-15 minutes or until golden brown, checking often to prevent burning.

5. Let cool before removing from the cookie sheet. Makes one dozen.

Almond Delight Ice-Cream Pie

I am happy to share this wonderful quick ice cream alternative with you. The main ingredient of this delicious pie is Tofutti, a frozen dessert available in most health food stores. I often prepare this simple dessert and keep it in the freezer for a spur of the moment treat or special occassion. Who would guess that tofu replaces the eggs and cream in this cholesterol-free gourmet dessert.

You Will Need

Almond Crust

1½ cups	toasted almonds, chopped
1 Tbsp	canola oil
1½ Tbsp	honey or brown rice syrup

Filling

¼ cup	shredded coconut (fine), unsweetened and lightly toasted
1 Tbsp	honey or brown rice syrup
¼ cup	almond or peanut butter
3 Tbsp	toasted almonds, chopped
2 pints	Vanilla Tofutti Nondairy Frozen Dessert

Carob Drizzle

¼ cup	carob chips

Step by Step

Almond Crust

Coat a 9-inch pie plate* with non-stick spray. Mix the crust ingredients and press the mixture firmly onto bottom and up the sides of the pie plate. May use wax paper on top to prevent sticking to your fingers when pressing crust mixture. Freeze while preparing the filling.

* Can be made in an 8 x 8 inch pan and cut in squares as presented above.

Filling

1. In a small bowl mix the coconut, syrup, almond butter, and almonds.
2. Place the ice cream in a large bowl and stir to soften. Stir in the almond mixture. Spoon into chilled crust. Sprinkle additional toasted almonds over pie and/or drizzle with melted carob chips. Freeze for at least 2 hours or until firm.

Carob Drizzle

In a small microwavable dish, melt carob chips on high for 15-30 seconds.* Stir to ensure smoothness. With a fork, drizzle over the pie.

* Carob chips will crystalize if overheated. The time depends on your microwave.

No-Bake Brownies

A delicious brownie, this recipe uses carob chips instead of chocolate chips. I like this recipe because it is quick and requires no baking. For an easy make-ahead recipe for unexpected company, roll the brownie mixture in the shape of a log, wrap in plastic wrap and freeze. Cut and serve at a moments notice.

You Will Need

1 pkg	graham cracker crumbs
½ cup	walnuts, chopped
⅓ cup	cup water
3 Tbsp	non-dairy milk powder
¾ cup	carob chips
1 tsp	vanilla
3-5 drops	peppermint essence (optional)

May roll in plastic wrap in the shape of a log. Freeze. Thaw for 15 minutes before slicing and serving.

Step by Step

1. In a food processor grind the crackers until fine. It should yield about 1¾ cup.

2. Combine graham cracker crumbs and walnuts.

3. In a saucepan, mix water and milk powder. Cook over medium heat until warm. Add all other ingredients to the saucepan. Stir until melted and thoroughly combined.

4. Remove from heat. Add cracker-walnut mixture. Mix well.

5. Press into oiled 8-in. square pan. Let sit 30 minutes. Cut and serve.

Carob is naturally sweet and low in fat; it is high in calcium as well as other vitamins and minerals. It tastes and looks enough like chocolate to be used as a substitute. Carob is free of tannin, caffeine, or theobromine found so abundantly in cocoa, and have been associated with headaches and depression.

259

GLOSSARY FOR RECIPES

Almond Butter: Roasted almonds, made into butter. Almonds are superior to peanuts nutritionally.

Baking Powder, Rumford: Preferable to regular baking powders in that it is aluminum-free though it does contain baking soda that is objectionable to some.

Bakon Seasoning: Hickory smoked dry torula yeast is a concentrated food contributing to good nutrition, while enhancing the flavor of many foods. If you cannot find this seasoning use Bacon-Bits, doubled amount.

Bragg's Amino's: Made from soybeans, is similar to soy sauce, but not as strong and not fermented. It has amino acids and minerals, but a little lower in sodium than regular soy sauce.

Brown Rice Syrup: A thick, sweet syrup used interchangeably with honey or other liquid sweeteners.

Carob Chips: Choose dairy-free, barley malt-sweetened carob chips.

Cashews: To prepare raw cashews for recipes in this cookbook, rinse them before adding to the other ingredients.

Coconut: Unsweetened shredded coconut is used in these recipes.

Flaxseed Meal: Ground flax seed.

McKay's chicken seasoning: This chicken-like all-vegetarian seasoning contains no animal fat.

Non-Dairy Milk Powder: A delicious substitute made from brown rice, soybeans, oats, almonds, etc.

Nutritional Yeast Flakes: The flakes are yellow in color and have a cheese-like flavor. This is not a baking yeast.

Sesame Tahini: A thick, smooth paste made from ground sesame seeds.

Sucanat: Made from organic sugar cane juice in granulated form. It is unrefined and retains all of the vitamins and minerals provided by nature. An excellent substitute for brown sugar and can be used interchangeably in baked goods or for any recipe that calls for sugar sweetening.

Tofutti Sour Cream: Non-dairy imitation sour cream available in health food stores.

Most items are available in health food stores.

Index

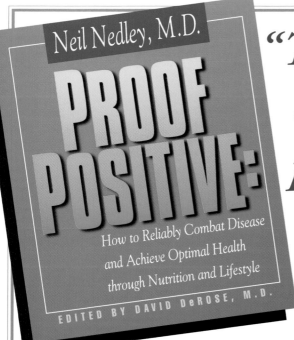

Neil Nedley, M.D.

PROOF POSITIVE:

How to Reliably Combat Disease and Achieve Optimal Health through Nutrition and Lifestyle

EDITED BY DAVID DeROSE, M.D.

"The most useful book for health promotion ever written in this generation."

J.A. SCHARFFENBERG M.D.
*Nutrition Researcher and
Adjunct Prof. of Nutrition
Loma Linda University*

Your health is in the news these days. The meat you eat is on the front page of the paper. Conflicting studies about cancer pop up continually. Where do you turn when it comes to living your best?

Dr. Nedley's book *Proof Positive: How to Reliably Combat Disease and Achieve Optimal Health through Nutrition and Lifestyle*, is the resource you need to determine what does and doesn't work when it comes to your health.

In this highly acclaimed book, *Proof Positive* presents a wide scope of directly usable, positively proven health facts for preventing and treating many diseases and conditions. Supported by the latest and most accurate medical and scientific information, *Proof Positive* is the guide in achieving your best possible health.

Learn how to attain and maintain good health by natural means, and avoid or reduce the use of prescription drugs.

For those suffering from long-term illness and afflictions, *Proof Positive* shows how to strengthen the body's immune system, overcome addictions, increase reasoning ability, and cope with stress.

For the price of a 15-minute doctor's visit, you will have true and amazing facts that you can rely on. Whether it is the latest diet fad or the hottest health claim, there is a sea of "cure-alls" and medicines. With this book, get the proof: *Proof Positive*.

Proof Positive…
Hardback 8"x10", 584 pages, Over 500 Full Color Charts and Illustrations, Fully Referenced.
$59.00

Call Today!

Nedley Publishing

1-888-778-4445 OR (580)223-5980

NOTES

NOTES

NOTES

NOTES

NOTES